OUT OF
THE BEST
BOOKS

OUT OF THE BEST BOOKS

AN ANTHOLOGY OF LITERATURE

VOLUME 1:
THE INDIVIDUAL AND HUMAN VALUES

Bruce B. Clark and Robert K. Thomas

1964

Published by Deseret Book Company, Salt Lake City, Utah

Printed by

DESERET NEWS PRESS

in the United States of America

To Ouida and Shirley,
our special Relief Society teachers

Preface

The principal idea behind this book is that the best way to study literature is to read it—that the work of literature itself is more important than anything that can be said about it. When asked two years ago if I could make any recommendation that might strengthen the literature program of the Relief Society, I suggested one thing only: for the women of the Relief Society individually to read the selections of literature and then in a group discuss them rather than have lectures, however good they might be, on works that most of the women have not read. If my observations are correct, the Relief Society literature program has for years functioned about as follows in most wards and stakes, branches and missions: (a) An excellent text (generally a standard college text) has been selected; (b) excellent lessons have been written and printed in the *Relief Society Magazine*; (c) excellent stake and ward literature leaders have been chosen who have spent many hours preparing excellent lessons (usually lectures); (d) then these lessons (lectures) have been delivered to groups of women in the wards and branches who for the most part have not read the works being discussed. How much better if the women could come together and talk about selections, even a single short story or a single poem, that all had read! Literature is vivid and exciting and provocative—but only when we have read it. Therefore, with the hope that it will be *read and discussed* by thousands of women throughout the world, this book has been prepared and published for use in the literature program of the Relief Society of The Church of Jesus Christ of Latter-day Saints.

In addition to this general statement, the following ten comments on the nature and purposes of the book should be helpful to those who use it:

(1) This book, *The Individual and Human Values*, is intended for use in the Relief Society program for two

years, 1964-65 and 1965-66. Section 1, "The Appreciation and Criticism of Literature," contains selections for October and November 1964; Section 2, "Faith in God and Man," contains selections for December 1964 and January 1965; Section 3, "Right and Wrong Attitudes," contains selections for six months—February, March, April, May, October, and November of 1965; Section 4, "Good versus Evil," contains selections for December 1965 and January 1966; Section 5, "The Place of Suffering in Life," contains selections for February and March 1966; and Section 6, "Facing Death," contains selections for April and May 1966. The *Relief Society Magazine* will print monthly lessons, as in the past, suggesting how the selections may be effectively used in the Relief Society program.

(2) Although the book is intended primarily for use in the Relief Society literature program, it is so designed that it should be valuable as a book for the entire family in the home library. The hope is that most families of the Church will want to use this work, and subsequent volumes to be published, to let literature enrich family life as only literature can.

(3) Literature and education have always held a treasured place in the Latter-day Saint Church. Always there has been an emphasis in the Church on the value of learning and of reading good books. Hence the present book is not a new emphasis but simply a new focus on an old emphasis. And we are pleased to announce that this volume, *The Individual and Human Values,* is intended as only the first part of a three-part work entitled *Out of the Best Books: An Anthology of Literature.* The second volume, to be called *Marriage and the Family,* is planned for 1966-68; and the third volume, to be called *The Community,* is planned for 1968-70.

(4) Three standards have controlled the selection of each work of literature included: (a) that it be literature of high quality; (b) that it explore subject matter and con-

vey a theme of value to the women of the Church and their families; (c) that it be written in such a way as to be understandable and meaningful to most of the readers for whom intended.

Some readers may feel that with several of the selections we have violated the third standard because the selections are too difficult. But all should remember that what is difficult for some readers may not be difficult for other readers, and that often the most difficult is also the most rewarding. Most things of value cannot be obtained at a cheap price, as Mortimer Adler says in his brilliant little essay later in this book. Two things are necessary for excellence in literature—artistic form and significant content. We have insisted on both qualities for each work included.

(5) In each section of the book there are some relatively difficult selections and some relatively easy ones, which should make the book useful for all levels of readers in the Relief Society program. Comments in the *Relief Society Magazine* lessons will suggest ways of using these selections for different groups.

(6) All of the selections in this volume are by non-L.D.S. authors, drawn from the "literature of the world." Nor have we tried to limit the selections strictly to those that conform in every detail to Latter-day Saint doctrines and practices. But in a larger sense we have chosen those works that harmonize with and enrich the ideals of gospel living. Many of the selections expose attitudes and practices to be avoided, but all are in a broad sense constructive and affirmative. Indeed, a basic purpose in writing this book has been to discuss works of literature that support the principles of the Gospel. Our first responsibility as readers in the Church is to study the scriptures and the writings of the prophets, ancient and modern. But we can also enrich and strengthen our spiritual lives by reading the high-quality literature of the world. Hence this book.

(7) As the first chapter of our work makes clear, there are four basic ways to approach and discuss literature. Each has its strengths and weaknesses; ideally they should supplement and support each other. Practically, however, the first or so-called Platonic approach is the one which should prove most useful to members of the Church, since it takes advantage of our common beliefs to establish the basis for critical understanding.

In our discussions, therefore, we usually stress this method. In addition, we often comment on the significance of form, the author's background, or the critical history of a given work—the other three approaches—but we believe an examination of the *content* and *meaning* of great poetry and prose is an obvious starting place for developing literary judgment.

Experience persuades us that the best story or poem for group discussion is one that focuses on some psychological, philosophical, or ethical question, yielding insight into human values, ideals, truths, problems, and frustrations. We have tried to choose selections rich in such insights, and we have also tried to emphasize these insights in our discussions of these works.

(8) Most of the selections are drawn from English and American literature. However, a generous sampling of selections from the great literature of other languages is included, sufficient to give a flavoring of world culture, and corresponding with the world-wide spread of the Relief Society program and the Church.

(9) Most of the selections are either poems or short stories. Novels and dramas would have been equally good—or even better—except for length. We have chosen poems and stories because they say a great deal in a few words. They are short enough to be printed in a limited space and to be read and discussed in a limited time, thus fitting comfortably into the Relief Society program, and at the same time they are significant in substance. There-

fore, some 65 poems and stories, with interpretive discussions, comprise the bulk of this book. These are not presented as "the best" poems and stories but are mere samplings from hundreds of selections in the literature of the world that would be equally good, equally appropriate.

(10) Each selection is accompanied by a critical discussion of it. This is intended to be suggestive and provocative but should in no way stop class leaders and readers from interpreting the selections themselves. Every reader should bring all of his experience in literature and life to assist in understanding a work, and each reader because of different experiences will understand it a little differently. We have done our best to suggest meaningful readings of each work, but we claim no infallibility in literary interpretation, and we encourage readers to explore meanings in the poems and stories that we may have missed or even misrepresented. Our comments are at best merely suggestive, and very incomplete.

Bruce B. Clark
June, 1964

A Note about the Authors:

Robert K. Thomas, who has written the essay on literary criticism on pp. 3 to 14 of Section 1, is Assistant Professor of English and Director of the Honors Program at Brigham Young University. He served for several years as a High Councilman and Bishop's Counselor in various wards and stakes in Provo, Utah, and is now serving as Bishop of the B.Y.U. Second Ward.

Bruce B. Clark, who has written the remainder of the book, is Professor of English and Chairman of the English Department at Brigham Young University. He served for seven years as a Bishop and for three years as a High Councilman in the West Sharon Stake in Provo-Orem, Utah, and has recently been called to serve for the second time as a Bishop, of the B.Y.U. Forty-Second Ward.

ACKNOWLEDGMENTS

Selections under copyright are reprinted by permission and courtesy of publishers indicated below:

Mortimer J. Adler and Publishers Newspaper Syndicate: for "What Makes a Great Book?" by Mortimer J. Adler.

Thomas S. Brush: for "Birthday Party" by Katharine Brush, copyright 1946, originally published in *The New Yorker*, March 16, 1946.

Jacques Chambrun, Inc.: for "The Sick Child" by Colette, reprinted from *Mademoiselle*, July, 1947, copyright 1947 by Street & Smith Publications, Inc.

Chatto & Windus, Ltd.: for "Dulce et Decorum Est" by Wilfred Owen, from *The Collected Poems of Wilfred Owen*, reprinted by permission of New Directions, Publishers.

P. F. Collier & Son: for "Boless" by Maxim Gorky.

Thomas Y. Crowell Company: for "Three Arshins of Land" by Leo N. Tolstoi, from *Popular Legends*.

Crown Publishers, Inc.: for excerpts from "The Pardoner's Tale" from Geoffrey Chaucer's *Canterbury Tales* rendered into modern English by J. U. Nicolson, copyright 1934 by Covici, Friede, Inc.

E. P. Dutton & Co., Inc.: for "War" by Luigi Pirandello, from *The Medals and Other Stories*.

Harcourt, Brace & World, Inc.: for "The New Dress" by Virginia Woolf, from *A Haunted House and Other Short Stories*.

Little Brown & Company: for "I Never Saw a Moor" by Emily Dickinson, from *The Complete Poems of Emily Dickinson*.

The Macmillan Company: for "Poetry" from *Collected Poems* by Marianne Moore, copyright 1935 by Marianne Moore; and for "Karma" from *Collected Poems* by Edwin Arlington Robinson, copyright 1925 by Edwin Arlington Robinson, renewed 1953 by Ruth Nivison and Barbara R. Holt.

New Directions: for "And Death Shall Have No Dominion" by Dylan Thomas, from *The Collected Poems of Dylan Thomas*, copyright 1957 by New Directions.

TABLE OF CONTENTS

SECTION ONE

The Appreciation and Criticism of Literature
Supplement to Section One

THE APPRECIATION AND CRITICISM OF LITERATURE

The value of good reading consists, first, in selecting good books and, second, in seeing clearly what is therein written. —President David O. McKay

Most of us feel that we can "appreciate" literature in the same sense that we appreciate other things. Because we are reasonably comfortable in knowing what we like, even if we can't always explain why, few of us aspire to become critics—literary or otherwise. At best, being a critic implies a wisdom which most of us don't claim; at worst, it suggests mere complaining. The Scriptures help us recognize the responsibility of being a judge, and we are all a little uncomfortable in the presence of the fault-finder.

But it is important to remember that, in one sense, we must always judge. Our most basic gift from God is free agency, our right to choose, and in choice there is always judgment — whether we recognize it or not. When we accept one course of action and reject another we have made a critical discrimination; our very salvation depends upon proper choices. Those who cannot easily see the judgments behind their choices are to be pitied; those who refuse to see them may need to be exhorted—but both must be helped. For failure to recognize the key role of judgment in *any* choice can be tragic—affecting us spiritually and temporally—as crucial distinctions are destroyed and differences blurred. One extreme result of this, as noted by Isaiah, was that the people of his time felt justified in calling "evil good and good evil," in putting "darkness for light and light for darkness." This same surrender of judgment was insisted upon by Korihor, the Anti-Christ, in the *Book of Mormon*. He stressed that no action in itself was to be condemned, that "whatsoever a man did was no crime." If, as this position suggests, no one is held accountable for his acts, we can avoid most critical evaluation; but if we accept accountability we must become critics—and not simply literary ones. We must learn to choose the best in every area of our lives. Our *conduct* should reflect a superior choice, as well as the paintings we admire, the music we enjoy, and the books we read. Originally, to criticize meant to discern—to see differences and evaluate them—and this meaning is still at the heart of all effective criticism.

This discernment begins at a very informal and individual level. When we say that we like a poem, an attitude, or a friend, we have discerned qualities which seem superior, and therefore appealing, to us. If we are content with such casual discriminations, if we do not try to analyze or focus our experience, our "criticism" is no more than the simplest kind of appreciation, a state in which vague but positive feelings of identification become the basis for judgment. Original meanings for "criticism" and "appreciation" were very close; both stressed careful distinction and thoughtful evaluation. Over the years, however, appreciation has tended to lose its precise focus. Increasingly, it has suggested an immediate, highly personal and emotional reaction. There is nothing wrong with this stage of evaluation—it is where we all begin—but appreciation at this level is almost impossible to share. This is why we are so ill at ease when we try to explain or justify our preference. We are often driven to the lame, "Well, I don't know; I just like it, that's all." The fundamental problem here is that no two backgrounds are similar enough to make subjective appreciation interchangeable. Even children in the same household will reflect the differing points of view which their status in the family makes inevitable. If understanding is difficult and agreement hard to arrive at in families, how much more frustrating are attempts to communicate our personal admirations to those of markedly different backgrounds. Yet because no joy is complete until it is shared, we still try to transfer our appreciation, unaware that the characteristics which distinguish ordinary appreciation—vagueness, a positive identification, and strong but random emotion—are hopeless barriers to an understanding, by others, of the things we cherish, whether they be material beauties or spiritual truths.

The vagueness of mere appreciation is fatal because fool's gold has a deceptive glitter to the casually discriminating glance. We must learn precise differences if we are to estimate values. Exact knowledge is not the enemy of insight. A fact is not only the base from which the artist may spring his imaginative creation; it is also a place where anyone may stand and try to share the artist's perspective. The simple, positive stress of appreciation, which at first seems so attractive, is finally equally unrewarding. Lehi, in the *Book of Mormon*, gives us the key here: good is seen most clearly in contrast to evil. This is not to support the widespread belief that criticism is fundamentally negative, that to discriminate effectively we should concentrate on picking out flaws. Good criticism is never carping. Perhaps the greatest critical precept ever written is the "golden rule." If we "do unto others as we would have others do unto us," we are not unaware of weaknesses—either in ourselves or others. But faults are not significant for their own sake. If they must be pointed out, they are pointed out to help. Weakness is not a stopping-place; it is a stepping-stone. And even here, as Scripture reminds us, we will be better able to see the mote in our brother's eye, if we have learned to recognize the beam in our own. The final characteristic of appreciation—its strong but random emotion—needs the corrective of objective reflection and the testifying direction of the Holy Ghost lest we confuse extraneous feelings with the emotion which is a living part of any memorable occurrence. When William Wordsworth discusses the writing of poetry he emphasizes that "it takes its origin in emotion recollected in tranquillity." If an emotion is really a necessary part of the poetic source, it can be recreated

and will be free of feelings not appropriate to the essence
of the experience.

Good criticism attempts to remedy the shortcomings of
appreciation by deepening, enlarging, and objectifying our
efforts. As we grow into critical maturity, we learn that to
see sensitively and precisely is to go far beyond a shallow
appreciation. We begin to see—and see clearly—relationships that escaped us before, and we are able to talk about
them in a way that is meaningful to others. In comprehend-
ing the whole—that "compound in one" of good and bad
which Lehi describes—we develop an encompassing awareness of problems and a resulting insight that makes it possible for us to communicate with those whose backgrounds
are different from, perhaps even opposed to, our own. Subjective emotion is not played down in good criticism, but we
find that emotion which is appropriate can be discussed
reasonably. We begin to understand what, by its very
nature, is too personal to be transferred, and we learn how
to convey reactions to things we cherish as objectively as
possible.

If we assume, at this point, that the difference between
ordinary appreciation and discriminating criticism is evident, and that the necessity for a critical temper is established, we are prepared to discuss the methods by which
we can all enrich our critical insights. Among the bewildering array of critical positions which seem to be available,
how can an amateur hope to find, much less use effectively,
the approach which is best? Fortunately, the problem is not
quite so complex as it appears. Since all criticism implies
standards, the possible critical positions are limited by the
source of these standards. Historically, the sources have
been four: (1) ultimate, transcendental values, often philosophical or religious, which the critic brings to his task from
some outside source; (2) the work itself, which is viewed as
being so unique that it sets its own standards; (3) the author, whose total environment becomes the criteria for

understanding; and (4) the audience, from whose many interpretations of a given work an acceptable synthesis has finally emerged. If these seem a bit difficult to follow when stated so abstractly, they will become clearer as they are described in detail and seen in action.

The first position, often identified with Plato, a Greek philosopher who lived about four centuries before Christ, is a very persuasive one. Plato makes no real distinction between literary and other kinds of criticism. Everything is evaluated by the same ultimate standard. Since, for Plato, the world about us is only a world of appearance, and only the ideal is "real," he checks everything by its approximation to the concept of truth which undergirds all his evaluation. It is important to remember that the standard he uses is not influenced by the work being considered; nor does it reflect the time in which the work was written. Plato's ideal truth becomes a yardstick against which anything can be measured, for ultimate truth is not distinguishable from ultimate goodness or ultimate beauty.

We need not argue Plato's philosophy here; it is his method which interests us. Whenever we judge on the basis of fundamental beliefs, we are using the Platonic method. As Mormons we are clearly in the Platonic tradition, since it is impossible for most of us not to use the principles of the Restored Gospel as our critical yardstick, no matter what we are evaluating. Unfortunately, we are sometimes embarrassed or defensive about this when we have no need to be. It is a thoroughly legitimate critical position. Certain themes in modern fiction *will* be offensive to us because they are so directly at odds with principles which we hold sacred. This is bound to be reflected in our reactions. It is a little foolish to ask for complete objectivity in such cases. We *do* need to recognize our bias, but we don't have to apologize for it. We only need to be aware of the strengths and weaknesses of our position as critical method. The real advantage of a Platonic approach lies in the ease with which our position can be understood by those who share our basic tenets. We need spend little time in justifying our standards; they will be recognized and accepted within our group. One danger, however, in espousing such a position is the temptation to apply our standards without enough thought. It is possible, for instance, to object to Nathaniel Hawthorne's *The Scarlet Letter* as a tale of adultery, but to do so is to miss Hawthorne's real theme —the consequences of sin—to focus solely on one of the devices by which this profoundly moral and uplifting story is told. Another difficulty in using the Platonic method alone is that it is not very meaningful outside the believing group. To people who do not share our ultimate beliefs, criticism based upon them is at best irrelevant and at worst incomprehensible. If we can never wholly escape our religious or philosophical orientation—and most of us surely have no desire to—we must recognize that we limit our audience in keeping rigorously to it as the sole source of our critical standards.

To illustrate the use of this method consider the following poem:

Days

Daughters of Time, the hypocritic days,
Muffled and dumb like barefoot dervishes,
And marching single in an endless file,
Bring diadems and fagots in their hands.
To each they offer gifts after his will,
Bread, kingdoms, stars, and sky that holds them all.
I, in my pleachéd garden watched the pomp,
Forgot my morning wishes, hastily
Took a few herbs and apples, and the Day
Turned and departed silent. I, too late,
Under her solemn fillet saw the scorn.

Unless we recognize this poem, and thereby identify both author and historical period, there is little need, in using a Platonic method, to try to discern either. Since we are gauging by profound truth, this alone is what we are looking for, and so we concentrate on the "message" of the poem. At first reading this seems to be a slightly unconventional poem on neglected opportunity. Because part of our belief is the necessity for each man "to work out his salvation" we are interested enough to read it again. This time we see that the theme is a little more complex than we thought. "Hypocritic days" suggests that we are deceived by what seem to be equal and endless opportunities. We then realize that the deception is not in the opportunities—they really are endless and magnificent—but in our base and unimaginative choices. Our "pleachéd garden"—that is, our hopelessly routine life—makes us insensitive to anything except the most obvious outward show. Our choices are inevitable and dismaying. We choose herbs (help for pain?) and apples (obvious satisfactions?) instead of the "sky that holds them all"—and we are immediately reminded of "seek ye first the kingdom of God . . . and all these things shall be added unto you." We leave this poem with our idea of opportunity deepened: perhaps the problem is not that we are away from home when opportunity knocks but that our homes must teach us to choose greatly from the gamut of daily opportunities which surround us.

The second position—the one in which the work itself becomes the source of critical standards—is usually associated with Aristotle, Plato's pupil. Without really rejecting a Platonic approach, for Aristotle is always aware that no one judges in a vacuum, he does try to make criticism less parochial. If we can't be totally objective, we may be able to find some elements on which there can be widespread agreement within a given context. To keep these elements from having strong religious or philosophic connotations, he emphasizes *form*. Since he is not talking about ultimates, he can talk about beauty quite apart from truth; so we are not surprised to find Aristotle gauging beauty solely on the basis of harmony and size. To stress harmony is to concentrate on relationships, and we soon see that

organic relationship is the key to Aristotle's method. When
each part is in dynamic and illuminating relationship to
every other part, we have a superior work. If critical
principles are formulated, they must evolve out of the works
themselves. Aristotle's famous "rules" for tragedy (which
succeeding generations have applied in a very un-Aris-
totelian manner) were established by seeing many tragedies. Creative works are sub-divided to the lowest of
artistic denominators in the hope that agreement on formal
relationships can be achieved without getting involved in
ultimates of any kind.

The main strength of such an attempt is immediately
evident. It approaches "scientific" criticism. Communica-
tion, at one level, seems to be clearly possible. Where the
Platonic method, used by critics with differing basic values,
often results in mere hostility, the Aristotelian builds
bridges. Where the Platonic critic can ignore history and
biography, but not philosophy, the Aristotelian can almost
ignore history, biography and philosophy—but not quite.
The great strength of the Aristotelian approach is, poten-
tially, its greatest weakness. Since we can only be truly
objective about those things which concern us not at all,
this critical position can obtain agreement, but often at the
expense of significance. It can degenerate into a sterile
manipulation of formal elements. Yet it need not, and over
the years it has become a very popular and useful approach.
It is restated in such well-known definitions of good writing
as "proper words in proper places" and in such influential
assertions as "nothing can permanently please which does
not contain in itself the reason why it is so." In an age when
no religion or philosophy can claim the allegiance of a ma-
jority of men, Aristotle's pragmatic method is an extremely
welcome bond.

To see it in action, let's consider the same poem we
viewed earlier but this time from an Aristotelian standpoint.
We still do not need to know who wrote it or when, and

we avoid the prose paraphrase of its "message," which is so often the hallmark of the Platonic approach. We concentrate rather on internal relationships. To begin, we note its overall form. The lines are unrhymed and uneven metrically, nor does it fit any of the standard verse patterns common in English poetry. Yet we note that there is a culmination of the first five lines in the sixth (even the length of the line reinforces this) and then a shift from metaphoric description of opportunity to the author's reaction to it in the last five lines. This rough balance and contrast is typical of the conflict which *is* the poem. "Hypocritic days" prepares us for the unreconciled "diadems and fagots," "bread . . . stars." By the end of the poem we realize that the conflict may not only be unresolved; it may even seem to be unresolvable. As man grows up, his daily requirements lead him to impose his will upon nature. Only a "pleachéd" or controlled garden will satisfy his needs. His problem is not that he is simply lulled into a false position by the regularity and monotony of each day's passing. The lines of the poem do not move easily. The meter is as irregular as life itself. The only pattern is opposition. The days may serve, but they do not cooperate. They are muffled in the beginning and still hooded ("solemn fillet") at the end. The balance between possibility and expedience is almost exact. The "scorn" which might precipitate action comes "too late." Nothing in such an interpretation suggests that the condition presented is either good or bad. It simply *is,* and the poem is your experience of it.

To the Platonic and Aristotelian positions a third is added by Longinus, a Greek living in Rome during the first century A.D. Again without rejecting earlier approaches Longinus gives such emphasis to the author—finding the "sublime" in the "ring of greatness in the author's soul"— that his name is often associated with criticism which attempts to explain a work in the light of the writer or his environment. The famous French critic Sainte-Beuve

(1804-1869) is unmistakably Longinian when he defines a classic as "an author who has enriched the human mind." His equally famous contemporary, Hippolyte Taine (1828-1893), is in the same vein when he insists that any creative work is only the "fossil shell" of its creator, a transcript of the author's "race, place, and time." Even the attempts of modern psychological criticism to probe into the mind of the artist are clearly Longinian.

The strength of this approach is that it accounts for things. We can understand Milton's tremendous interest in space when we know that he was blind. Emily Dickinson's repeated images of herself as a bride take on an added poignancy when we know of her withdrawn, single life. The difficulty here is that we can spend so much time learning about the poet that we never get around to reading his poetry, or we may read everything with such a biographical bias that we praise or blame unfairly. Yet this approach can be very useful. Let us demonstrate this by considering once more the poem we have been using.

It is important now to find out that "Days" was written in 1857 by an American, Ralph Waldo Emerson, who was the leading exponent of transcendentalism. This point of view—for it was hardly more formal than that—was an extremely individual one, but the "day" was a symbol which most of the transcendentalists shared. The twenty-four hour day, that is day and night, was an epitome of life, with its positive and negative aspects fused into a whole. Each day, in fact, was a commentary on life, and this helps explain Emerson's personification of Time and Day. "Morning wishes" becomes more meaningful as we realize that, in transcendentalism, morning is the symbol of youthful purity, the uncorrupted divine in man. Even such choices as "dervishes" are explained when we know the unusual interest of many transcendentalists in the East and Eastern religion. A dervish is usually a wandering priest, often under vows of poverty, who lives an austere life of the spirit while serving humbly. Such a symbol has all the right connotations for Emerson and his circle. But perhaps the most transcendental view in the whole poem is the *silence* of the day, the *dumbness* of the dervishes. For nature reveals to man only what he is ready to receive; the gifts to each are "after his will." If man can remember his "morning wishes" and choose according to them, he will retain his divinity.

The final source—the audience—is given its classical formulation by Horace, a very practical Roman who lived during the half century before Christ. He is quite aware of the other critical positions, but he adds a charmingly down-to-earth touch. He mentions that, in addition to the usual places that we should check in trying to form an estimate of a book, we should stop in at the booksellers! If intelligent people have kept a book in demand over the years, we cannot ignore this appeal, whether the work fits any of our usual standards or not. The weakness of this approach is that it cannot be applied to contemporary works; its strength is the weight of evidence which reviews, discussions, and comments over the centuries can provide. Many books which we call "Classics" have received this designation simply because they have endured. Horace would not have us underestimate the test of time.

Since "Days" is only a hundred years old, we still cannot expect the synthesis of critical judgment which Horace prizes. But we have been able to balance the vague and somewhat mystical interpretations of Emerson's contemporaries with the overly simple paraphrases of some of his early twentieth century detractors. If the poem continues to be read, it will gradually integrate the best of many interpretations. Perhaps our grandchildren will see this poem in the critical perspective most of us now have toward the works of Milton.

We can aid in this process of assimilation by trying to harmonize some elements of the criticism expended in this essay on "Days," for the best criticism is rarely one position alone. If, at a Platonic level, we stressed our deepening awareness of the nature of opportunity and the necessity for making significant choices, our Aristotelian approach jolted us a bit in showing that awareness of opposition may not be much help in overcoming it. From a Longinian point of view, however, we surmise that Emerson felt that it could be overcome if we remained sensitive to the divine in us. And, since we usually end on a Platonic note, we suddenly remember some lines from the *Book of Mormon* which help to synthesize our reactions. We are in opposition, "enemies" to God and all that he stands for, and we are without much hope unless we yield ourselves to "the enticings of the Holy Spirit."

An understanding of the four positions outlined above, with the yardsticks which grow out of them, will give anyone all the theory he needs to become an excellent, even a professional, critic. But the intent of this essay is not to prepare professional critics. It is to give confidence to those who recognize that they must discern and evaluate but who have been overawed by the critical paraphernalia which often surrounds a given work, or, even more distressing, do not understand enough about critical method to know where to begin. It seems to bring the problem to manageable size to realize that all critical approaches can be subsumed under four basic views. The background which *you* bring is a legitimate source of critical standards; the relationships *you* see are meaningful; the ring of greatness *you* hear is significant; and the final thrill *you* feel in finding yourself in agreement with great critics is given an added glow when you, in your own way and by your own efforts, are now capable of "selecting good books and seeing clearly what is therein written."[1]

---

[1]As indicated in the Preface, this essay on literary criticism on the preceding twelve pages has been written by Robert K. Thomas. All of the book from here on has been selected and written by Bruce B. Clark.

Supplement to "The Appreciation and Criticism of Literature"

As a supplement to "The Appreciation and Criticism of Literature," we attach six brief selections—three poems, two essays, and a short story. Each is concerned with reading and understanding literature. They are not intended to cover all the myriad views of the world's critics about the nature and value of literature. The scope of criticism is too vast and varied. They are intended simply to make a few special comments on literature that will be both interesting and stimulating.

Of Studies

by Sir Francis Bacon

Studies serve for delight, for ornament, and for ability. Their chief use for delight is in privateness and retiring; for ornament, is in discourse; and for ability, is in the judgment and disposition of business. For expert men can execute, and perhaps judge of particulars, one by one; but the general counsels, and the plots and marshaling of affairs, come best from those that are learned. To spend too much time in studies is sloth; to use them too much for ornament is affectation; to make judgment wholly by their rules is the humor of a scholar. They perfect nature, and are perfected by experience; for natural abilities are like natural plants, that need pruning by study; and studies themselves do give forth direction too much at large, except they be bounded in by experience. Crafty men contemn studies, simple men admire them, and wise men use them; for they teach not their own use; but that is a wisdom without them, and above them, won by observation. Read not to contradict and confute; nor to believe and take for granted; nor to find talk and discourse; but to weigh and consider. Some books are to be tasted, others to be swallowed, and some few to be chewed and digested; that is, some books are to be read only in parts; others to be read, but not curiously; and some few to be read wholly, and with diligence and attention. Some books also may be read by deputy, and extracts made of them by others; but that would be only in the less important arguments, and the meaner sort of books; else distilled books are like common distilled waters, flashy things. Reading maketh a full man; conference a ready man; and writing an exact man. And therefore, if a man write little, he had need have a great memory; if he confer little, he had need have a present wit: and if he read little, he had need have much cunning, to seem to know that he doth not. Histories make men wise; poets witty; the mathematics subtile; natural philosophy deep; moral grave; logic and rhetoric able to contend. "Abeunt studia in mores."[1] Nay, there is no stond or impediment in the wit but may be wrought out by fit studies; like as diseases of the body may have appropriate exercises. Bowling is good for the stone and reins; shooting for the lungs and breast; gentle walking for the stomach; riding for the head; and the like. So if a man's wit be wandering, let him study the mathematics; for in demonstrations, if his

---

[1]"Studies pass over into manners."

wit be called away never so little, he must begin again. If his wit be not apt to distinguish or find differences, let him study the school-men; for they are *cymini* sectores.[1] If he be not apt to beat over matters, and to call up one thing to prove and illustrate another, let him study the lawyers' cases. So every defect of the mind may have a special receipt.

Discussion of "Of Studies"

Francis Bacon (1561-1626) was not primarily a man of literature. He was an eminent statesman (Lord Chancellor of England) and philosopher (*The Advancement of Learning, Novum Organum, New Atlantis,* and other works) who, on the side, wrote dozens of little essays so crisp in style and so clear in meaning, so thoughtful and stimulating and altogether delightful, that literature reaches out to embrace him. Or rather, he reached out to embrace literature.

This famous old essay on "Studies" may seem quaintly archaic to most readers, but after 350 years it still is stimulating reading. Moreover, what it says about books and reading them still seems pertinent and sound. For it is perhaps even more true today than it was 350 years ago that wise men *use* books; that "some books are to be tasted, others to be swallowed, and some few to be chewed and digested"; and also that "reading maketh a full man, conference [that is, conversation] a ready man, and writing an exact man."

---

[1]Splitters of cumin (that is, splitters of hairs).

What Makes a Great Book?

by Mortimer J. Adler

Great books are those that contain the best materials on which the human mind can work in order to gain insight, understanding, and wisdom. Each of them, in its own way, raises the recurrent basic questions which men must face. Because these questions never are completely solved, these books are the sources and monuments of a continuing intellectual tradition.

Carl Van Doren once referred to great books as "the books that never have to be written again." They are the rare, perfect achievements of sustained excellence. Their beauty and clarity show that they are masterpieces of the fine as well as of the liberal arts. Such books justifiably are called great whether they are books of science, poetry, theology, mathematics, or politics.

The richness of great books shows itself in the many levels of meaning they contain. They lend themselves to a variety of interpretations. This does not mean that they are ambiguous or that their integrity is compromised. The different interpretations complement one another and allow the reader to discover the unity of the work from a variety of perspectives. We need not read other books more than once to get all that they have to say. But we can always go deeper into great books. As sources of enlightenment, they are inexhaustible.

The interest in many good books that are written is limited to a definite period of history. They do not exhibit the universal appeal that results from dealing with the fundamental questions which confront men in all times and places and in a way that men in all times and places can understand. Great books, on the contrary, transcend the provincial limits of their origin. They remain as world literature. The ones we are sure are great are the ones men everywhere turn to again and again through the centuries.

In view of this, it is often said that great books must pass the test of time. This is quite true. But it is not the passage of time that makes the books great. They were great when they were written. An enduring interest in a book merely confirms its greatness. We may consider some contemporary books great, but we cannot be sure. Their excellence still remains to be proved before the tribunal of the ages.

Mark Twain once remarked that "The great books are the books that everyone wishes he *had* read, but no one *wants* to read." People wish they had read them because they are the indispensable material of a liberal education. They shy away from reading them because these books require thought. And thinking is hard. It is probably one of the most painful things that human beings are called upon to do.

The great books are not easy to read. No one should expect to understand them very well on a first reading, nor even to master them fully after many readings. I have often said that they are the books which are over everyone's head all of the time. That is why they must be read and reread. That is also why they are good for us. Only the things which are over our head can lift us up.

Like all the other good things in life, what the great books have to offer is hard to get. But it is precisely because great books are difficult that they are more readable and more worth reading than other books. It is precisely because they raise problems which they do not finally answer that they can provoke us to think, inquire, and discuss. It is precisely because their difficulty challenges our skill in reading that they can help us to improve that skill. It is precisely because they often challenge our accepted prejudices and our established opinions that they can help us to develop our critical faculties.

Comment on "What Makes a Great Book?"

Mortimer J. Adler (1902-   ) is a distinguished American college professor, philosopher, and literary critic. As will be apparent to all readers, his "What Makes a Great Book?" is an excellent brief statement on the challenge and reward of first-quality reading. The statement is forcefully clear and self-explanatory.

Ode on a Grecian Urn

by John Keats

I

Thou still unravish'd bride of quietness,
    Thou foster-child of silence and slow time,
Sylvan historian, who canst thus express
    A flowery tale more sweetly than our rhyme:
What leaf-fring'd legend haunts about thy shape
    Of deities or mortals, or of both,
        In Tempe or the dales of Arcady?
    What men or gods are these? What maidens loth?
What mad pursuit? What struggle to escape?
        What pipes and timbrels? What wild ecstasy?

II

Heard melodies are sweet, but those unheard
    Are sweeter; therefore, ye soft pipes, play on;
Not to the sensual ear, but, more endear'd,
    Pipe to the spirit ditties of no tone:
Fair youth, beneath the trees, thou canst not leave
    Thy song, nor ever can those trees be bare;
        Bold Lover, never, never canst thou kiss,
Though winning near the goal—yet, do not grieve;
        She cannot fade, though thou hast not thy bliss,
    For ever wilt thou love, and she be fair!

III

Ah, happy, happy boughs! that cannot shed
    Your leaves, nor ever bid the Spring adieu;
And, happy melodist, unwearied,
    For ever piping songs for ever new;
More happy love! more happy, happy love!
    For ever warm and still to be enjoy'd,
        For ever panting, and for ever young;
All breathing human passion far above,
    That leaves a heart high-sorrowful and cloy'd,
        A burning forehead, and a parching tongue.

IV

Who are these coming to the sacrifice?
    To what green altar, O mysterious priest,
Lead'st thou that heifer lowing at the skies,
    And all her silken flanks with garlands drest?
What little town by river or sea shore,
    Or mountain-built with peaceful citadel,
        Is emptied of this folk, this pious morn?
And, little town, thy streets for evermore
    Will silent be; and not a soul to tell
        Why thou art desolate, can e'er return.

V

O Attic[1] shape! Fair attitude! with brede[2]
    Of marble men and maidens overwrought,
With forest branches and the trodden weed;
    Thou, silent form, dost tease us out of thought
As doth eternity: Cold Pastoral!
    When old age shall this generation waste,
        Thou shalt remain, in midst of other woe
        Than ours, a friend to man, to whom thou say'st,
Beauty is truth, truth beauty,—that is all
        Ye know on earth, and all ye need to know.

Discussion of "Ode on a Grecian Urn"

John Keats (1795-1821) published his first poem at the age of 20 and died the brief span of five years later at the age of 25, yet he is without question one of the great poets of the world. His short life is filled with tragedy— the death of both his parents and one beloved brother, his own sickness with tuberculosis, periods of extreme poverty,

[1]It was in Attica that Greek civilization found its purest expression.
[2]"Brede" means embroidery.

turbulent love, and finally his own premature death. But his life is also filled with beauty, and with a total dedication to the pursuit of beauty in poetry. Altogether he completed only one small volume of poems. How could he have written more in so brief a time? Indeed, the remarkable thing is that he wrote so much in less than five years—less because he didn't really write great poetry (except in a few little poems) until 1819. And by 1820 the tuberculosis that was soon to kill him had already so weakened him that he could write only intermittently and feverishly. In less than one year (1819) Keats wrote enough great poetry to place him forever among the foremost of English poets — an achievement unparalleled in the entire history of literature. And what are his "great" poems? All the world knows them—"The Eve of St. Agnes," "Ode to a Nightingale," "Ode on a Grecian Urn," "To Autumn," the *Hyperion* fragments, several other odes, and a number of sonnets. Not many—but oh the quality!

Like most of Keats's poems, "Ode on a Grecian Urn" makes its primary appeal to the aesthetic sensitivities of the reader. It is beautifully written, with a liquid smoothness of melody and a "choked-in richness" of sensuous imagery that thrill a reader sensitive to beauty in sound and rhythm. Moreover, its ten-line stanzas have just the right combination of structural uniformity and variation to give a pleasing sense of artistic harmony without monotony.

But the poem also has substance. First of all, it describes some scenes carved and painted on the sides of a Grecian urn or vase. Although references to them are intermixed, the reader should be able to identify at least four scenes: (1) a youth underneath some trees playing on a pipe, (2) a priest leading a heifer to the sacrificial altar, followed by a processional of people who have "emptied" the little town in which they live, (3) a youth and maiden in love, their lips almost—but not quite—touching in a kiss, (4) some flirtatious girls running with some young men in laughing pursuit. Such are the descriptive details of the poem.

Its meaning is deeper, however. Various comments are made in the poem contrasting "heard melodies" that are sweet with "unheard melodies" that are sweeter, a kiss or a musical playing that in real life would be experienced briefly and gone but that "cannot fade" on the urn, trees that in the world of reality shed their lovely leaves but on the urn keep their loveliness forever. Finally, in the closing stanza, the poet comments that the urn with its scenes "teases" out a thought. What is this thought, this central idea of the poem? Already we have suggested it: the poem contrasts the temporariness of fading beauty in real life with the relative permanence of beauty as it is caught and preserved in art. Thus, when "old age shall this generation waste," the beautiful urn—and all other works of art, including literature—"shall remain," proclaiming to the world that "Beauty is truth, truth beauty." So read, the poem is one of the great statements on the enduring power and value of art.

This is the theme of the poem. But as an exquisite work of art itself, it is greater than its meaning, greater than the details of its parts. Flawless in craftsmanship, it is one of the great short poems of the world—an experience in beauty and truth.[1]

---

[1]The reader will observe that in this discussion the criticism has been principally a combination of Platonic and Aristotelian approaches, with occasional comments of a Longinian or Horatian nature as needed to fill in background and identify the significance of the poem. The same method, with perhaps even more Platonic emphasis, will be used for most of the works that follow, resulting, we feel, in a focus on ethical and artistic meaning and value. To avoid monotony, however, we will not often employ the terms Platonic, etc., in our discussions. Such repetition would be pointlessly artificial.

The Celestial Omnibus

by E. M. Forster

The boy who resided at Agathox Lodge, 28, Buckingham Park Road, Surbiton, had often been puzzled by the old sign-post that stood almost opposite. He asked his mother about it, and she replied that it was a joke, and not a very nice one, which had been made many years back by some naughty young men, and that the police ought to remove it. For there were two strange things about this sign-post; first, it pointed up a blank alley, and, secondly, it had painted on it, in faded characters, the words, "To Heaven."

"What kind of young men were they?" he asked.

"I think your father told me that one of them wrote verses, and was expelled from the University and came to grief in other ways. Still, it was a long time ago. You must ask your father about it. He will say the same as I do, that it was put up as a joke."

"So it doesn't mean anything at all?"

She sent him upstairs to put on his best things, for the Bonses were coming to tea, and he was to hand the cake-stand.

It struck him, as he wrenched on his tightening trousers, that he might do worse than ask Mr. Bons about the sign-post. His father, though very kind, always laughed at him—shrieked with laughter whenever he or any other child asked a question or spoke. But Mr. Bons was serious as well as kind. He had a beautiful house and lent one books, he was a churchwarden, and a candidate for the County Council; he had donated to the Free Library enormously, he presided over the Literary Society, and had Members of Parliament to stop with him—in short, he was probably the wisest person alive.

Yet even Mr. Bons could only say that the sign-post was a joke —the joke of a person named Shelley.

"Of course!" cried the mother; "I told you so, dear. That was the name."

"Had you never heard of Shelley?" asked Mr. Bons.

"No," said the boy, and hung his head.

"But is there no Shelley in the house?"

"Why, yes!" exclaimed the lady, in much agitation. "Dear Mr. Bons, we aren't such Philistines as that. Two at the least. One a wedding present, and the other, smaller print, in one of the spare rooms."

"I believe we have seven Shelleys," said Mr. Bons, with a slow smile. Then he brushed the cake crumbs off his stomach, and, to-gether with his daughter, rose to go.

The boy, obeying a wink from his mother, saw them all the way to the garden gate, and when they had gone he did not at once return to the house, but gazed for a little up and down Buckingham Park Road.

His parents lived at the right end of it. After No. 39 the quality of the houses dropped very suddenly, and 64 had not even a separate servants' entrance. But at the present moment the whole road looked rather pretty, for the sun had just set in splendour, and the inequalities of rent were drowned in a saffron afterglow. Small birds twittered, and the breadwinners' train shrieked musically down through the cutting—that wonderful cutting which has drawn to itself the whole beauty out of Surbiton, and clad itself, like any Alpine valley, with the glory of the fir and the silver birch and the primrose. It was this cutting that had first stirred desires within the boy—desires for something just a little different, he knew not what, desires that would return whenever things were sunlit, as they were this evening, running up and down inside him, up and down, up and down, till he would feel quite unusual all over, and as likely as not would want to cry. This evening he was even sillier, for he slipped across the road towards the sign-post and began to run up the blank alley.

The alley runs between high walls—the walls of the gardens of "Ivanhoe" and "Bella Vista," respectively. It smells a little all the way, and is scarcely twenty yards long, including the turn at the end. So not unnaturally the boy soon came to a standstill. "I'd like to kick that Shelley," he exclaimed, and glanced idly at a piece of paper which was pasted on the wall. Rather an odd piece of paper, and he read it carefully before he turned back. This is what he read:

S. AND C.R.C.C.
ALTERATION IN SERVICE

Owing to lack of patronage the Company are regretfully compelled to suspend the hourly service, and to retain only the

Sunrise and Sunset Omnibuses,

which will run as usual. It is to be hoped that the public will patronize an arrangement which is intended for their convenience. As an extra inducement, the Company will, for the first time, now issue

Return Tickets!

(available one day only), which may be obtained of the driver. Passengers are again reminded that *no tickets are issued at the other end,* and that no complaints in this connection will receive consideration from the Company. Nor will the Company be responsible for any negligence or stupidity on the part of Passengers, nor for Hailstorms, Lightning, Loss of Tickets, nor for any Act of God.

For the Direction.

Now he had never seen this notice before, nor could he imagine where the omnibus went to. S. of course was for Surbiton, and R.C.C. meant Road Car Company. But what was the meaning of the other C? Coombe and Malden, perhaps, or possibly "City." Yet it could not hope to compete with the South-Western. The whole thing, the boy reflected, was run on hopelessly unbusinesslike lines. Why no tickets from the other end? And what an hour to start! Then he realized that unless the notice was a hoax, an omnibus must have been starting just as he was wishing the Bonses good-bye. He peered at the ground through the gathering dusk, and there he saw what might or might not be the marks of wheels. Yet nothing had come out of the alley. And he had never seen an omnibus at any time in the Buckingham Park Road. No: it must be a hoax, like the sign-post, like the fairy tales, like the dreams upon which he would wake suddenly in the night. And with a sigh he stepped from the alley—right into the arms of his father.

Oh, how his father laughed! "Poor, poor Popsey!" he cried, "Diddums! Diddums! Diddums think he'd walky-palky up to Evvink!" And his mother, also convulsed with laughter, appeared on the steps of Agathox Lodge.

"Don't Bob!" she gasped. "Don't be so naughty! Oh, you'll kill me! Oh, leave the boy alone!"

But all that evening the joke was kept up. The father implored to be taken too. Was it a very tiring walk? Need one wipe one's shoes on the door-mat? And the boy went to bed feeling faint and sore, and thankful for only one thing—that he had not said a word about the omnibus. It was a hoax, yet through his dreams it grew more and more real, and the streets of Surbiton, through which he saw it driving, seemed instead to become hoaxes and shadows. And very early in the morning he woke with a cry, for he had a glimpse of its destination.

He struck a match, and its light fell not only on his watch but also on his calendar, so that he knew it to be half-an-hour to sunrise. It was pitch dark, for the fog had come down from London in the night, and all Surbiton was wrapped in its embraces. Yet he sprang out and dressed himself, for he was determined to settle once for all which was real: the omnibus or the streets. "I shall be a fool one way or the other," he thought, "until I know." Soon he was shivering in the road under the gas lamp that guarded the entrance to the alley.

To enter the alley itself required some courage. Not only was it horribly dark, but he now realized that it was an impossible terminus for an omnibus. If it had not been for a policeman, whom he heard approaching through the fog, he would never have made the attempt. The next moment he had made the attempt and failed. Nothing. Nothing but a blank alley and a very silly boy gaping at its dirty floor. It *was* a hoax. "I'll tell papa and mamma," he decided. "I deserve it. I deserve that they should know. I am too silly to be alive." And he went back to the gate of Agathox Lodge.

There he remembered that his watch was fast. The sun was not risen; it would not rise for two minutes. "Give the bus every chance," he thought cynically, and returned into the alley.

But the omnibus was there.

II

It had two horses, whose sides were still smoking from their journey, and its two great lamps shone through the fog against the alley's walls, changing their cobwebs and moss into tissues of fairyland. The driver was huddled up in a cape. He faced the blank wall, and how he had managed to drive in so neatly and so silently was one of the many things that the boy never discovered. Nor could he imagine how ever he would drive out.

"Please," his voice quavered through the foul brown air, "please, is that an omnibus?"

"Omnibus est," said the driver, without turning around. There was a moment's silence. The policeman passed, coughing, by the entrance of the alley. The boy crouched in the shadow, for he did not want to be found out. He was pretty sure, too, that it was a Pirate; nothing else, he reasoned, would go from such odd places and at such odd hours.

"About when do you start?" he tried to sound nonchalant.

"At sunrise."

"How far do you go?"

"The whole way."

"And can I have a return ticket which will bring me all the way back?"

"You can."

"Do you know, I half think I'll come." The driver made no answer. The sun must have risen, for he unhitched the brake. And scarcely had the boy jumped in before the omnibus was off.

How? Did it turn? There was no room. Did it go forward? There was a blank wall. Yet it was moving—moving at a stately pace through the fog, which had turned from brown to yellow. The thought of warm bed and warmer breakfast made the boy feel faint. He wished he had not come. His parents would not have approved. He would have gone back to them if the weather had not made it impossible. The solitude was terrible; he was the only passenger. And the omnibus, though well-built, was cold and somewhat musty. He drew his coat round him, and in so doing chanced to feel his pocket. It was empty. He had forgotten his purse.

"Stop!" he shouted. "Stop!" And then, being of a polite disposition, he glanced up at the painted notice-board so that he might call the driver by name. "Mr. Browne! stop; oh, do please stop!"

Mr. Browne did not stop, but he opened a little window and looked in at the boy. His face was a surprise, so kind it was and modest.

"Mr. Browne, I've left my purse behind. I've not got a penny. I can't pay for the ticket. Will you take my watch, please? I am in the most awful hole."

"Tickets on this line," said the driver, "whether single or return can be purchased by coinage from no terrene mint. And a chronometer, though it had solaced the vigils of Charlemagne, or measured the slumbers of Laura, can acquire by no mutation the double-cake that charms the fangless Cerberus of Heaven!" So saying, he handed in the necessary ticket, and while the boy said "Thank you," continued, "Titular pretensions, I know it well, are vanity. Yet they merit no censure when uttered on a laughing lip, and in an homonymous world are in some sort useful, since they do serve to distinguish one Jack from his fellow. Remember me, therefore, as Sir Thomas Browne."

"Are you a Sir? Oh, sorry!" He had heard of these gentlemen drivers. "It *is* good of you about the ticket. But if you go on at this rate, however does your bus pay?"

"It does not pay. It was not intended to pay. Many are the faults of my equipage; it is compounded too curiously of foreign woods; its cushions tickle erudition rather than promote repose; and my horses are nourished not on the evergreen pastures of the moment, but on the dried bents and clovers of Latinity. But that it pays!— that error at all events was never intended and never attained."

"Sorry again," said the boy rather hopelessly. Sir Thomas looked sad, fearing that, even for a moment, he had been the cause of sadness. He invited the boy to come up and sit beside him on the box, and together they journeyed on through the fog, which was now changing from yellow to white. There were no houses by the road; so it must be either Putney Heath or Wimbledon Common.

"Have you been a driver always?"

"I was a physician once."

"But why did you stop? Weren't you good?"

"As a healer of bodies I had scant success, and several score of my patients preceded me. But as a healer of the spirit I have succeeded beyond my hopes and my deserts. For though my draughts were not better nor subtler than those of other men, yet, by reason of the cunning goblets wherein I offered them, the queasy soul was ofttimes tempted to sip and be refreshed."

"The queasy soul," the boy murmured; "if the sun sets with trees in front of it, and you suddenly come strange all over, is that a queasy soul?"

"Have you felt that?"

"Why, yes."

After a pause he told the boy a little, a very little, about the journey's end. But they did not chatter much, for the boy, when he liked a person, would as soon sit silent in his company as speak, and this, he discovered, was also the mind of Sir Thomas Browne and of many others with whom he was to be acquainted. He heard, however, about the young man Shelley, who was now quite a famous person, with a carriage of his own, and about some of the other drivers who are in the service of the Company. Meanwhile the light grew stronger, though the fog did not disperse. It was now more like mist than fog, and at times would travel quickly across them, as if it were part of a cloud. They had been ascending too, in a most puzzling way; for over two hours the horses had been pulling against the collar, and even if it were Richmond Hill they ought to have been at the top long ago. Perhaps it was Epsom, or even the North Downs; yet the air seemed keener than that which blows on either. And as to the name of their destination, Sir Thomas Browne was silent.

Crash!

"Thunder, by Jove!" said the boy, "and not so far off either. Listen to the echoes! It's more like mountains."

He thought, not very vividly, of his father and mother. He saw them sitting down to sausages and listening to the storm. He saw his own empty place. Then there would be questions, alarms, theories, jokes, consolations. They would expect him back at lunch. To lunch he would not come, nor to tea, but he would be in for dinner, and so his day's truancy would be over. If he had had his purse he would have bought them presents—not that he should have known what to get them.

Crash!

The peal and the lightning came together. The cloud quivered as if it were alive, and torn streamers of mist rushed past. "Are you afraid?" asked Sir Thomas Browne.

"What is there to be afraid of? Is it much farther?"

The horses of the omnibus stopped just as a ball of fire burst up and exploded with a ringing noise that was deafening but clear, like the noise of a blacksmith's forge. All the cloud was shattered.

"Oh, listen, Sir Thomas Browne! No, I mean look; we shall get a view at last. No, I mean listen; that sounds like a rainbow!"

The noise had died into the faintest murmur, beneath which another murmur grew, spreading stealthily, steadily, in a curve that widened but did not vary. And in widening curves a rainbow was spreading from the horses' feet into the dissolving mists.

"But how beautiful! What colours! Where will it stop? It is more like the rainbows you can tread on. More like dreams."

The colour and the sound grew together. The rainbow spanned an enormous gulf. Clouds rushed under it and were pierced by it, and still it grew, reaching forward, conquering the darkness, until it touched something that seemed more solid than a cloud.

The boy stood up. "What is that out there?" he called. "What does it rest on, out at that other end?"

In the morning sunshine a precipice shone forth beyond the gulf. A precipice—or was it a castle? The horses moved. They set their feet upon the rainbow.

"Oh, look" the boy shouted. "Oh, listen! Those caves—or are they gateways? Oh, look between those cliffs at those ledges. I see people! I see trees!"

"Look also below," whispered Sir Thomas. "Neglect not the diviner Acheron."

The boy looked below, past the flames of the rainbow that licked against their wheels. The gulf also had cleared, and in its depths there flowed an everlasting river. One sunbeam entered and struck a green pool, and as they passed over he saw three maidens rise to the surface of the pool, singing, and playing with something that glistened like a ring.

"You down in the water—" he called.

They answered, "You up on the bridge—" There was a burst of music. "You up on the bridge, good luck to you. Truth in the depth, truth on the height."

"You down in the water, what are you doing?"

Sir Thomas Browne replied: "They sport in the mancipiary possession of their gold"; and the omnibus arrived.

III

The boy was in disgrace. He sat locked up in the nursery of Agathox Lodge, learning poetry for a punishment. His father had said, "My boy! I can pardon anything but untruthfulness," and had caned him, saying at each stroke, "There is *no* omnibus, *no* driver, *no* bridge, *no* mountain; you are a *truant*, a *guttersnipe*, a *liar*." His father could be very stern at times. His mother had begged him to say he was sorry. But he could not say that. It was the greatest day of his life, in spite of the caning and the poetry at the end of it.

He had returned punctually at sunset—driven not by Sir Thomas Browne, but by a maiden lady who was full of quiet fun. They had talked of omnibuses and also of barouche landaus. How far away her gentle voice seemed now! Yet it was scarcely three hours since he had left her up the alley.

His mother called through the door. "Dear, you are to come down and to bring your poetry with you."

He came down, and found that Mr. Bons was in the smoking-room with his father. It had been a dinner party.

"Here is the great traveller!" said his father grimly. "Here is the young gentleman who drives in an omnibus over rainbows, while young ladies sing to him." Pleased with his wit, he laughed.

"After all," said Mr. Bons, smiling, "there is something a little like it in Wagner. It is odd how, in quite illiterate minds, you find glimmers of Artistic Truth. The case interests me. Let me plead for the culprit. We have all romanced in our time, haven't we?"

"Hear how kind Mr. Bons is," said his mother, while his father said, "Very well. Let him say his Poem, and that will do. He is going away to my sister on Tuesday, and *she* will cure him of this alley-sloping." (Laughter.) "Say your Poem."

The boy began. " 'Standing aloof in giant ignorance.' "

His father laughed again — roared. "One for you, my son! 'Standing aloof in giant ignorance!' I never knew these poets talked sense. Just describes you. Here, Bons, you go in for poetry. Put him through it, will you, while I fetch up the whisky?"

"Yes, give me the Keats," said Mr. Bons. "Let him say his Keats to me."

So for a few moments the wise man and the ignorant boy were left alone in the smoking-room.

" 'Standing aloof in giant ignorance, of thee I dream and of the Cyclades, as one who sits ashore and longs perchance to visit—' "

"Quite right. To visit what?"

" 'To visit dolphin coral in deep seas,' " said the boy, and burst into tears.

"Come, come why do you cry?"

"Because — because all these words that only rhymed before, now that I've come back they're me."

Mr. Bons laid the Keats down. The case was more interesting than he had expected. *"You?"* he exclaimed. "This sonnet, *you?"*

"Yes—and look further on: 'Aye, on the shores of darkness there is light, and precipices show untrodden green.' It *is* so, sir. All these things are true."

"I never doubted it," said Mr. Bons, with closed eyes.

"You—then you believe me? You believe in the omnibus and the driver and the storm and that return ticket I got for nothing and—"

"Tut, tut! No more of your yarns, my boy. I meant that I never doubted the essential truth of Poetry. Some day, when you have read more, you will understand what I mean."

"But, Mr. Bons, it *is* so. There *is* light upon the shores of darkness. I have seen it coming. Light and a wind."

"Nonsense," said Mr. Bons.

"If I had stopped! They tempted me. They told me to give up my ticket—for you cannot come back if you lose your ticket. They called from the river for it, and indeed I was tempted, for I have never been so happy as among those precipices. But I thought of my mother and father, and that I must fetch them. Yet they will not come, though the road starts opposite our house. It has all happened as the people up there warned me, and Mr. Bons has disbelieved me like everyone else. I have been caned. I shall never see that mountain again."

"What's that about me?" said Mr. Bons, sitting up in his chair very suddenly.

"I told them about you, and how clever you were, and how many books you had, and they said, 'Mr. Bons will certainly disbelieve you.' "

"Stuff and nonsense, my young friend. You grow impertinent. I—well—I will settle the matter. Not a word to your father. I will

cure you. Tomorrow evening I will myself call here to take you for a
walk, and at sunset we will go up this alley opposite and hunt for
your omnibus, you silly little boy."

His face grew serious, for the boy was not disconcerted, but
leapt about the room singing, "Joy! joy! I told them you would believe
me. We will drive together over the rainbow. I told them that you
would come." After all, could there be anything in the story? Wagner? Keats? Shelley? Sir Thomas Browne? Certainly the case was
interesting.

And on the morrow evening, though it was pouring with rain,
Mr. Bons did not omit to call at Agathox Lodge.

The boy was ready, bubbling with excitement, and skipping
about in a way that rather vexed the President of the Literary Society. They took a turn down Buckingham Park Road, and then—
having seen that no one was watching them—slipped up the alley.
Naturally enough (for the sun was setting) they ran straight against
the omnibus.

"Good heavens!" exclaimed Mr. Bons. "Good gracious heavens!"

It was not the omnibus in which the boy had driven first, nor
yet that in which he had returned. There were three horses—black,
gray, and white, the gray being the finest. The driver, who turned
round at the mention of goodness and of heaven, was a sallow
man with terrifying jaws and sunken eyes. Mr. Bons, on seeing him,
gave a cry as if of recognition, and began to tremble violently.

The boy jumped in.

"Is it possible?" cried Mr. Bons. "Is the impossible possible?"

"Sir; come in, sir. It is such a fine omnibus. Oh, here is his
name—Dan someone."

Mr. Bons sprang in too. A blast of wind immediately slammed
the omnibus door, and the shock jerked down all the omnibus blinds,
which were very weak on their springs.

"Dan . . . Show me. Good gracious heavens We're moving."

"Hooray!" said the boy.

Mr. Bons became flustered. He had not intended to be kid-
napped. He could not find the door-handle nor push up the blinds.
The omnibus was quite dark, and by the time he had struck a match,
night had come on outside also. They were moving rapidly.

"A strange, a memorable adventure," he said, surveying the
interior of the omnibus, which was large, roomy, and constructed
with extreme regularity, every part exactly answering to every other
part. Over the door (the handle of which was outside) was written,
"Lasciate ogni baldanza voi che entrate"—at least, that was what

was written, but Mr. Bons said that it was Lashy arty something, and that baldanza was a mistake for speranza. His voice sounded as if he was in church. Meanwhile, the boy called to the cadaverous driver for two return tickets. They were handed in without a word. Mr. Bons covered his face with his hand and again trembled. "Do you know who that is!" he whispered, when the little window had shut upon them. "It is the impossible."

"Well, I don't like him as much as Sir Thomas Browne, though I shouldn't be surprised if he had even more in him."

"More in him?" He stamped irritably. "By accident you have made the greatest discovery of the century, and all you can say is that there is more in this man. Do you remember those vellum books in my library, stamped with red lilies? This—sit still, I bring you stupendous news!—*this is the man who wrote them.*"

The boy sat quite still. "I wonder if we shall see Mrs. Gamp?" he asked, after a civil pause.

"Mrs.—?"

"Mrs. Gamp and Mrs. Harris. I like Mrs. Harris. I came upon them quite suddenly. Mrs. Gamp's bandboxes have moved over the rainbow so badly. All the bottoms have fallen out, and two of the pippins off her bedstead tumbled into the stream."

"Out there sits the man who wrote my vellum books!" thundered Mr. Bons, "and you talk to me of Dickens and Mrs. Gamp?"

"I know Mrs. Gamp so well," he apologized. "I could not help being glad to see her. I recognized her voice. She was telling Mrs. Harris about Mrs. Prig."

"Did you spend the whole day in her elevating company?"

"Oh, no. I raced. I met a man who took me out beyond to a race-course. You run, and there are dolphins out at sea."

"Indeed. Do you remember the man's name?"

"Achilles. No; he was later. Tom Jones."

Mr. Bons sighed heavily. "Well, my lad, you have made a miserable mess of it. Think of a cultured person with your opportunities! A cultured person would have known all these characters and known what to have said to each. He would not have wasted his time with a Mrs. Gamp or a Tom Jones. The creations of Homer, of Shakespeare, and of Him who drives us now, would alone have contented him. He would not have raced. He would have asked intelligent questions."

"But, Mr. Bons," said the boy humbly, "you will be a cultured person. I told them so."

"True, true, and I beg you not to disgrace me when we arrive.

No gossiping. No running. Keep close to my side, and never speak
to these Immortals unless they speak to you. Yes, and give me the
return tickets. You will be losing them."

The boy surrendered the tickets, but felt a little sore. After all,
he had found the way to this place. It was hard first to be disbelieved and then to be lectured. Meanwhile, the rain had stopped,
and moonlight crept into the omnibus through the cracks in the blinds.

"But how is there to be a rainbow?" cried the boy.

"You distract me," snapped Mr. Bons. "I wish to meditate on
beauty. I wish to goodness I was with a reverent and sympathetic
person."

The lad bit his lip. He made a hundred good resolutions. He
would imitate Mr. Bons all the visit. He would not laugh, or run, or
sing, or do any of the vulgar things that must have disgusted his
new friends last time. He would be very careful to pronounce their
names properly, and to remember who knew whom. Achilles did
not know Tom Jones—at least, so Mr. Bons said. The Duchess of
Malfi was older than Mrs. Gamp—at least, so Mr. Bons said. He
would be self-conscious, reticent, and prim. He would never say
he liked anyone. Yet, when the blind flew up at a chance touch of his
head, all these good resolutions went to the winds, for the omnibus
had reached the summit of a moonlit hill, and there was the chasm,
and there, across it, stood the old precipices, dreaming, with their
feet in the everlasting river. He exclaimed, "The mountain! Listen
to the new tune in the water! Look at the camp fires in the ravines,"
and Mr. Bons, after a hasty glance, retorted, "Water? Camp fires?
Ridiculous rubbish. Hold your tongue. There is nothing at all."

Yet, under his eyes, a rainbow formed, compounded not of
sunlight and storm, but of moonlight and the spray of the river.
The three horses put their feet upon it. He thought it the finest
rainbow he had seen, but did not dare to say so, since Mr. Bons said
nothing was there. He leant out—the window had opened—and
sang the tune that rose from the sleeping waters.

"The prelude of Rhinegold?" said Mr. Bons suddenly. "Who
taught you these *leit motifs?*" He, too, looked out of the window.
Then he behaved very oddly. He gave a choking cry and fell back
onto the omnibus floor. He writhed and kicked. His face was green.

"Does the bridge make you dizzy?" the boy asked.

"Dizzy!" gasped Mr. Bons. "I want to go back. Tell the driver."

But the driver shook his head.

"We are nearly there," said the boy. "They are asleep. Shall
I call? They will be pleased to see you, for I have prepared them."

Mr. Bons moaned. They moved over the lunar rainbow, which ever and ever broke away behind their wheels. How still the night was! Who would be sentry at the Gate?

"I am coming," he shouted, again forgetting the hundred resolutions. "I am returning—I, the boy."

"The boy is returning," cried a voice to other voices, who repeated, "The boy is returning."

"I am bringing Mr. Bons with me."

Silence.

"I should have said Mr. Bons is bringing me with him."

Profound silence.

"Who stands sentry?"

"Achilles."

And on the rocky causeway, close to the springing of the rainbow bridge, he saw a young man who carried a wonderful shield.

"Mr. Bons, it is Achilles, armed."

"I want to go back," said Mr. Bons.

The last fragment of the rainbow melted, the wheels sang upon the living rock, the door of the omnibus burst open. Out leapt the boy—he could not resist—and sprang to meet the warrior, who, stooping suddenly, caught him on his shield.

"Achilles!" he cried, "let me get down, for I am ignorant and vulgar, and I must wait for that Mr. Bons of whom I told you yesterday."

But Achilles raised him aloft. He crouched on the wonderful shield, on heroes and burning cities, on vineyards graven in gold, on every dear passion, every joy, on the entire image of the Mountain that he had discovered, encircled, like it, with an everlasting stream. "No, no," he protested, "I am not worthy. It is Mr. Bons who must be up here."

But Mr. Bons was whimpering, and Achilles trumpeted and cried, "Stand upright upon my shield!"

"Sir, I did not mean to stand! something made me stand. Sir, why do you delay? Here is only the great Achilles, whom you knew."

Mr. Bons screamed, "I see no one. I see nothing. I want to go back." Then he cried to the driver, "Save me! Let me stop in your chariot. I have honoured you. I have quoted you. I have bound you in vellum. Take me back to my world."

The driver replied, "I am the means and not the end. I am the food and not the life. Stand by yourself, as that boy has stood. I cannot save you. For poetry is a spirit; and they that would worship it must worship in spirit and in truth."

Mr. Bons—he could not resist—crawled out of the beautiful omnibus. His face appeared, gaping horribly. His hands followed, one gripping the step, the other beating the air. Now his shoulders emerged, his chest, his stomach. With a shriek of "I see London," he fell—fell against the hard, moonlit rock, fell into it as if it were water, fell through it, vanished, and was seen by the boy no more.

"Where have you fallen to, Mr. Bons? Here is a procession arriving to honour you with music and torches. Here come the men and women whose names you know. The mountain is awake, the river is awake, over the race-course the sea is awakening those dolphins, and it is all for you. They want you—"

There was the touch of fresh leaves on his forehead. Someone had crowned him.

ΤΕΛΟΣ

♦

From the *Kingston Gazette, Surbiton Times,* and *Raynes Park Observer.*

The body of Mr. Septimus Bons has been found in a shockingly mutilated condition in the vicinity of the Bermondsey gas-works. The deceased's pockets contained a sovereign-purse, a silver cigar-case, a bijou pronouncing dictionary, and a couple of omnibus tickets. The unfortunate gentleman had apparently been hurled from a considerable height. Foul play is suspected, and a thorough investigation is pending by the authorities.

Discussion of "The Celestial Omnibus"

E. M. Forster (1879-   ) is a celebrated English novelist (*A Passage to India, Where Angels Fear to Tread, The Longest Journey, A Room With a View, and Howard's End*), literary critic (*Aspects of the Novel*), and short-story writer (two volumes). "The Celestial Omnibus" combines his interests as a critic and as a creative writer.

The reader may, on first reading the story, wonder why "The Celestial Omnibus" is included in this book, and particularly in the opening section on literary criticism. Certainly it is a strange story, and it may not even seem to make sense. In fact, it doesn't make sense on a literal level. If we read it literally as the story of a boy and an old man who make an actual trip on a "celestial omnibus" to heaven, out of which the old man plunges back to earth, the story is worse than unrealistic—it is silly.

But if it doesn't make sense on a literal level, to what level must we go for it to make sense? The answer is, of course, to the level of symbol and allegory. On this level we see Mr. Bons as representing one approach (the wrong one) to literature, and the boy as representing another approach (the right one).

Years ago I took a Shakespeare course from a famous Shakespearean scholar. I looked forward to the course with excitement —and left it with disappointment. In it we learned every detail of Shakespeare's life, every date in and around his career, multitudinous facts about the publication of all his plays, and about their sources, innumerable items of information about the Shakespearean theater, and the language of Shakespeare's London, and the politics of Shakespeare's England. Everything, in short, except an understanding of Shakespeare's writings. We had missed the most important thing; and with this missed, all of the other things were of little importance.

Mr. Bons is this kind of literary scholar. He prides himself in his knowledge of books and their authors. He knows all of the birth dates, death dates, and publication dates—all of the facts about all the books and who wrote them—everything except what is in the books. He knows everything, that is, except the one thing that is important. Therefore, he is uncomfortable in heaven with the authors and the immortal living characters of their books, and he tumbles back to earth.

The boy, on the other hand, knows few of the external facts. But he knows the *insides* of the books. He has read them, and they have delighted him. Hence he is on friendly, comfortable terms with authors and characters. He is neither awed nor alienated by literature. He simply *enjoys* it, responding spontaneously to what is there. Pompous Mr. Bons condescendingly and scornfully calls the boy "illiterate," but the truth is that the boy knows much more of what is important about literature than does Mr. Bons. And, which is most important of all, his "attitude" is right. Therefore, he remains in heaven, chatting with the authors and characters.

If one searches he can find many scriptures that suggest the essence of this story: "The letter killeth, but the spirit giveth life." (II Corinthians 3:6) "And a little child shall lead them." (Isaiah 11:6) "Except ye . . .become as little children, ye shall not enter into the kingdom of heaven." (Matthew 18:3) (In this story, heaven is, of course, *literary* heaven.) And there are other scriptures.

We do need to approach literature "as a little child." We need to be humble, and teachable, and curious, and filled with wonder over all new and beautiful things. Some people pride themselves in the books they own, as Mr. Bons did. But one never owns a book by buying it. One buys merely paper and thread and printer's ink. The only way to own a book is to read it and let it digest into the blood of one's heart and the marrow of one's bones, or even the cells of one's brain.

Perhaps the best statement on the meaning of this story comes right in the story itself, spoken by the driver near the story's end, as he paraphrases scripture to say:

"I am the means and not the end. I am the food and not the life. . . . For poetry is a spirit; and they that would worship it must worship in spirit and in truth."

As one further thought for consideration on this story, note that Mr. Bons's attitude towards literature may be even worse than that of the boy's father: the father openly scorns it, but Mr. Bons destroys it with pompous erudition. And as still another thought for pondering, note the rich implications of the fact that the mysterious driver of the omnibus on the second day is Dante, author of *The Divine Comedy*.

Poetry

by Marianne Moore

I, too, dislike it: there are things that are important beyond all
    this fiddle.
    Reading it, however, with a perfect contempt for it, one
    discovers in it after all, a place for the genuine.
        Hands that can grasp, eyes
        that can dilate, hair that can rise
            if it must, these things are important not because a

high-sounding interpretation can be put upon them but because
    they are useful. When they become so derivative as to
    become unintelligible, the same thing may be said for all
        of us, that we do not admire what
        we cannot understand: the bat
            holding on upside down or in quest of something to

eat, elephants pushing, a wild horse taking a roll, a tireless wolf
    under a tree, the immovable critic twitching his skin like a
    horse that feels a flee, the base—
    ball fan, the statistician—
        nor is it valid
            to discriminate against 'business documents and

school-books'; all these phenomena are important. One must
    make a distinction however: when dragged into prominence
    by half poets, the result is not poetry, nor till the poets
        among us can be
        'literalists of
        the imagination'—above
            insolence and triviality and can present

for inspection, 'imaginary gardens with real toads in them,'
    shall we have it. In the meantime, if you demand on the
    one hand, the raw material of poetry in
        all its rawness and
        that which is on the other hand
            genuine, you are interested in poetry.

Comment on "Poetry"

Marianne Moore (1887-   ) is an American poet and literary critic characterized by an unusual ability to say important things both sharply and powerfully, and in both prose and poetry.

Her famous little poem "Poetry" is at once both a criticism of bad poetry by "half-poets" and a defense of good poetry by "genuine" poets. The work speaks for itself and needs no explaining.

Some Remarks on "Flower in the Crannied Wall"

One of the most interesting arguments I ever heard on literature occurred several years ago at Brigham Young University. Two English teachers were talking about what makes great literature. To clinch a point, one quoted to the other Tennyson's[1] little poem "Flower in the Crannied Wall":

> Flower in the crannied wall,
> I pluck you out of the crannies,
> I hold you here, root and all, in my hand,
> Little flower—but *if* I could understand
> What you are, root and all, and all in all,
> I should know what God and man is.

"Now that," said the one teacher, "is profound poetry."

"I don't like it," said the other.

"But you have to like it if you like good poetry," said the first. "Listen to it again." And he quoted it once more from beginning to end, his voice even more reverent than on the first recitation. "Don't you see?" he continued. "If we could understand what makes the sap rise in the stem, the greenness spread through the leaves, and the color brighten in the delicate flower petals, we *would* comprehend the mystery of God's creative powers. The whole essence of life is in this little flower. Don't you see?" he repeated.

"The more you talk about it, the worse it sounds," retorted the second teacher. "Why, it isn't even grammatical: 'I should know what God and man *is*'!"

"Obviously you don't even understand the poem," said the first. "A plural verb would ruin it. Tennyson is pointing out the oneness of God and man as aspects of eternal life in the universe. He is suggesting the divine spark of God that illuminates man's nature and unites him

---

[1]For some brief comments on the life and work of Alfred, Lord Tennyson (1809-1892), see pp. 476-77.

with God, and unites all living things. Don't you see?" he said for a third time.

"It's even worse than before," exploded the second teacher. "If you pull a flower out of the ground and hold it in your hand, what do you have? A wilted weed, and that is all."

★   ★   ★

Which teacher was right? The answer is that each was right—from his point of view. The first would call the second a cynical realist, and the second would call the first a sentimental idealist. Most of us will probably side with the idealist, but we need to recognize that the realist also has a point.

The incident is cited here to show that, whatever other differences and likenesses we as readers may have, we differ finally in our tastes. Some of us like one kind of literature, some a different kind. And all of us vary from time to time depending on the mood we are in.

We hope that in this book there are selections to suit many tastes and many moods. However, not all types of literature are represented, for we have emphasized those works that harmonize with ideals of Christian living. But within these standards we have tried to select poems and stories of many types and with many appeals to reach the varied interests, attitudes, and moods of the members of the Church.

SECTION TWO

Faith in God and Man

FAITH IN GOD AND MAN

Introductory Comments

Through the centuries men of literature, and especially poets, have traditionally been champions of the spirit and defenders of the faith.

This may not seem so to present-day readers, however, because in the twentieth century pessimism and negativism have spread as a dominant force in philosophy and literature, reflecting the fears and frustrations of modern man. Often in our contemporary age the most brilliant and powerful literature has also been the most despairing.

Note, as one example of many that might be used, the poems of Anglo-American T. S. Eliot (1888-   ) such as "The Waste Land," "Gerontian," "The Love Song of J. Alfred Prufrock," and "The Hollow Men." Such poems should not be interpreted as necessarily Eliot's own philosophy; he has, in fact, written some deeply religious poems expressing quite contrary views. Rather, they should be seen as Eliot's attempt to reflect what he felt was the tragedy of modern man, living in a spiritual wasteland with faith and confidence dead, unable to believe in either God or man, torn by petty fears and wasting his days in trivial pursuits, prematurely aged and world-weary. If the reader wishes to explore these poems, he might turn first to "The Hollow Men," which represents the "wasteland" world in miniature. Religion for the "modern" men in this poem has degenerated to empty ritualism, and existence has become a monotony of directionless routine. So frustrated are they that even sentences break off unfinished. And so pathetically weak have they become compared with their faith-strong ancestors that even death has deteriorated to a whining pathos as they look to a world which will end "not with a bang but a whimper." This is artistically rich and excellent poetry, but its view of life is bleak and dismal.

Even more harshly extreme as a reflection of twentieth-century despair is such a poem as "Original Sin" by Robinson Jeffers (1887-1962), another strong-voiced American poet:

> The man-brained and man-handed ground-ape, physically
> The most repulsive of all hot-blooded animals
> Up to that time of the world: they had dug a pitfall
> And caught a mammoth, but how could their sticks and stones
> Reach the life in that hide? They danced around the pit, shrieking
> With ape excitement, flinging sharp flints in vain, and the stench of their bodies
> Stained the white air of dawn; but presently one of them
> Remembered the yellow dancer, wood-eating fire
> That guards the cave-mouth: he ran and fetched him, and others
> Gathered sticks at the wood's edge; they made a blaze
> And pushed it into the pit, and they fed it high, around the mired sides
> Of their huge prey. They watched the long hairy trunk
> Waver over the stifle-trumpeting pain,
> And they were happy.
>
> Meanwhile the intense color and nobility of sunrise,
> Rose and gold and amber, flowed up the sky. Wet rocks were shining, a little wind
> Stirred the leaves of the forest and the marsh flag-flowers; the soft valley between the low hills
> Became as beautiful as the sky; while in its midst, hour after hour, the happy hunters
> Roasted their living meat slowly to death.
>
> These are the people.
> This is the human dawn. As for me, I would rather
> Be a worm in a wild apple than a son of man.
> But we are what we are, and we might remember
> Not to hate any person, for all are vicious;
> And not to be astonished at any evil, all are deserved;
> And not fear death; it is the only way to be cleansed.

In his poetry as a whole Jeffers argues that human society has become so degenerate that the only way to escape contamination is to flee civilization and live isolated in nature. ("It would be better for men to be few and live far apart, where none could infect another; then slowly the sanity of field and mountain and the cold ocean and glittering stars might enter their minds," he says in "May-June 1940.") Although it may seem difficult to believe, Jeffers seems absolutely sincere and consistent in his argument that civilization is doomed by its own decadence, and the sooner the earth is cleansed by the removal of man the better. Repeatedly in his poems he contrasts the brutality and ugliness of man with the magnificent beauty of the non-human universe. (See "Apology for Bad Dreams" as the best example of this contrast.) Thus "Original Sin" is for Jeffers a characteristic poem—its first stanza describing savage cave-men frenziedly torturing a great mammoth by roasting it alive in a pit, its second stanza describing a contrastingly beautiful scene in non-human nature, and its third stanza grotesquely asserting that the poet "would rather be a worm in a wild apple than a son of man."

These poems by Eliot and Jeffers are here cited as examples of many contemporary works of literature that are equally pessimistic, grim, and negative. There is much power in such literature; there is not much optimism.[1] •

Traditionally, however, literature has, as already stated, been the bulwark of man's faith and the guardian of his spiritual ideals, as well as the goad to his conscience.

We now turn to a small group of poems, mostly by English authors, as representative of the poet's traditional faith in God and in man; and we go first to several poems

---

[1]These comments should not be taken as an indictment of modern literature. Power, beauty, and rich meaning are all found abundantly in the literature of our century, even though it does tend to be dominantly pessimistic. Fortunately, the pessimism is not unbroken. In fact, many evidences in the literature of the past twenty-five years suggest that a reaffirmation of spiritual values may be the direction literature will take in the next several decades. And in any case, modern literature is extraordinarily challenging and provocative.

by William Wordsworth, the great fountainhead of romanticism. After Wordsworth there is a discussion of several poems by Robert Browning, followed with individual poems by William Blake, Emily Dickinson, Francis Thompson, Gerard Manley Hopkins (two poems), and Edith Sitwell.

William Wordsworth: Affirmer of Spiritual Values

Occasionally in the world of literature there is a writer so gifted and so wise that he seems to speak with a voice of divine authority. Such a writer was William Wordsworth (1770-1850), who, a century and a half ago, created poems of such simple beauty and such enduring truth that their appeal and greatness seem forever assured. If we Latter-day Saints take seriously the Lord's commandment to seek words of wisdom out of the best books,[1] we will do well to study the poems of Wordsworth, for in all literature there are few other first-quality poets who shaped so many religious and ethical truths into works of art. As Coleridge says, Wordsworth was "friend of the wise and teacher of the good,"[2] who, in Matthew Arnold's words, came to a world of "doubts, disputes, distractions, fears" and brought stability through the "healing power" of his poetry.[3]

As a poet Wordsworth has obvious faults: he is sometimes over-sentimental, sometimes sing-songy, sometimes dull, sometimes wordy ("wordy Wordsworth" his enemies called him), sometimes pompous in trivialities. If one judges him by the poorest of his poems, he is little better than a shallow rhymester. Indeed, in the entire history of English poetry there is probably no other great poet who wrote so much mediocre poetry. Yet judged by his best work— and a writer should always be judged by his best—Wordsworth achieves distinction among the world's greatest poets. As Russell Noyes says, "Wordsworth was the most truly original genius of his age and exerted a power over the poetic destinies of his century unequaled by any of his contemporaries."[4] More than any other poet he stands as the great shaper of the whole romantic movement in western

---

[1]Doctrine and Covenants, 88:118 and 109:14.
[2]See Coleridge's poem "To Willam Wordsworth."
[3]See Arnold's poem "Memorial Verses."
[4]Russell Noyes, *English Romantic Poetry and Prose* (New York: Oxford University Press, 1956), p. 237.

world literature and probably, all things considered, must be recognized as the greatest English poet between Milton and Browning. In an age of great poets, Wordsworth stands highest of all. His poems are not so challengingly mystical as Blake's, nor so hauntingly musical as Coleridge's, nor so soaringly lyrical as Shelley's, nor so exuberantly variable as Byron's, nor so enchantingly euphonical as Keats's, nor so stingingly satirical as Burns's—yet he is greater than all these, for more than any of them he spoke enduring truths in words of beauty, and that is the essence of great poetry. His poetry—not individual poems but his work as a whole—has more breadth, more depth, more psychological and ethical richness, and a more impressive combination of lofty thought and eloquent music than that of the others. From Wordsworth more than from any other poet we learn, as Ernest Bernbaum says, "the beauty and happiness of plain living and high thinking."[1]

---

[1]Ernest Bernbaum, *Anthology of Romanticism* (New York: Ronald Press, 1948), p. 187.

Ode: Intimations of Immortality from Recollections of Early Childhood

by William Wordsworth

I

There was a time when meadow, grove, and stream,
The earth and every common sight,
          To me did seem
        Apparelled in celestial light,
The glory and the freshness of a dream.
        It is not now as it hath been of yore;—
      Turn wheresoe'er I may,
          By night or day,
The things which I have seen I now can see no more.

II

      The rainbow comes and goes,
      And lovely is the rose,
      The moon doth with delight
Look round her when the heavens are bare,
      Waters on a starry night
      Are beautiful and fair;
    The sunshine is a glorious birth;
    But yet I know, where'er I go,
That there hath past away a glory from the earth.

III

Now, while the birds thus sing a joyous song,
      And while the young lambs bound
        As to the tabor's sound,
To me alone there came a thought of grief:
A timely utterance gave that thought relief,
        And I again am strong:
The cataracts blow their trumpets from the steep;
No more shall grief of mine the season wrong;
I hear the echoes through the mountains throng,
The winds come to me from the fields of sleep,
        And all the earth is gay;
          Land and sea
    Give themselves up to jollity,
        And with the heart of May

Doth every beast keep holiday;—
Thou child of joy,
Shout round me, let me hear thy shouts, thou happy
Shepherd-boy!

IV

Ye blessed creatures, I have heard the call
Ye to each other make; I see
The heavens laugh with you in your jubilee;
My heart is at your festival,
My head hath its coronal,
The fulness of your bliss, I feel—I feel it all.
Oh evil day! if I were sullen
While Earth herself is adorning,
This sweet May-morning,
And the children are culling
On every side,
In a thousand valleys far and wide,
Fresh flowers; while the sun shines warm,
And the babe leaps up on his mother's arm:—
I hear, I hear, with joy I hear!
—But there's a tree, of many, one,
A single field which I have looked upon,
Both of them speak of something that is gone:
The pansy at my feet
Doth the same tale repeat:
Whither is fled the visionary gleam?
Where is it now, the glory and the dream?

V

Our birth is but a sleep and a forgetting;
The Soul that rises with us, our life's Star,
Hath had elsewhere its setting,
And cometh from afar:
Not in entire forgetfulness,
And not in utter nakedness,
But trailing clouds of glory do we come
From God, who is our home:
Heaven lies about us in our infancy!

Shades of the prison-house begin to close
    Upon the growing boy,
But he beholds the light, and whence it flows,
    He sees it in his joy;
The youth, who daily farther from the east
    Must travel, still is Nature's priest,
    And by the vision splendid
    Is on his way attended;
At length the man perceives it die away,
And fade into the light of common day.

VI

Earth fills her lap with pleasures of her own;
Yearnings she hath in her own natural kind,
And, even with something of a mother's mind.
    And no unworthy aim,
    The homely nurse doth all she can
To make her foster-child, her inmate man,
    Forget the glories he hath known,
And that imperial palace whence he came.

VII

Behold the child among his new-born blisses,
A six years' darling of a pigmy size!
See, where 'mid work of his own hand he lies,
Fretted by sallies of his mother's kisses,
With light upon him from his father's eyes!
See, at his feet, some little plan or chart,
Some fragment from his dream of human life,
Shaped by himself with newly-learned art;
    A wedding or a festival,
    A mourning or a funeral;
        And this hath now his heart,
    And unto this he frames his song:
        Then will he fit his tongue
To dialogues of business, love, or strife;
    But it will not be long
    Ere this be thrown aside,
    And with new joy and pride
The little actor cons another part;

Filling from time to time his "humorous stage"
With all the persons, down to palsied age,
That life brings with her in her equipage;
    As if his whole vocation
    Were endless imitation.

VIII

Thou, whose exterior semblance doth belie
    Thy Soul's immensity;
Thou best philosopher, who yet dost keep
Thy heritage, thou eye among the blind,
That, deaf and silent, read'st the eternal deep,
Haunted for ever by the eternal mind,—
        Mighty Prophet! Seer blest!
    On whom those truths do rest,
Which we are toiling all our lives to find,
In darkness lost, the darkness of the grave;
Thou, over whom thy immortality
Broods like the day, a master o'er a slave,
A presence which is not to be put by;
Thou little child, yet glorious in the might
Of heaven-born freedom on thy being's height,
Why with such earnest pains dost thou provoke
The years to bring the inevitable yoke,
Thus blindly with thy blessedness at strife?
Full soon thy Soul shall have her earthly freight,
And custom lie upon thee with a weight,
Heavy as frost, and deep almost as life!

IX

    O joy! that in our embers
    Is something that doth live,
    That nature yet remembers
    What was so fugitive!
The thought of our past years in me doth breed
Perpetual benediction: not indeed
For that which is most worthy to be blest—
Delight and liberty, the simple creed
Of childhood, whether busy or at rest,
With new-fledged hope still fluttering in his breast:—

Not for these I raise
The song of thanks and praise;
But for those obstinate questionings
Of sense and outward things,
Fallings from us, vanishings;
Blank misgivings of a creature
Moving about in worlds not realised,
High instincts before which our mortal nature
Did tremble like a guilty thing surprised:
But for those first affections,
Those shadowy recollections,
Which, be they what they may,
Are yet the fountain light of all our day,
Are yet a master light of all our seeing;
Uphold us, cherish, and have power to make
Our noisy years seem moments in the being
Of the eternal Silence; truths that wake,
To perish never;
Which neither listlessness, nor mad endeavour,
Nor man nor boy,
Nor all that is at enmity with joy,
Can utterly abolish or destroy!
Hence in a season of calm weather
Though inland far we be,
Our Souls have sight of that immortal sea
Which brought us hither,
Can in a moment travel thither,
And see the children sport upon the shore,
And hear the mighty waters rolling evermore.

X

Then sing, ye birds, sing, sing a joyous song!
And let the young lambs bound
As to the tabor's sound!
We in thought will join your throng,
Ye that pipe and ye that play,
Ye that through your hearts to-day
Feel the gladness of the May!
What though the radiance which was once so bright
Be now for ever taken from my sight,
Though nothing can bring back the hour
Of splendour in the grass, of glory in the flower;

We will grieve not, rather find
Strength in what remains behind;
In the primal sympathy
Which having been must ever be;
In the soothing thoughts that spring
Out of human suffering;
   In the faith that looks through death,
In years that bring the philosophic mind .

XI

And O, ye fountains, meadows, hills, and groves,
Forebode not any severing of our loves!
Yet in my heart of hearts I feel your might;
I only have relinquished one delight
To live beneath your more habitual sway.
I love the brooks which down their channels fret,
Even more than when I tripped lightly as they;
The innocent brightness of a new-born Day
   Is lovely yet;
The clouds that gather round the setting sun
Do take a sober colouring from an eye
That hath kept watch o'er man's mortality;
Another race hath been, and other palms are won.
Thanks to the human heart by which we live.
To me the meanest flower that blows can give
Thoughts that do often lie too deep for tears.

Discussion of "Intimations of Immortality"

Wordsworth's poem best known to Latter-day Saints
is this famous ode just quoted, for it is the fullest and most
beautiful expression in all literature harmonious with the
unique Latter-day Saint doctrine of pre-existence, which
extends immortality in both directions, not only forward
into post-mortality following death and resurrection, but
also backward into pre-mortality before birth.[1] All Christian churches recognize life after death, and many Christian
people have a sort of inherent feeling that there is life before birth; but The Church of Jesus Christ of Latter-day
Saints alone teaches as an official doctrine that we mortals
existed as individual spirit children with God our Father
and exercised our free agency for development in a pre-
mortal state. Wordsworth was not, of course, a Latter-
day Saint and perhaps never heard of "Mormonism," for,
born in 1770, he was an old man when the Gospel came
to England and he died, in 1850, when the Church was
still very young. But he might well have been an inspired
forerunner of the Gospel when in 1805, the very year of
Joseph Smith's birth, he wrote:

> Our birth is but a sleep and a forgetting:
> The soul that rises with us, our life's star,
>   Hath had elsewhere its setting,
>   And cometh from afar:
>   Not in entire forgetfulness,
>   And not in utter nakedness,
> But trailing clouds of glory do we come
> From God, who is our home.

These eight lines come out of the middle of the beautiful
"Immortality" ode. To understand fully what Wordsworth is saying we need to know some background to the
poem. We need to know that Wordsworth was endeavor-

---

[1]When criticized by sectarian leaders for teaching the "heretical" doctrine
of pre-existence in this poem, Wordsworth said that he did not intend to propound
such a belief. But his "retraction" seems more a distaste for argument than a
reversal of conviction.

ing to lift his friend Coleridge out of the despondency into which Coleridge was plunged because of the personal tragedy of his life and because he could no longer respond to the beauties of nature around him, which heretofore had been the source of his creative inspiration. "I see, not feel, how beautiful they are," said Coleridge in his sadly beautiful poem "Dejection: An Ode."

Samuel Taylor Coleridge[1] was not only Wordsworth's great friend but also a brilliant poet and literary critic, probably the most learned poet of his generation. His skill as a poet and his powers of the imagination were astonishing, and yet his personal life was shattered by an agonizing marriage failure, years of excruciating physical sickness, and a woeful lack of self-discipline that threatened to wreck him spiritually and mentally as well as physically. All of this anguish is reflected in Coleridge's "Dejection: An Ode." And Wordsworth's "Immortality" ode was written as a direct answer to Coleridge's poem, especially to the central problem of the poem — Coleridge's spiritual despondency caused by a lack of responsiveness to the inspiring beauties of nature.

To understand Wordsworth's poem we also need to examine its form. Structurally it is what we call an "irregular ode." Each stanza in number of lines, rhyme pattern, length of lines, and meter within the lines is different from every other stanza. Yet rhythm, rhyme, sound, and imagery are at all times so expertly controlled and so harmoniously related to meaning that the result is a rich work of art—a miniature symphony of sound fused with a provocative essay of meaning.

The 204 lines of the poem are grouped into eleven stanzas, but in idea-development the work has only three sections. The first four stanzas comprise the first section, in which Wordsworth agrees with Coleridge that as we grow older we can no longer respond spontaneously to the

---

[1]For more extensive comments on Coleridge's life and works, see pp. 321-22.

beauties of nature as a child does. Then in the next section, stanzas 5 through 8, Wordsworth endeavors to explain why this is so: that when we were young we were close to God and hence close to the creations of God in nature, but that as we grow older the "prison house" of mortality closes around us and we seem to grow apart from nature. But, continues Wordsworth in the closing section (stanzas 9 through 11), we should not grieve over our loss of spontaneous joy in nature, for in the wisdom of maturity that gives us thoughtful insight into the truth of immortality we have "abundant recompense"[1] for all our loss:

> What though the radiance which was once so bright
> Be now for ever taken from my sight,
>   Though nothing can bring back the hour
> Of splendour in the grass, of glory in the flower;
>   We will grieve not, rather find
>   Strength in what remains behind;
>   In the primal sympathy
>   Which having been must ever be;
>   In the soothing thoughts that spring
>   Out of human suffering;
>   In the faith that looks through death,
> In years that bring the philosophic mind.

And so, through the contemplation of God-created beauty in nature, has come a greater and more compassionate understanding of man in relation to eternity.

> Thanks to the human heart by which we live,
> Thanks to its tenderness, its joys, and fears,
> To me the meanest flower that blows can give
> Thoughts that do often lie too deep for tears.

---

[1]This phrase is from "Lines Composed a Few Miles Above Tintern Abbey," another of Wordsworth's great psychological-philosophical poems.

Notes on "The Prelude"

Wordsworth's "Intimations of Immortality" ode is well known in the L.D.S. Church. Most of his other poems are, unfortunately, very little known, yet in them are ideas just as beautifully expressed and as harmonious with gospel teachings as those in the "Immortality" ode. (However, it would be wrong to stress Wordsworth's harmony with L.D.S. Church doctrine too far. Many of his ideas are extraordinarily parallel, but others of them are quite otherwise, and in early life he even had strong Pantheistic leanings, reflected in some of his poems.)

Wordsworth's greatest long poem is *The Prelude,* that massive and unique autobiographical work concerned with the "growth of a poet's mind," as its sub-title indicates. The poem is so long and full that only brief passages can be cited here; but it is so pertinent that not to discuss it would be a mistake. Written in dignified, stately, sonorous blank verse, it is the fullest poetic treatment in the English language of how childhood experiences and attitudes during the "seedtime"[1] of one's life gradually shape the habits and personality and character of adulthood. A powerful message on the importance of proper environment and training in childhood is implied throughout this long poem, for, as Wordsworth says elsewhere, "The child is father of the man."[2] And out of all the miscellaneous and sometimes discordant experiences of life "the immortal spirit grows like harmony in music."[3]

In *The Prelude* we find one of the most eloquent tributes in all literature to the power of nature to dignify and ennoble man:

> If in my youth I have been pure in heart,
> If, mingling with the world, I am content

---

[1] "Fair seed-time had my soul, and I grew up/Fostered alike by beauty and by fear," Wordsworth says in *The Prelude,* Book I, lines 301-02.

[2] See Wordsworth's short lyric "My Heart Leaps Up When I Behold a Rainbow in the Sky."

[3] *The Prelude,* Book I, line 341.

With my own modest pleasures, and have lived
With God and Nature communing, removed
From little enmities and low desires—
. . . . . . if in these times of fear,
This melancholy waste of hopes o'erthrown,
If, 'mid indifference and apathy,
And wicked exultation when good men
On every side fall off, we know not how,
To selfishness, disguised in gentle names
Of peace and quiet and domestic love
Yet mingled not unwillingly with sneers
On visionary minds; if in this time
Of dereliction and dismay, I yet
Despair not of our nature, but retain
A more than Roman confidence, a faith
That fails not, in all sorrow my support,
The blessing of my life—the gift is yours,
Ye winds and sounding cataracts! 'tis yours,
Ye mountains! thine, O Nature! Thou hast fed
My lofty speculations; and in thee,
For this uneasy heart of ours, I find
A never-failing principle of joy
And purest passion.[1]

The Prelude goes on to talk of the innate nobility that is man's heritage, and of how, when he conquers the base animal instincts within himself, man can move toward the potentiality of godliness that is his, for "there's not a man that lives who hath not known his godlike hours."[2]

In the remaining books of *The Prelude*, fourteen long books in all, Wordsworth talks of many further things that shape one's life for good or bad, especially how faith in immortality can lift one to nobility in mortality.

I had inward hopes
And swellings of the spirit, was rapt and soothed
Conversed with promises, had glimmering views
How life pervades the undecaying mind;

[1]*The Prelude*, Book II, lines 427-51.
[2]*The Prelude*, Book III, lines 190-91.

> How the immortal soul with God-like power
> Informs, creates, and thaws the deepest sleep
> That time can lay upon her; how on earth,
> Man, if he do but live within the light
> Of high endeavours, daily spreads abroad
> His being armed with strength that cannot fail.[1]

And the conclusion of this lengthy meditation on life and the universe is

> Faith in life endless, the sustaining thought
> Of human Being, Eternity, and God.[2]

Two closely related themes are dominant above all others throughout *The Prelude* and in Wordsworth's poetry as a whole: (1) the power of nature to elevate and ennoble the mind of man and (2) the dignity and nobility inherent in all human life. In "Michael," Wordsworth's greatest short narrative poem, we find his most dramatic treatment of these two themes. But "Michael" will not be discussed here because it fits more appropriately in a later section and will be reserved for there.[3]

---

[1]*The Prelude*, Book IV, lines 162-71.
[2]*The Prelude*, Book XIV, lines 204-05.
[3]See pp. 405-19. For a discussion of still other poems by Wordsworth, see pp. 229-30 for "*The World Is Too Much With Us*" and pp. 469-72 for "*We Are Seven.*"

Character of the Happy Warrior

by William Wordsworth

Who is the happy warrior ? Who is he
That every man in arms should wish to be?
—It is the generous spirit, who, when brought
Among the tasks of real life, hath wrought
Upon the plan that pleased his boyish thought:
Whose high endeavours are an inward light
That makes the path before him always bright:
Who, with a natural instinct to discern
What knowledge can perform, is diligent to learn;
Abides by this resolve, and stops not there,
But makes his moral being his prime care;
Who, doomed to go in company with pain,
And fear, and bloodshed, miserable train!
Turns his necessity to glorious gain;
In face of these doth exercise a power
Which is our human nature's highest dower;
Controls them and subdues, transmutes, bereaves
Of their bad influence, and their good receives:
By objects, which might force the soul to abate
Her feeling, rendered more compassionate;
Is placable—because occasions rise
So often that demand such sacrifice;
More skilful in self-knowledge, even more pure,
As tempted more; more able to endure,
As more exposed to suffering and distress;
Thence, also, more alive to tenderness.
—'T is he whose law is reason; who depends
Upon that law as on the best of friends;
Whence, in a state where men are tempted still
To evil for a guard against worse ill,
And what in quality or act is best
Doth seldom on a right foundation rest,
He labours good on good to fix, and owes
To virtue every triumph that he knows:
—Who, if he rise to station of command,
Rises by open means; and there will stand
On honourable terms, or else retire,
And in himself possess his own desire;
Who comprehends his trust, and to the same
Keeps faithful with a singleness of aim;

And therefore does not stoop, nor lie in wait
For wealth, or honours, or for worldly state;
Whom they must follow; on whose head must fall,
Like showers of manna, if they come at all:
Whose powers shed round him in the common strife,
Or mild concerns of ordinary life,
A constant influence, a peculiar grace;
But who, if he be called upon to face
Some awful moment to which Heaven has joined
Great issues, good or bad for human kind,
Is happy as a lover; and attired
With sudden brightness, like a man inspired;
And, through the heat of conflict, keeps the law
In calmness made, and sees what he foresaw;
Or if an unexpected call succeed,
Come when it will, is equal to the need:
—He who, though thus endued as with a sense
And faculty for storm and turbulence,
Is yet a soul whose master-bias leans
To homefelt pleasures and to gentle scenes;
Sweet images! which, wheresoe'er he be,
Are at his heart; and such fidelity
It is his darling passion to approve;
More brave for this, that he hath much to love: —
'T is, finally, the man, who, lifted high,
Conspicuous object in a nation's eye,
Or left unthought-of in obscurity, —
Who, with a toward or untoward lot,
Prosperous or adverse, to his wish or not—
Plays, in the many games of life, that one
Where what he most doth value must be won:
Whom neither shape of danger can dismay,
Nor thought of tender happiness betray;
Who, not content that former worth stand fast,
Looks forward, persevering to the last,
From well to better, daily self-surpast:
Who, whether praise of him must walk the earth
For ever, and to noble deeds give birth,
Or he must fall, to sleep without his fame,
And leave a dead unprofitable name—
Finds comfort in himself and in his cause;

And, while the mortal mist is gathering, draws
His breath in confidence of Heaven's applause:
This is the happy warrior; this is he
That every man in arms should wish to be.

Discussion of "Character of the Happy Warrior"

Not so philosophically or artistically rich[1] as *The Prelude* and the "Intimations of Immortality" ode but even more directly centered around an ethical message is "Character of the Happy Warrior," which is Wordsworth's fullest description of what he felt man at his best should be. In a narrow sense it characterizes what a military officer ought to be but in a larger sense is a portrait of an ideal leader of men. Such an ideal leader is a man "whose high endeavors are an inward light that makes the path before him always bright," one who "makes his moral being his prime care," and who is

even more pure,
As tempted more; more able to endure,
As more exposed to suffering and distress;
Thence, also, more alive to tenderness.

Such a man "labors good on good to fix, and owes to virtue every triumph that he knows." And, if he rises to a position of importance, he will do so "by open means" only and remain there "on honorable terms" only. He is trustworthy and dedicated but also humble and unworldly. He is a man whose reasoned control of himself is absolute and whose sole motivation for achievement is the common good, a man so wise and stable that "through the heat of conflict he keeps the law in calmness made," a man who, though destined to wrestle with great issues, still "leans to homefelt

---

[1] Lack of artistic richness seriously lessens the poetic attractiveness of "Character of the Happy Warrior." Most readers prefer poetry that communicates through metaphors and other figurative, imagistic phrases. But the language here tends to be direct and literal. The form is blank verse, but it is more prosaic and "flat" than that of Wordsworth's great blank verse poems such as "Michael" and *The Prelude,* or of such a poem as "Intimations of Immortality." Indeed, a good case could be made for calling "Character of the Happy Warrior" a prose essay in iambic pentameter rhythm rather than a genuine poem. The work is included here not for its artistry of language but for its loftiness of message.

pleasures and to gentle scenes. . . . More brave for this,
that he hath much to love." The ideal leader is finally he
who

> Plays, in the many games of life, that one
> Where what he most doth value must be won:
> Whom neither shape of danger can dismay,
> Nor thought of tender happiness betray;
> Who, not content that former worth stand fast,
> Looks forward, persevering to the last,
> From well to better, daily self-surpast.

He is not concerned for fame; indeed, he is indifferent to
both fame and obscurity. Rather his concern is for an un-
deviating devotion to some good cause, and he works unselfishly towards this goal "in confidence of Heaven's applause."

What a difference there would be in the world if every
military leader, every civic leader, every industrial leader,
every religious leader, every political leader had these lofty
rules of conduct steadily in mind and followed them! There
is perhaps no higher code of ethics recorded anywhere than
Wordsworth's except in that greatest of all sermons spoken
on a mountain by the Saviour of the world. And fortunately, Wordsworth is consistent, even as Christ was, in his
insistence upon honor in human affairs. For example, in
"Dion," a poem written late in his life, Wordsworth further
explores ethics in leadership, specifically the problem of
whether a good end ever justifies evil means to attain that
end, and concludes:

> Him only pleasure leads, and peace attends,
> Whose means are fair and spotless as his ends.

Robert Browning: Psychologist of Human Souls

Equal to Wordsworth as an affirmer of human values, and even greater as a poet—probably the greatest English poet since Milton, in fact—is Robert Browning (1812-1889). His brilliant dramatic monologues, dramatic soliloquies, and psychological soul-studies probe as meaningfully into human personality and character as any poems ever written; and his long masterpiece, *The Ring and the Book,* is one of the great poems of the world. Browning's writing is complex and difficult, but wonderfully rewarding.

The words "robust optimist" have so often been used to describe Browning that they now seem almost part of his name. Fortunately, they fit this great man whose total affirmation of life both here and hereafter is so vigorous that it is attractive even to readers who may not share it. Strangely, his most widely known statement of optimism, "God's in his Heaven—All's right with the world," from his drama *Pippa Passes,* is an extreme view that Browning himself recognized as unrealistic. He put the words into the mouth of a naive little girl, and to ascribe the point of view as Browning's own would be as wrong as to identify Browning with the hypocritically self-righteous Johannes Agricola or the debased Caliban or other equally unattractive characters created by Browning. Nevertheless, he does firmly believe that God is in Heaven controlling the universe and that, while much is wrong with the world, the potentiality of man in this life is great and the confidence with which he can look forward to life beyond death is equally great.

Occasionally Browning speaks directly of himself and his views, as in the "Epilogue to *Asolando*" when he describes himself as

One who never turned his back but marched breast forward,
Never doubted clouds would break,

Never dreamed, though right were worsted, wrong would triumph,
Held we fall to rise, are baffled to fight better,
    Sleep to wake.

At other times Browning speaks his views not directly but through the words of one of his characters, as in the great soul-study "Saul" where the redemptive power of music is explored, or in "Fra Lippo Lippi" when the wordly but exuberantly likeable Fra Lippo says,

                    This world's no blot for us,
        Nor blank; it means intensely, and means good.

And earlier says, referring to his purpose in painting,

        If you get simple beauty and nought else,
        You get about the best thing God invents.

But even more vividly than when Browning speaks explicitly through himself or through his characters, he ironically communicates his views to us indirectly and upside-down through his unattractive characters. In fact, the bulk of what we know about Browning's specific views we infer in this manner. We sense his admiration for sincerity and honesty and simple goodness because the proud, jealous Duke of Ferrara in "My Last Duchess" is so arrogantly materialistic, and because the dying Bishop in Saint Praxed's Church and the soliloquizing monk in the Spanish Cloister are so sensually worldly and (the latter at least) so hypocritically self-righteous. We know that Browning believes man has the responsibility and opportunity, in this life, to work towards his own eternal salvation because the despicable Johannes Agricola (see "Johannes Agricola in Meditation") and the degenerate Caliban (see "Caliban Upon Setebos") believe otherwise, thinking themselves destined to inherit (Johannes) or endure (Caliban) the unalterable whims of an irresponsible God who predestines them to their reward or doom. And we know that Browning believes earthly man should live his daily experiences to the fullest capability in joy and meaning without brooding about the hopes of the past (see "The Last Ride Together") or procrastinating the desires of the present (see "The Statue and the Bust") or rationalizing one's failures (see "Andrea del Sarto").

Out of and through all his poems Browning emerges not only as a great poet but as the most vigorously optimistic writer of his age, with an unwavering faith in God and immortality and a great confidence in man. We now turn to two full poems—"A Grammarian's Funeral" and "An Epistle of Karshish"—to explore some of the details of Browning's faith:[1]

A Grammarian's Funeral

by Robert Browning

Let us begin and carry up this corpse,
    Singing together.
Leave we the common crofts, the vulgar thorpes,[2]
    Each in its tether
Sleeping safe on the bosom of the plain,
    Cared-for till cock-crow;
Look out if yonder be not day again
    Rimming the rock-row![3]
That's the appropriate country; there, man's thought,
    Rarer, intenser,   10
Self-gathered for an outbreak, as it ought,
    Chafes in the censer.[4]
Leave we the unlettered plain its herd and crop;
    Seek we sepulture
On a tall mountain, citied to the top,
    Crowded with culture!
All the peaks soar, but one the rest excels;
    Clouds overcome it;
No! yonder sparkle is the citadel's
    Circling its summit.   20
Thither our path lies; wind we up the heights;
    Wait ye the warning?

---

[1]For an analysis of other poems by Browning, see pp. 234-42 and 459-68.
[2]*Crofts* are enclosed farm lands, and *thorpes* are small villages.
[3]The sun's rays are just touching the rocky tops of the mountains.
[4]*In the censer* means in the crater of a smoking volcano.

Our low life was the level's and the night's;
 He's for the morning.
Step to a tune, square chests, erect each head,
 'Ware the beholders!
This is our master, famous, calm and dead,
 Borne on our shoulders.
Sleep, crop and herd! sleep, darkling thorpe and croft,
 Safe from the weather!   30
He whom we convoy to his grave aloft,
 Singing together,
He was a man born with thy face and throat,
 Lyric Apollo![1]
Long he lived nameless; how should Spring take note
 Winter would follow?
Till lo, the little touch, and youth was gone!
 Cramped and diminished,
Moaned he, "New measures, other feet anon!
 My dance is finished"?   40
No, that's the world's way (keep the mountain-side,
 Make for the city!);[2]
He knew the signal, and stepped on with pride
 Over men's pity;
Left play for work, and grappled with the world
 Bent on escaping;
"What's in the scroll," quoth he, "thou keepest furled?[3]
 Show me their shaping,
Theirs who most studied man, the bard and sage—
 Give"—So, he gowned him,[4]   50
Straight got by heart that book to its last page;
 Learned, we found him;
Yea, but we found him bald too, eyes like lead,
 Accents uncertain;
"Time to taste life," another would have said,
 "Up with the curtain!"
This man said rather, "Actual life comes next?
 Patience a moment!
Grant I have mastered learnings crabbed text,
 Still there's the comment.   60

---

[1] *Apollo* is the Greek god of music and of manly beauty.
[2] This and later passages in parentheses indicate directions given to the other pallbearers by the speaker of the poem.
[3] A *scroll* was a manuscript used before the printing of books.
[4] *He gowned him* means that he put on the scholastic gown.

Let me know all! Prate not of most or least,
 Painful or easy!
Even to the crumbs I'd fain eat up the feast,
 Aye, nor feel queasy."
Oh, such a life as he resolved to live,
 When he had learned it,
When he had gathered all books had to give!
 Sooner, he spurned it.
Image the whole, then execute the parts—
 Fancy the fabric   70
Quite, ere you build, ere steel strike fire from quartz,
 Ere mortar dab brick!

(Here's the town-gate reached; there's the market-place
 Gaping before us.)
Yea, this in him was the peculiar grace
 (Hearten our chorus!)
That before living he'd learn how to live—
 No end to learning;
Earn the means first—God surely will contrive
 Use for our earning.   80
Others mistrust and say, "But time escapes;
 Live now or never!"
He said, "What's time? Leave Now for dogs and apes!
 Man has Forever."
Back to his book then; deeper drooped his head;
 Calculus racked him,[1]
Leaden before, his eyes grew dross of lead;
 Tussis attacked him.[2]
"Now, master, take a little rest!"—not he!
 (Caution redoubled,   90
Step two abreast, the way winds narrowly!)
 Not a whit troubled,
Back to his studies, fresher than at first,
 Fierce as a dragon
He (soul-hydroptic with a sacred thirst)[3]
 Sucked at his flagon.
Oh, if we draw a circle premature,
 Heedless of far gain,

---

[1]*Calculus* was a disease called "the stone."
[2]*Tussis* was bronchial cough.
[3]*Soul-hydroptic* means soul-thirsty.

Greedy for quick returns of profit, sure
    Bad is our bargain!   100
Was it not great? did not he throw on God
    (He loves the burthen)—
God's task to make the heavenly period
    Perfect the earthen?
Did not he magnify the mind, show clear
    Just what it all meant?
He would not discount life, as fools do here,
    Paid by instalment.
He ventured neck or nothing—heaven's success
    Found, or earth's failure: 110
"Wilt thou trust death or not?" He answered "Yes!
    Hence with life's pale lure!"
That low man seeks a little thing to do,
    Sees it and does it;
This high man, with a great thing to pursue,
    Dies ere he knows it;
That low man goes on adding one to one,
    His hundred's soon hit;
This high man, aiming at a million,
    Misses an unit.   120
That, has the world here—should he need the next,
    Let the world mind him.
This, throws himself on God, and unperplexed
    Seeking shall find him.
So, with the throttling hands of death at strife,
    Ground he at grammar;
Still, through the rattle, parts of speech were rife;[1]
    While he could stammer
He settled *Hoti's* business—let it be!—
    Properly based *Oun*—
Gave us the doctrine of the enclitic *De*,[2]
    Dead from the waist down.
Well, here's the platform, here's the proper place;
    Hail to your purlieus,[3]
All ye highfliers of the feathered race,
    Swallows and curlews!

[1]The *rattle* refers to the death rattle in his throat.
[2]*Hoti, oun,* and *de* are Greek particles meaning *that, therefore,* and *toward.*
They involve technical points of grammar.
[3]*Purlieus* are bird haunts on the mountain peaks.

    Here's the top-peak; the multitude below
        Live, for they can there;
    This man decided not to Live but Know—
        Bury this man there?   140
    Here—here's his place, where meteors shoot, clouds form,
        Lightnings are loosened,
    Stars come and go! Let joy break with the storm,
        Peace let the dew send!
    Lofty designs must close in like effects;
        Loftily lying,
    Leave him—still loftier than the world suspects,
        Living and dying.

Discussion of "A Grammarian's Funeral"

We especially feel Browning's vigorous affirmation
of life in the several poems, including "A Grammarian's
Funeral," that develop his doctrine of "success in failure,"
the "philosophy of the imperfect"—that man should direct
all his energy toward achieving high goals, even impossibly
high goals, for to set low goals and achieve them is to fail
whereas to set high goals and strive unceasingly toward
them is to succeed even though the goals may not be fully
reached. Browning would on this point agree with the
pathetic Andrea del Sarto (in his poem of that title), who
broodingly acknowledges that "a man's reach should exceed his grasp, or what's a heaven for?" He hated all
forms of avoidable mediocrity and half-effort. For him,
anything worth doing was worth doing well, with complete energy and devotion.

Browning's fullest and most explicit treatment of this
philosophy is found in "A Grammarian's Funeral." Part
of his purpose in the poem is to catch the inexhaustible thirst
for knowledge of the scholars of the early Renaissance.

Although the term "grammarian" may suggest otherwise, the dead grammarian is a learned scholar, loved and honored by his disciples; and he is now being carried to the top of a lofty mountain for burial at sunrise. The speaker of the poem is a disciple especially devoted to the dead grammarian, and he is talking to the other pallbearers as he leads them to the burial spot.

In the first section of 28 lines the speaker points out, as the bearers climb the mountain, that the mountain peak is the "appropriate" spot for burial because it is lofty as the scholar in learning was also lofty. "Our low life was the level's and the night's," says the disciple. "He's for the morning."

In the second section, lines 29 to 72, the speaker points out how his master spent the years of his youth and young manhood searching, searching—unknown, unrecognized, withdrawn from life in a total dedication to learning. "Long he lived nameless" as he "left play for work" yearning "let me know all!"

And in the long closing section, lines 73 to 148, the total search to know all continues. Some who know him criticize the grammarian for not living while he has a chance. "Time escapes; live now or never!" they say. But he answers, "What's time? Leave Now for dogs and apes! Man has Forever." And back to his books he goes, physically half dead, intellectually even more dedicated. Now, years later, he is dead, and his disciples are carrying his body to the burial spot. Did he learn all? No, the goal was impossibly high. He learned much, but not all. Nevertheless, in the devoted pursuit of a high goal that he could not quite reach he succeeded more than lesser people who set and achieve little goals. Says his disciple,

> If we draw a circle premature,
> > Heedless of far gain,
> Greedy for quick returns of profit, sure
> > Bad is our bargain!

A little later he further explains:

> That low man seeks a little thing to do,
>   Sees it and does it;
> This high man, with a great thing to pursue,
>   Dies ere he knows it.
> That low man goes on adding one to one,
>   His hundred's soon hit;
> This high man, aiming at a million,
>   Misses an unit.
> That, has the world here—should he need the next,
>   Let the world mind him!
> This, throws himself on God, and unperplexed
>   Seeking shall find him.

Thus "trusting death"—that is, having confidence in the eternal progression possible through immortality—the grammarian accepts "earth's failure" as the price of "heaven's success." And his disciples honor him by burying him on the mountain peak, for "lofty designs must close in like effects."

> Here's the top-peak; the multitude below
>   Live, for they can, there;
> This man decided not to Live but Know—
>   Bury this man there?
> Here—here's his place, where meteors shoot, clouds form,
>   Lightnings are loosened,
> Stars come and go!

The one problem for the modern reader of this poem is in deciding not to side with the grammarian's critics who felt that he was wasting his time in a grubby search for knowledge, that he would have been wiser to live life to the fullest as Browning advocated in other poems. But Browning's point is that whatever one chooses to do should be done with energy and enthusiasm and devotion. Pillowy, "lukewarm," easy, directionless, undisciplined mediocrity was as distasteful to Browning as St. John in the Book of Revelation recorded it as being to Jesus Christ.[1]

---

[1]Revelation 3:15-16 reads: "I know thy works, that thou art neither cold nor hot: I would thou wert cold or hot. So then because thou art lukewarm and neither cold nor hot, I will spue thee out of my mouth."

An Epistle, Containing the Strange Medical Experience of Karshish, the Arab Physician

by Robert Browning

Karshish, the picker-up of learning's crumbs,
The not-incurious in God's handiwork—
This man's-flesh He hath admirably made,
Blown like a bubble, kneaded like a paste,
To coop up and keep down on earth a space   5
That puff of vapor from His mouth, man's soul—
To Abib, all-sagacious in our art,
Breeder in me of what poor skill I boast,
Like me inquisitive how pricks and cracks
Befall the flesh through too much stress and strain,   10
Whereby the wily vapor fain would slip
Back and rejoin its source before the term—
And aptest in contrivance (under God)
To baffle it by deftly stopping such—
The vagrant Scholar to his Sage at home   15
Sends greetings (health and knowledge, fame with peace)
Three samples of true snakestone—rarer still,[1]
One of the other sort, the melon-shaped
(But fitter, pounded fine, for charms than drugs);
And writeth now the twenty-second time.   20

   My journeyings were brought to Jericho;[2]
Thus I resume. Who studious in our art
Shall count a little labor unrepaid?
I have shed sweat enough, left flesh and bone
On many a flinty furlong of this land.   25
Also, the country-side is all on fire
With rumors of a marching hitherward;
Some say Vespasian cometh, some, his son.[3]
A black lynx snarled and pricked a tufted ear;
Lust of my blood inflamed his yellow balls;   30
I cried and threw my staff and he was gone.
Twice have the robbers stripped and beaten me,
And once a town declared me for a spy;
But at the end, I reach Jerusalem,

---

[1]*Snake-stone* is a stone used as a charm to cure snake bites.
[2]*Jericho* was an important city of ancient Palestine. Karshish's last letter covered his travels as far as Jericho.
[3]*Vespasian* (9-79 A.D.) led a campaign against the Jews in 67 A.D. His son Titus destroyed Jerusalem in 70 A.D.

Since this poor covert where I pass the night, 35
This Bethany, lies scarce the distance thence
A man with plague-sores at the third degree
Runs till he drops down dead. Thou laughest here!
'Sooth, it elates me, thus reposed and safe,
To void the suffering of my travel-scrip 40
And share with thee whatever Jewry yields.
A viscid choler is observable
In tertians, I was nearly bold to say;[1]
And falling-sickness hath a happier cure
Than our school wots of; there's a spider here[2] 45
Weaves no web, watches on the ledge of tombs,
Sprinkled with mottles on an ash-gray back;
Take five and drop them . . . but who knows his mind,[3]
The Syrian runagate I trust this to?
His service payeth me a sublimate[4] 50
Blown up his nose to help the ailing eye.
Best wait; I reach Jerusalem at morn,
There set in order my experiences,
Gather what most deserves, and give thee all—
Or I might add, Judæa's gum-tragacanth[5] 55
Scales off in purer flakes, shines clearer-grained,
Cracks twixt the pestle and the porphyry—[6]
In fine, exceeds our produce. Scalp-disease
Confounds me, crossing so with leprosy—
Thou hadst admired one sort I gained at Zoar—[7] 60
But zeal outruns discretion. Here I end.

Yet stay; my Syrian blinketh gratefully,
Protesteth his devotion is my price—
Suppose I write what harms not, though he steal?
I half resolve to tell thee, yet I blush, 65
What set me off a-writing first of all.
An itch I had, a sting to write, a tang!
For, be it this town's barrenness—or else—
The Man had something in the look of him—
His case has struck me far more than 'tis worth. 70

---

[1] *Tertians* are persons afflicted with intermittent fever.
[2] The use of *spiders* in medicine is an old practice.
[3] *His mind* refers to the mind of the messenger who is to carry the letter.
[4] A *sublimate* is some kind of medicine.
[5] *Gum-tragacanth* is a kind of gum used in medicine.
[6] *The porphyry* is a kind of stone used for pulverizing drugs.
[7] *Zoar* is a city southeast of the Dead Sea.

So, pardon if—lest presently I lose
In the great press of novelty at hand
The care and pains this somehow stole from me—
I bid thee take the thing while fresh in mind,
Almost in sight—for, wilt thou have the truth?   75
The very man is gone from me but now,
Whose ailment is the subject of discourse.
Thus then, and let thy better wit help all!

  'Tis but a case of mania-subinduced
By epilepsy, at the turning-point   80
Of trance prolonged unduly some three days;
When, by the exhibition of some drug[1]
Or spell, exorcization, stroke of art[2]
Unknown to me and which 'twere well to know,
The evil thing out-breaking all at once   85
Left the man whole and sound of body indeed—
But, flinging (so to speak) life's gates too wide,
Making a clear house of it too suddenly,
The first conceit that entered might inscribe
Whatever it was minded on the wall   90
So plainly at that vantage, as it were,
(First come, first served) that nothing subsequent
Attaineth to erase those fancy-scrawls
The just-returned and new-established soul
Hath gotten now so thoroughly by heart   95
That henceforth she will read or these or none.
And first—the man's own firm conviction rests
That he was dead (in fact they buried him)
—That he was dead and then restored to life
By a Nazarene physician of his tribe: 100
—Sayeth, the same bade "Rise," and he did rise.
"Such cases are diurnal," thou wilt cry.[3]
Not so this figment!—not, that such a fume,[4]
Instead of giving way to time and health,
Should eat itself into the life of life,   105
As saffron tingeth flesh, blood, bones and all!
For see, how he takes up the after-life.
The man—it is one Lazarus, a Jew,

---

[1]*Exhibition* means the act of administering a remedy.
[2]*Exorcization* is the act of expelling an evil spirit by the use of a holy name.
[3]*Diurnal* means daily.
[4]*Such a fume* means such a vaporish fancy.

Sanguine, proportioned, fifty years of age,
The body's habit wholly laudable,   110
As much, indeed, beyond the common health
As he were made and put aside to show.
Think, could we penetrate by any drug
And bathe the wearied soul and worried flesh,
And bring it clear and fair, by three days' sleep!   115
Whence has the man the balm that brightens all?
This grown man eyes the world now like a child.
Some elders of his tribe, I should premise,
Led in their friend, obedient as a sheep,
To bear my inquisition. While they spoke,   120
Now sharply, now with sorrow—told the case—
He listened not except I spoke to him,
But folded his two hands and let them talk,
Watching the flies that buzzed: and yet no fool.
And that's a sample how his years must go.   125
Look, if a beggar, in fixed middle-life,
Should find a treasure—can he use the same
With straitened habits and with tastes starved small,
And take at once to his impoverished brain
The sudden element that changes things,   130
That sets the undreamed-of rapture at his hand
And puts the cheap old joy in the scorned dust?
Is he not such an one as moves to mirth—
Warily parsimonious, when no need,
Wasteful as drunkenness at undue times?   135
All prudent counsel as to what befits
The golden mean, is lost on such an one;
The man's fantastic will is the man's law.
So here—we call the treasure knowledge, say,
Increased beyond the fleshly faculty—   140
Heaven opened to a soul while yet on earth,
Earth forced on a soul's use while seeing heaven;
The man is witless of the size, the sum,
The value in proportion of all things,
Or whether it be little or be much.   145
Discourse to him of prodigious armaments
Assembled to besiege his city now,
And of the passing of a mule with gourds—
'Tis one! Then take it on the other side,
Speak of some trifling fact—he will gaze rapt   150

With stupor at its very littleness
(Far as I see), as if in that indeed
He caught prodigious import, whole results;
And so will turn to us the bystanders
In ever the same stupor (note this point)   155
That we too see not with his opened eyes.
Wonder and doubt come wrongly into play,
Preposterously, at cross purposes.
Should his child sicken unto death—why, look
For scarce abatement of his cheerfulness,   160
Or pretermission of the daily craft![1]
While a word, gesture, glance from that same child
At play or in the school or laid asleep
Will startle him to an agony of fear,
Exasperation, just as like. Demand   165
The reason why—" 'Tis but a word," object—
"A gesture"—he regards thee as our lord
Who lived there in the pyramid alone,
Looked at us—dost thou mind?—when, being young,
We both would unadvisedly recite   170
Some charm's beginning, from that book of his,
Able to bid the sun throb wide and burst
All into stars, as suns grown old are wont.
Thou and the child have each a veil alike
Thrown o'er your heads, from under which ye both   175
Stretch your blind hands and trifle with a match
Over a mine of Greek fire, did ye know![2]
He holds on firmly to some thread of life
(It is the life to lead perforcedly)
Which runs across some vast distracting orb   180
Of glory on either side that meager thread,
Which, conscious of, he must not enter yet—
The spiritual life around the earthly life.
The law of that is known to him as this,
His heart and brain move there, his feet stay here.   185
So is the man perplexed with impulses
Sudden to start off crosswise, not straight on,
Proclaiming what is right and wrong across,
And not along, this black thread through the blaze—
"It should be" balked by "here it cannot be."   190

---

[1]*Pretermission* means omission, interruption.
[2]*Greek fire* refers to some highly inflammable substance, supposed to contain sulphur, niter, and naptha.

And oft the man's soul springs into his face
As if he saw again and heard again
His sage that bade him "Rise" and he did rise.
Something, a word, a tick o' the blood within
Admonishes; then back he sinks at once   195
To ashes, who was very fire before,
In sedulous recurrence to his trade
Whereby he earneth him the daily bread;
And studiously the humbler for that pride,
Professedly the faultier that he knows   200
God's secret, while he holds the thread of life.
Indeed the especial marking of the man
Is prone submission to the heavenly will—
Seeing it, what it is, and why it is.
'Sayeth, he will wait patient to the last   205
For that same death which must restore his being
To equilibrium, body loosening soul
Divorced even now by premature full growth;
He will live, nay, it pleaseth him to live
So long as God please, and just how God please.   210
He even seeketh not to please God more
(Which meaneth, otherwise) than as God please.
Hence, I perceive not he affects to preach
The doctrine of his sect whate'er it be,
Make proselytes as madmen thirst to do;   215
How can he give his neighbor the real ground,
His own conviction? Ardent as he is—
Call his great truth a lie, why, still the old
"Be it as God please" reassureth him.
I probed the sore as thy disciple should.   220
"How, beast," said I, "this stolid carelessness
Sufficeth thee, when Rome is on her march
To stamp out like a little spark thy town,
Thy tribe, thy crazy tale, and thee at once?"
He merely looked with his large eyes on me.   225
The man is apathetic, you deduce?
Contrariwise, he loves both old and young,
Able and weak, affects the very brutes
And birds—how say I? flowers of the fields—
As a wise workman recognizes tools   230
In a master's workshop, loving what they make.
Thus is the man as harmless as a lamb;

Only impatient, let him do his best,
At ignorance and carelessness and sin—
An indignation which is promptly curbed: 235
As when in certain travel I have feigned
To be an ignoramus in our art
According to some preconceived design,
And happed to hear the land's practitioners,
Steeped in conceit sublimed by ignorance,   240
Prattle fantastically on disease,
Its cause and cure—and I must hold my peace!

   Thou wilt object—Why have I not ere this
Sought out the sage himself, the Nazarene
Who wrought this cure, inquiring at the source,   245
Conferring with the frankness that befits?
Alas! it grieveth me, the learned leech[1]
Perished in a tumult many years ago,
Accused—our learning's fate—of wizardry,
Rebellion, to the setting up a rule   250
And creed prodigious as described to me.
His death, which happened when the earthquake fell[2]
(Prefiguring, as soon appeared, the loss
To occult learning in our lord the sage
Who lived there in the pyramid alone),   255
Was wrought by the mad people—that's their wont!
On vain recourse, as I conjecture it,
To his tried virtue, for miraculous help—
How could he stop the earthquake? That's their way!
The other imputations must be lies;   260
But take one, though I loath to give it thee,
In mere respect for any good man's fame.
(And after all, our patient Lazarus
Is stark mad; should we count on what he says?
Perhaps not; though in writing to a leech   265
'Tis well to keep back nothing of a case.)
This man so cured regards the curer, then,
As—God forgive me! who but God himself,
Creator and sustainer of the world,
That came and dwelt in flesh on it awhile!   270

---

[1]*Leech* was merely a slang term for doctor, not derogatory in any sense.
[2]*The earthquake* at the time of the crucifixion is recorded in *Matthew*, 27:51.
—"And behold, the veil of the temple was rent in twain from the top to the bottom; and the earth did quake, and the rocks rent."

—'Sayeth that such an one was born and lived,
Taught, healed the sick, broke bread at his own house,
Then died, with Lazarus by, for aught I know,
And yet was . . . what I said nor choose repeat,
And must have so avouched himself, in fact,   275
In hearing of this very Lazarus,
Who saith—but why all this of what he saith?
Why write of trivial matters, things of price
Calling at every moment for remark?
I noticed on the margin of a pool   280
Blue-flowering borage, the Aleppo sort,[1]
Aboundeth, very nitrous. It is strange!

    Thy pardon for this long and tedious case,
Which. now that I review it, needs must seem
Unduly dwelt on, prolixly set forth!   285
Nor I myself discern in what is writ
Good cause for the peculiar interest
And awe indeed this man has touched me with.
Perhaps the journey's end, the weariness
Had wrought upon me first. I met him thus: 290
I crossed a ridge of short sharp broken hills
Like an old lion's cheek teeth. Out there came
A moon made like a face with certain spots
Multiform, manifold, and menacing;
Then a wind rose behind me. So we met   295
In this old sleepy town unaware,
The man and I. I send thee what is writ.
Regard it as a chance, a matter risked
To this ambiguous Syrian—he may lose,
Or steal, or give it thee with equal good.   300
Jerusalem's repose shall make amends
For time this letter wastes, thy time and mine;
Till when, once more thy pardon and farewell!

    The very God! think, Abib; dost thou think?
So, the All-Great, were the All-Loving too—   305
So, through the thunder comes a human voice
Saying, "O heart I made, a heart beats here!
Face, my hands fashioned, see it in myself!

---

[1] *Borage* is a plant supposed to have properties of exhilaration. *Aleppo* is a town in Syria.

Thou hast no power nor mayst conceive of mine,
But love I gave thee, with myself to love,   310
And thou must love me who have died for thee!"
The madman saith He said so; it is strange.

Discussion of "An Epistle of Karshish"

This long and complex poem is perhaps the most successful effort in the world's poetry to recreate the tremendous impact of Christ's mission upon an ancient non-believer
who is so overwhelmed by it all that in bafflement he almost
believes. The poem is not history and should not be read
as history. It is an art creation, attempting to capture the
spirit rather than merely the factual details of how Christ's
life and message must have affected those who only half
knew and understood it.

Karshish and Abib are imaginary characters. The
Epistle purports to be written in 66 A.D. from Bethany in
Judea by the traveling scholar-physician Karshish to his
master, Abib.

The first two sections, through line 61, are merely
introductory as Karshish tells Abib of his travels to a number of places, different people and things he has seen, and
various medicines he has used in the treatment of epilepsy
and other sicknesses. The reader will almost certainly find
these lines tedious and not very meaningful, as Browning
intended.

Then Karshish, almost as an after-thought, says, "Yet
stay." Something is on his mind that he wants to talk
about. Before the reader moves further in the poem he
should study the account in John 11:1-44 of Christ's raising
of Lazarus from the dead, for it is about Lazarus that
Karshish wishes to talk. He has met Lazarus and been
puzzled by him. "The man had something in the look of
him," says Karshish in line 69, something that Karshish

cannot forget. Lazarus, having felt the power of Christ,
is a man incapable of doubt.

> And first—the man's own firm conviction rests
> That he was dead (in fact they buried him)
> —That he was dead and then restored to life
> By a Nazarene physician of his tribe:
> —'Sayeth, the same bade "Rise," and he did rise.
>   (lines 97-101)

Karshish is both intrigued and baffled by Lazarus.
Karshish does not himself know Christ—is, in fact, not
even of the Jewish faith. And he does not really believe
Lazarus. Yet he cannot fully doubt him. Lazarus has the
unshakeable faith, quiet yet absolute, of one who simply
knows. "This grown man eyes the world now like a child."
(line 117) His conviction needs no arguing to support it.
He serenely *knows,* and Karshish, a non-believer, is deeply
moved by the whole experience.

And so the "epistle" goes on, line after line. Often
an expression comes into Lazarus's face "as if he saw again
and heard again his sage that bade him 'Rise' and he did
rise," says Karshish. Again and again Karshish starts to
end the letter to Abib, and then goes on talking about
Lazarus, unable to dismiss the incident from his thoughts.
One might suppose Lazarus to be a madman or a fanatic,
says Karshish, but it is not so—the man is "harmless as a
lamb." (line 232) Patiently, steadfastly, unwaveringly he
waits for the death that will take him back to his Master.
The whole thing is incomprehensible to Karshish.

In the section beginning with line 243 Karshish says
to Abib, you may wonder why I have not sought out "the
Nazarene who wrought this cure" to learn for myself all
about him. But I cannot, Karshish explains, for he was
killed by a mob of people because he was accused of wizardry and then failed to stop an earthquake. (Obviously
Karshish is all confused about the facts of Christ's death,
just as a person in Christ's time might well have been con-

fused when getting the information through hearsay, as Karshish did. Browning makes the "epistle" all the more realistic by this brilliant handling of the probability of confusion.)

In the passage beginning with line 267 Karshish, now almost overcome by what he is saying, comments that Lazarus believes his healer was actually God:

> This man so cured regards the curer, then,
> As—God forgive me! who but God himself,
> Creator and sustainer of the world,
> That came and dwelt in flesh on it awhile!
> —'Sayeth that such an one was born and lived,
> Taught, healed the sick, broke bread at his own house,
> Then died, with Lazarus by, for aught I know.

Of course this simply could not be, says Karshish, and asks Abib's "pardon for this long and tedious" letter. (line 283) I have talked much too long about the whole thing, he says —and then goes on talking longer about it. So tremendously has he been impressed that, try as he will, he cannot cast it from his mind.

The thought that finally overwhelms him most of all, in the brief closing passage of the poem, is the magnificent concept of God as a being of Love as well as of Power:

> The very God! think, Abib; dost thou think?
> So, the All-Great, were the All-Loving too—
> So, through the thunder comes a human voice
> Saying, "O heart I made, a heart beats here!
> Face, my hands fashioned, see it in myself!"

And not only a being of love, but also a being, divinely perfected, in the glorified form of man himself. The whole thing is utterly beyond comprehension for Karshish, but also beyond dismissal. He cannot believe, yet he cannot *not* believe. And so brilliant is Browning's handling of the whole poem that the reader is fully caught up in the wonder of it all, just as Karshish was. Christ, the Creator and Redeemer of the world, and mankind's loving Elder Brother!

The Lamb

by William Blake

Little Lamb, who made thee?
Dost thou know who made thee?
Gave thee life, and bid thee feed
By the stream and o'er the mead;
Gave thee clothing of delight,
Softest clothing, woolly, bright;
Gave thee such a tender voice,
Making all the vales rejoice?
Little Lamb, who made thee?
Dost thou know who made thee?

Little Lamb, I'll tell thee,
Little Lamb, I'll tell thee,
He is called by thy name,
For he calls himself a Lamb,
He is meek, and he is mild;
He became a little child
I a child, and thou a lamb,
We are called by his name.
Little Lamb, God bless thee!
Little Lamb, God bless thee!

Discussion of "The Lamb"

One can say unequivocally of William Blake (1757-1827), as one can say of few men, here was a genius—a fiery, many-sided, mystic genius. Self-educated, he was vastly learned in some areas and startlingly blind in others. Isolated from the world around him, he yet was decades ahead of his time. Violently imaginative and defiantly thoughtful, he tore away the husks of all things external and temporary in an effort to get at Truth. And when he found it, as often as not he would then reject it in search of even more vital truth. He spent his whole life isolated and largely unknown in London, and yet his mind ranged wider and deeper than that of all his contemporaries. His personal life was as gentle and simple as his art was violent and visionary. And when we speak of his art, we must include painting as well as poetry, for he was equally gifted in each field. Yet like many great artists, he was inconsistent to the point of contradiction. And the simplicity of some of his poems is exceeded only by the complexity of others of them.

With a writer of such scope, obviously one cannot say of any single poem, this is typical. "The Lamb," exquisitely artistic and melodious yet wondrously simple, is typical of one phase of Blake's poetry, but is as different as it could be from the fierce, angry tone of other poems and the entangled symbols of still other poems. It is here included, then, not to represent Blake but to stand alone as an attractive melody of reverent love for Christ, the Creator.

Although Blake says many things in his poems, including some vigorously argumentative things, and at times even some extremely unorthodox and almost blasphemous things, his most central message is built around two commandments: be free, and love all things. "For every thing that lives is Holy," he says in "A Song of Liberty." He is also a champion of the power of truth ("Truth can never be told so as to be understood and not be believed," he says in *The Marriage of Heaven and Hell*) and a protector of the innocent:

> He who mocks the infant's faith
> Shall be mock'd in age and death.
> He who shall teach the child to doubt
> The rotting grave shall ne'er get out.
>   (from "Auguries of Innocence")

I Never Saw a Moor

by Emily Dickinson

I never saw a moor,
I never saw the sea;
Yet know I how the heather looks,
And what a wave must be.

I never spoke with God,
Nor visited in Heaven;
Yet certain am I of the spot
As if the chart were given.

Discussion of "I Never Saw a Moor"

Greatest of all poetesses of the English language is America's Emily Dickinson (1830-1886). In hundreds of fastidious little poems she provokes, stimulates, charms, probes, delights, illuminates, and challenges. She is as profound as Wordsworth, as artistic as Hopkins, and as many-faceted in point of view as Blake; and yet she is also strikingly individual and more easily communicative than any of them. Her poetry is wonderfully deep and yet wonderfully simple.

Nothing need be said about "I Never Saw a Moor," which totally communicates its essence, except to remind the reader again that it is only one of many points of view expressed by Emily Dickinson.

Little Jesus

by Francis Thompson

Little Jesus, wast Thou shy
Once, and just so small as I?
And what did it feel like to be
Out of heaven, and just like me?
Didst Thou sometimes think of *there*,
And ask where all the angels were?

I should think that I would cry
For my house all made of sky;
I would look about the air,
And wonder where my angels were;
And at waking 'twould distress me—
Not an angel there to dress me!

Hadst Thou ever any toys,
Like us little girls and boys?
And didst Thou play in heaven with all
The angels, that were not too tall,
With stars for marbles? Did the things
Play *Can you see me?* through their wings?

Didst Thou kneel at night to pray,
And didst Thou join Thy hands, this way?
And did they tire sometimes, being young,
And make the prayer seem very long?
And dost Thou like it best, that we
Should join our hands to pray to Thee?
I used to think, before I knew,
The prayer not said unless we do.
And did Thy Mother at the night
Kiss Thee, and fold the clothes in right?
And didst Thou feel quite good in bed,
Kissed, and sweet, and Thy prayers said?

Thou canst not have forgotten all
That it feels like to be small;
And Thou know'st I cannot pray
To thee in my father's way—
When Thou wast so little, say,
Couldst Thou talk Thy Father's way?

So, a little Child, come down
And hear a child's tongue like Thy own;
Take me by the hand and walk,
And listen to my baby-talk.
To Thy Father show my prayer
(He will look, Thou art so fair),
And say: "O Father, I, Thy Son,
Bring the prayer of a little one."

And He will smile, that children's tongue
Has not changed since Thou wast young!

Discussion of "Little Jesus"

The simplicity of this little poem by Francis Thompson (1859-1907)[1] is equalled only by its loveliness. In artistry it is delicate, fragile, beautiful—and reminiscent of Blake. In tone it is tenderly reverent. And in subject matter it is an expression of total devotion and adoration. Some of its theological details will seem inaccurate to Latter-day Saint readers—such as the reference to angels' wings—but the poem is in all ways so lovely, so charming, so movingly spiritual that such technicalities should not be dwelt upon. Its message is so clear as to need no comment; indeed, a comment would spoil it.

[1] For a brief discussion of Francis Thompson's life and work, see pp. 348-51.

Two Poems by Gerard Manley Hopkins

Gerard Manley Hopkins (1844-1889) was in his brief forty-five years a musician, a painter, a Greek scholar (at University College in Dublin, Ireland), a poet, and, above all else, a devout Jesuit priest. Although he wrote quite a few poems during his years of spiritual devotion, he published none of them—and readers were not to know his extraordinary poetic genius until thirty years after his death when Robert Bridges, England's poet laureate, rescued them from oblivion in forgotten manuscripts and published them to the world in 1918. Since then his impact has been so vast that he is now regarded as the great Victorian forerunner of modern poetry, and modern poets are still trying to catch up with his exciting experiments in sprung rhythm, counterpoint, syncopation, and dissonance. Hopkins's poetry is difficult, but it is also immensely rewarding, with many passages that are startlingly original and some that are truly magnificent.

In subject matter Hopkins is rather conventional. Most of his poems are built around traditional religious themes, and many of them have the same theme: God is everywhere evident in nature; therefore we should acknowledge and worship Him.

Two of Hopkins's typically difficult yet also typically beautiful short poems are the sonnets "The Windhover" and "God's Grandeur." In each the central idea is simple and has been treated hundreds of times by other poets, including dozens of lesser poets; but each poem nevertheless is a vivid and fresh artistic creation.

The Windhover
To Christ Our Lord

by Gerard Manley Hopkins

I caught this morning morning's minion, king-
    dom of daylight's dauphin, dapple-dawn-drawn Falcon, in his
      riding
  Of the rolling level underneath him steady air, and striding
High there, how he rung upon the rein of a wimpling wing
In his ecstasy! then off, off forth on swing,
    As a skate's heel sweeps smooth on a bow-bend: the hurl and
      gliding
  Rebuffed the big wind. My heart in hiding
Stirred for a bird,—the achieve of, the mastery of the thing!

Brute beauty and valor and act, oh, air, pride, plume, here
    Buckle! And the fire that breaks from thee then, a billion
Times told lovelier, more dangerous, O my chevalier!

  No wonder of it: sheer plod makes plough down sillion
Shine, and blue-bleak embers, ah my dear,
    Fall, gall themselves, and gash gold-vermilion.

Discussion of "The Windhover"

In external form "The Windhover" is actually a regular Petrarchan sonnet with an octave (first eight lines)
rhyming abbaabba and a sestet (last six lines) rhyming
cdcdcd. But its inverted syntax (word order) is so unusual,
its rhythms so shimmeringly variable, and its word sounds
so startlingly alliterative that it may not seem like a sonnet.
Because the poem is unconventional and difficult and "different," we can expect different reactions to it. Some may
find it nothing more than a meaningless and not very at-

tractive jumble of words. Others will be excited by its rich
artistic beauty and moved by its equally rich meaning.

So extraordinary are the rhythms and word sounds
and figurative phrases of this poem that, especially when
real aloud—and all poems should be read aloud[1] to be
fully appreciated—it will have such impact on musically
sensitive ears that some readers will find it a work of sheer
and quivering beauty even though they don't understand
a thing that it says. Poetry—good poetry, that is—is in
part music, and our response to it should in part be aesthetic.
The only thing wrong with a solely aesthetic response is
that it is incomplete. To be really excellent a poem must
have not only beauty of form but also significance of content, and to be fully appreciated it must communicate not
only its beauty of language but also its meaning. What,
then, does "The Windhover" say? Is it, as one reader interpreted it, an adventurous fish story about a man who
caught a big "dauphin" (dolphin!)? Is it, as many not very
careful readers have loosely assumed, a pretty but vague
description of a lovely sunrise? Or is it, as its sub-title "To
Christ Our Lord" suggests, a poem of religious adoration?
The best way to read a poem is not to search for obscure
meanings but to accept the words for what they say. What
do the words of "The Windhover" say?

Any dictionary will tell us that a windhover, or kestrel,
is a small bird of the falcon family, named for its ability to
hover in the air with its head to the wind. A dictionary will
also tell us that a minion is a favorite or beloved one and
that a dauphin (French) is a prince, the eldest son and
heir to the throne. Therefore, the first two lines of the poem,
slightly paraphrased, simply say, I saw (caught—caught
sight of) this morning the beloved one (minion) of the

---

[1]Probably the best way to teach a poem, especially a good poem, is to read
it aloud skillfully. More can be said with voice tones and inflections and pauses
than can be said with a multitude of comments. But the reading must be skillful.
An unskilled reading of a poem is just as ruinous as an unskilled playing of a
musical composition. Nothing can kill a poem so dead as a poor reading of it
to an audience.

morning, the prince (dauphin) of the kingdom of daylight,
the falcon drawn in flight into the dapple (multi-colored)
dawn. These are simply parallel phrases naming and describing the windhover as it is seen against the morning
sky. The next four lines describe the characteristic flight
of the bird—as it skillfully rides the wind currents that roll
underneath it, and as it "strides" high in the air, hovering
almost motionless on a wimpling (rippling or quivering)
wing for a moment, then swooping down in a rapid but
graceful swing earthward, with all the controlled smoothness of a skater in a large circular glide. Some readers may
not be familiar with the windhover, but all have seen a
hawk or falcon in similar flight—hovering and swooping,
hovering and swooping—very skillful and very beautiful
motions. Indeed, as the poet says, such masterful flying
does conquer (rebuff) the big wind. No wonder that he
ends the octave with phrases expressing admiration for
the bird's skill and power—"the achieve of, the mastery of
the thing!"

Up to this point we have had, as here interpreted,
simply eight lines of rich description of the windhover in
its skillful morning flight with a closing comment on the
poet's regard for the bird. From here on the poem becomes more difficult, and the next statement is the most
difficult: "Brute beauty and valor and act, oh, air, pride,
plume, here buckle!" The key word is *buckle*, which has
a double meaning: either (1) to unite strongly, as to "buckle
together" or "buckle down" to accomplish a difficult task;
or (2) to "crumple" or "collapse," as the pillars of a building "buckled." Based on the first meaning, to unite strongly,
the statement says that the bird in its skill and power of
flight, in its conquering (rebuffing) of the opposition of
the wind, was both beautiful and courageous (valorous).

At this point, with this first interpretation of "buckle,"
the poem shifts abruptly from the bird to a comparison with
Christ (my "chevalier" or Saviour): "And the fire that

breaks from *thee* then, a billion times told lovelier, more dangerous, O my chevalier!" That is, the power (fire) of Christ is a billion times greater and more beautiful than the lesser power of the windhover. Why? In two vivid analogies the poet in the closing three lines explains. "No wonder of it." (It isn't difficult to understand.) For "sheer plod makes plough down sillion shine"—that is, as the plough thrusts its way through the resistance of the soil it is shined to a mirror-brilliance. (The "sillion" is the ridge between two furrows of ploughed land.) "And blue-bleak embers, ah my dear, fall, gall themselves, and gash gold-vermilion." An ember is a live coal of fire. A "blue-bleak" ember would have the fire almost gone in it. But what would happen if this dying ember were thrown or let fall through the air? The friction (resistance) of the air would burst it into flame. Thus again an object is made to shine brilliantly through meeting opposition. The windhover was beautiful and powerful because it conquered the opposition of the wind, but Christ is a billion times greater because he conquered the opposition of all the world.

So read, the poem is as profoundly beautiful in its meaning as it is shimmeringly beautiful in its artistry.

Some readers may prefer a slightly different and equally stirring interpretation. If the second meaning of buckle, to "crumple" or "collapse," is taken, then it is best to regard the bird from the beginning of the poem as a symbol of Christ, the eldest son and heir (dauphin)—first seen in His glory in Heaven, then seen plunging (buckling) earthward to fulfill His mission in mortality that ended with His crucifixion. Even in the moment of buckling, however, there was triumph, and Christ was "a billion times" greater in his earthly fall to temporary mortality than He otherwise would have been because He achieved greatness through taking upon Himself the opposition (sins) of all humanity and, like the bird and the ploughshare and the ember, found brilliance in conquering opposition. With this second and

more symbolic interpretation, the "blue-bleak embers" that
"fall, gall themselves, and gash gold-vermilion" at the end
of the poem probably should be seen as Christ's blood
spilling for humanity as He wept and later suffered on the
cross.

The reader may choose whichever interpretation he
prefers. They are essentially the same, and they are
equally beautiful and meaningful.

God's Grandeur

by Gerard Manley Hopkins

The world is charged with the grandeur of God.
   It will flame out, like shining from shook foil;
   It gathers to a greatness, like the ooze of oil
Crushed. Why do men then now not reck his rod?
Generations have trod, have trod, have trod;
   And all is seared with trade; bleared, smeared with toil;
   And wears man's smudge and shares man's smell: the soil
Is bare now, nor can foot feel, being shod.

And for all this, nature is never spent;
   There lives the dearest freshness deep down things;
And though the last lights off the black West went
   Oh, morning, at the brown brink eastward, springs—
Because the Holy Ghost over the bent
   World broods with warm breast and with ah! bright wings.

Discussion of "God's Grandeur"

"God's Grandeur" is almost equally beautiful and meaningful and not quite so difficult. It also is a Petrarchan sonnet, in what Hopkins called "standard rhythm counterpointed."

The poem opens with a statement of its central idea — that God's beauty and power are everywhere manifest in the world and "will flame out, like shining from shook foil." Line 4 asks why, if evidence of God is everywhere, do people not "reck his rod" — that is, acknowledge his power. The answer is given in lines 5 to 8: People for generations have become so smeared with the routine of work and the pursuit of worldly goals that they have driven spiritual values from their lives and have built barriers between them-

selves and God. The shoes in line 8 are a symbol of the man-
made barrier between man and God preventing man from
feeling God's presence.

The closing six lines develop the thought that, even
though people of the world have withdrawn from God, He
nevertheless everywhere manifests His creative power in
nature, as in the "dearest freshness" of "deep down things."
The whole poem ends with a rich description of God exer-
cising His power over all the world through the Holy Ghost,
symbolized here in the image of a dove (the Biblical sign of
the Holy Ghost) enfolding the world in protective wings.
The "bright wings" suggest the glory of God, and the
"warm breast" suggests His loving compassion.

Two spots of special difficulty are in the poem. One
is just a matter of unconventional word order. Hopkins
delighted (and artistically delights his readers) in saying
things differently, often just in putting old words in new
patterns. Lines 11 and 12 may seem difficult for this reason, especially because of the separation of the verb *springs*
from its subject *morning;* but they become immediately
clear (and not nearly so poetic) if we paraphrase them to
say: "Although darkness comes each night, we know that
light will return each morning"—because we know that
God's power controls the world.

The second problem spot is in lines 3 and 4 with the
words, "It gathers to a greatness, like the ooze of oil
crushed." Many readers will react negatively to these
words. They probably do not at first suggest beauty, and
they probably seem especially inappropriate as describing
the grandeur of God. But Hopkins was devoutly religious.
Surely he did not intend any blasphemy or irreligiousness.
What then should the words connote? As we think about
them some fresh ideas are suggested. Is there power in
oil, crushed as it has been for centuries in the deep caverns
of the earth? Is there not only the power of great pressure
that when released will erupt in a volcano of oil but also

the internal power that, released in combustion, will drive mighty engines? From another point of view, is there a quality to oil which makes it coalesce in unified droplets ("gather to a greatness") after being pressed flat (crushed)? And finally, is oil necessarily ugly as we at first think of it? Watch it spread as a film on water with its glimmering iridescence and its beauty will match the richness of the rainbow. "It gathers to a greatness, like the ooze of oil crushed." The words now are filled with tremulous loveliness and great latent power. Did Hopkins intend all of this? We can't be sure. But we can be sure that he intended a great deal—and that the poem as a whole is artistically rich and meaningful.

Still Falls the Rain
The Raids, 1940. Night and Dawn

by Edith Sitwell

Still falls the Rain —
Dark as the world of man, black as our loss —
Blind as the nineteen hundred and forty nails
Upon the Cross.

Still falls the Rain
With a sound like the pulse of the heart that is changed to the ham-
    mer-beat
In the Potter's Field, and the sound of the impious feet

On the Tomb:
               Still falls the Rain
In the Field of Blood where the small hopes breed and the human
    brain
Nurtures its greed, that worm with the brow of Cain.
Still falls the Rain
At the feet of the Starved Man hung upon the Cross.
Christ that each day, each night, nails there, have mercy on us —
On Dives and on Lazarus:
Under the rain the sore and the gold are as one.

Still falls the Rain —
Still falls the blood from the Starved Man's wounded Side:
He bears in His Heart all wounds, — those of the light that died,
The last faint spark
In the self-murdered heart, the wounds of the sad uncomprehending
    dark,

The wounds of the baited bear, —
The blind and weeping bear whom the keepers beat
On his helpless flesh . . . the tears of the hunted hare.

Still falls the Rain —
Then — O Ile leape up to my God: who pulles me doune —
See, see where Christ's blood streames in the firmament:[1]

---

    [1]from Act 5, Scene 2 of *The Tragical History of Doctor Faustus* by Chris-
topher Marlowe.

It flows from the Brow we nailed upon the tree
Deep to the dying, to the thirsting heart
That holds the fires of the world—dark-smirched with pain
As Caesar's laurel crown.

Then sounds the voice of One who like the heart of man
Was once a child who among beasts has lain—
"Still do I love, still shed my innocent light, my Blood, for thee."

Discussion of "Still Falls the Rain"

Edith Sitwell (1887-   ) is an English poetess of extraordinary power, both dramatically and artistically. Startling images and arresting rhythms combine to heighten her dramatic messages, as in "Still Falls the Rain."

This poem was written in bomb-devastated London at the beginning of World War II, but its point of view is universal, not national. It is the voice of anguished humanity acknowledging the world-wide guilt that shows itself in war and other man-made calamities. The poem is at one and the same time excitingly artistic and movingly religious.

The power of "Still Falls the Rain" derives most of all from its central symbol of the falling rain functioning on a triple level of meaning:

First, the rain symbolizes the falling bombs, raining their awful destruction on man and his "civilization."

Second, and more richly developed, the rain symbolizes the blood which after almost two thousand years continues to fall from Christ's wounds, as humanity, its heartbeat changed to a cruel hammer-beat, continues to crucify Christ by opposing His will and defying His counsel on how we should live. As we in our blind thoughtless-

ness and sin continue to rebel against Christ, we symbolic-
ally each year drive more nails into His torn and bleeding
body. As we live in greed and selfishness and cruelty,
Christ increasingly suffers, for He assumes the burden of
all man's suffering and sins: "He bears in His Heart all
wounds."

Finally—and the climax of the poem is in this—the
falling rain symbolizes the love of Christ that, despite our
rebellion against Him, despite our sins and unworthiness,
He continues to shower down upon us. In His great and
all-encompassing mercy, in his patiently enduring compassion, He still loves, still sheds his innocent light, his blood,
upon the people of the world—all the people, of all the
world.

SECTION THREE

Right and Wrong Attitudes

RIGHT AND WRONG ATTITUDES

Introductory Comments

Another major concern of literature, and of religion, is with right and wrong attitudes that men and women may hold. Anyone who has studied the New Testament knows how much attention Jesus gave to matters of "attitude," and anyone who has studied literature knows the equal attention given there. Selfishness versus unselfishness, spirituality versus materialism, integrity versus expediency, righteousness versus self-righteousness, humility versus pride, sincerity versus hypocrisy—these are the concerns of religion, and of literature.

Moreover, even as men of religion often stress good attitudes by exposing bad attitudes, so do men of literature. The goals of religion and literature are the same, and the methods tend to be the same. Sometimes religious leaders explicitly denounce evil attitudes, as did Jesus in the Twenty-third Chapter of St. Matthew when He seven times repeated the lashing words, "Woe unto you, scribes and Pharisees, hypocrites!" But often they deliver the message through a story, or parable as Jesus called it. This latter method, with the message implied in the story rather than made explicit, tends to be the way of literature.

In a group of nine stories and ten poems drawn from the literature of the world, plus four special Christmas selections (a story and three poems), we now explore the problem of good and bad attitudes.

The Necklace

by *Guy de Maupassant*

She was one of those pretty and charming girls who are some-times, as if by a mistake of destiny, born in a family of clerks. She had no dowry, no expectations, no means of being known, understood, loved, wedded by any rich and distinguished man; and she let herself be married to a little clerk at the Ministry of Public Instruction.

She dressed plainly because she could not dress well, but she was as unhappy as though she had really fallen from her proper sta-tion, since with women there is neither caste nor rank: and beauty, grace, and charm act instead of family and birth. Natural fineness, instinct for what is elegant, suppleness of wit, are the sole hierarchy, and make from women of the people the equals of the very greatest ladies.

She suffered ceaselessly, feeling herself born for all the delicacies and all the luxuries. She suffered from the poverty of her dwelling, from the wretched look of the walls, from the worn-out chairs, from the ugliness of the curtains. All those things, of which another woman of her rank would never even have been conscious, tortured her and made her angry. The sight of the little Breton peasant who did her humble housework aroused in her regrets which were despairing, and distracted dreams. She thought of the silent antechambers hung with Oriental tapestry, lit by tall bronze candelabra, and of the two great footmen in knee breeches who sleep in the big armchairs, made drowsy by the heavy warmth of the hot-air stove. She thought of the long *salons* fitted up with ancient silk, of the delicate furniture carrying priceless curiosities, and of the coquettish perfumed boudoirs made for talks at five o'clock with intimate friends, with men famous and sought after, whom all women envy and whose attention they all desire.

When she sat down to dinner, before the round table covered with a tablecloth three days old, opposite her husband, who uncovered the soup tureen and declared with an enchanted air, "Ah, the good *pot-au-feu!* I don't know anything better than that," she thought of dainty dinners, of shining silverware, of tapestry which peopled the walls with ancient personages and with strange birds flying in the midst of a fairy forest; and she thought of delicious dishes served on marvelous plates, and of the whispered gallantries which you listen to with a sphinxlike smile, while you are eating the pink flesh of a trout or the wings of a quail.

She had no dresses, no jewels, nothing. And she loved nothing but that; she felt made for that. She would so have liked to please, to be envied, to be charming, to be sought after.

She had a friend, a former schoolmate at the convent, who was rich, and whom she did not like to go and see any more, because she suffered so much when she came back.

But one evening, her husband returned home with a triumphant air, and holding a large envelope in his hand.

"There," said he. "Here is something for you."

She tore the paper sharply, and drew out a printed card which bore these words:

"The Minister of Public Instruction and Mme. Georges Ramponneau request the honor of M. and Mme. Loisel's company at the palace of the Ministry on Monday evening, January eighteenth."

Instead of being delighted, as her husband hoped, she threw the invitation on the table with disdain, murmuring:

"What do you want me to do with that?"

"But, my dear, I thought you would be glad. You never go out, and this is such a fine opportunity. I had awful trouble to get it. Everyone wants to go; it is very select, and they are not giving many invitations to clerks. The whole official world will be there."

She looked at him with an irritated glance, and said, impatiently:

"And what do you want me to put on my back?"

He had not thought of that; he stammered:

"Why, the dress you go to the theater in. It looks very well, to me."

He stopped, distracted, seeing his wife was crying. Two great tears descended slowly from the corners of her eyes toward the corners of her mouth. He stuttered:

"What's the matter? What's the matter?"

But, by violent effort, she had conquered her grief, and she replied, with a calm voice, while she wiped her wet cheeks:

"Nothing. Only I have no dress and therefore I can't go to this ball. Give your card to some colleague whose wife is better equipped than I."

He was in despair. He resumed:

"Come, let us see, Mathilde. How much would it cost, a suitable dress, which you could use on other occasions, something very simple?"

She reflected several seconds, making her calculations and wondering also what sum she could ask without drawing on herself an immediate refusal and a frightened exclamation from the economical clerk.

Finally, she replied, hesitatingly:

"I don't know exactly, but I think I could manage it with four hundred francs."

He had grown a little pale, because he was laying aside just that amount to buy a gun and treat himself to a little shooting next summer on the plain of Nanterre, with several friends who went to shoot larks down there, of a Sunday.

But he said:

"All right. I will give you four hundred francs. And try to have a pretty dress."

The day of the ball drew near, and Mme. Loisel seemed sad, uneasy, anxious. Her dress was ready, however. Her husband said to her one evening:

"What is the matter? Come, you've been so queer these last three days."

And she answered:

"It annoys me not to have a single jewel, not a single stone, nothing to put on. I shall look like distress. I should almost rather not go at all."

He resumed:

"You might wear natural flowers. It's very stylish at this time of the year. For ten francs you can get two or three magnificent roses."

She was not convinced.

"No; there's nothing more humiliating than to look poor among other women who are rich."

But her husband cried:

"How stupid you are! Go look up your friend Mme. Forestier, and ask her to lend you some jewels. You're quite thick enough with her to do that."

She uttered a cry of joy:

"It's true. I never thought of it."

The next day she went to her friend and told of her distress.

Mme. Forestier went to a wardrobe with a glass door, took out a large jewel-box, brought it back, opened it, and said to Mme. Loisel:

"Choose, my dear."

She saw first of all some bracelets, then a pearl necklace, then a Venetian cross, gold and precious stones of admirable workmanship. She tried on the ornaments before the glass, hesitated, could not make up her mind to part with them, to give them back. She kept asking:

"Haven't you any more?"

"Why, yes. Look. I don't know what you like."

All of a sudden she discovered, in a black satin box, a superb necklace of diamonds, and her heart began to beat with an immoderate desire. Her hands trembled as she took it. She fastened it around her throat, outside her high-necked dress, and remained lost in ecstasy at the sight of herself.

Then she asked, hesitating, filled with anguish:

"Can you lend me that, only that?"

"Why, yes, certainly."

She sprang upon the neck of her friend, kissed her passionately, then fled with her treasure.

The day of the ball arrived. Mme. Loisel made a great success. She was prettier than them all, elegant, gracious, smiling, and crazy with joy. All the men looked at her, asked her name, endeavored to be introduced. All the attachés of the Cabinet wanted to waltz with her. She was remarked by the minister himself.

She danced with intoxication, with passion, made drunk by pleasure, forgetting all, in the triumph of her beauty, in the glory of her success, in a sort of cloud of happiness composed of all this homage, of all this admiration, of all these awakened desires, and of that sense of complete victory which is so sweet to a woman's heart.

She went away about four o'clock in the morning. Her husband had been sleeping since midnight, in a little deserted anteroom, with three other gentlemen whose wives were having a very good time. He threw over her shoulders the wraps which he had brought, modest wraps of common life, whose poverty contrasted with the elegance of the ball dress. She felt this, and wanted to escape so as not to be remarked by the other women, who were enveloping themselves in costly furs.

Loisel held her back.

"Wait a bit. You will catch cold outside. I will go and call a cab."

But she did not listen to him, and rapidly descended the stairs. When they were in the street they did not find a carriage; and they began to look for one, shouting after the cabmen whom they saw passing by at a distance.

They went down toward the Seine, in despair, shivering with cold. At last they found on the quay one of those ancient noctambulant coupés which, exactly as if they were ashamed to show their misery during the day, are never seen round Paris until after night-fall.

It took them to their door in the Rue des Martyrs, and once more, sadly they climbed up homeward. All was ended for her. And as to him, he reflected that he must be at the Ministry at ten o'clock.

She removed the wraps which covered her shoulders, before the glass, so as once more to see herself in all her glory. But suddenly she uttered a cry. She no longer had the necklace around her neck!

Her husband, already half undressed, demanded:

"What is the matter with you?"

She turned madly towards him:

"I have—I have—I've lost Mme. Forestier's necklace."

He stood up, distracted.

"What!—how?—impossible!"

And they looked in the folds of her dress, in the folds of her cloak, in her pockets, everywhere. They did not find it.

He asked:

"You're sure you had it on when you left the ball?"

"Yes, I felt it in the vestibule of the palace."

"But if you had lost it in the street we should have heard it fall. It must be in the cab."

"Yes. Probably. Did you take his number?"

"No. And you, didn't you notice it?"

"No."

They looked, thunderstruck, at one another. At last Loisel put on his clothes.

"I shall go back on foot," said he, "over the whole route which we have taken to see if I can find it."

And he went out. She sat waiting on a chair in her ball dress, without strength to go to bed, overwhelmed, without fire, without a thought.

Her husband came back about seven o'clock. He had found nothing.

He went to Police Headquarters, to the newspaper offices, to offer a reward; he went to the cab companies—everywhere, in fact, whither he was urged by the least suspicion of hope.

She waited all day, in the same condition of mad fear before this terrible calamity.

Loisel returned at night with a hollow, pale face; he had discovered nothing.

"You must write to your friend," said he, "that you have broken the clasp of her necklace and that you are having it mended. That will give us time to turn round."

She wrote at his dictation.

At the end of a week they had lost all hope.

And Loisel, who had aged five years, declared:

"We must consider how to replace that ornament."

The next day they took the box which had contained it, and they went to the jeweler whose name was found within. He consulted his books.

"It was not I, madame, who sold that necklace; I must simply have furnished the case."

Then they went from jeweler to jeweler, searching for a necklace like the other, consulting their memories, sick both of them with chagrin and anguish.

They found, in a shop at the Palais Royal, a string of diamonds which seemed to them exactly like the one they looked for. It was worth forty thousand francs. They could have it for thirty-six thousand.

So they begged the jeweler not to sell it for three days yet. And they made a bargain that he should buy it back for thirty-four thousand francs, in case they found the other one before the end of February.

Loisel possessed eighteen thousand francs which his father had left him. He would borrow the rest.

He did borrow, asking a thousand francs of one, five hundred of another, five louis here, three louis there. He gave notes, took up ruinous obligations, dealt with usurers and all the race of lenders. He compromised all the rest of his life, risked his signature without even knowing if he could meet it; and, frightened by the pains yet to come, by the black misery which was about to fall upon him, by the prospect of all the physical privation and of all the moral tortures which he was to suffer, he went to get the new necklace, putting down upon the merchant's counter thirty-six thousand francs.

When Mme. Loisel took back the necklace, Mme. Forestier said to her, with a chilly manner:

"You should have returned it sooner; I might have needed it."

She did not open the case, as her friend had so much feared. If she had detected the substitution, what would she have thought, what would she have said? Would she not have taken Mme. Loisel for a thief?

Mme. Loisel now knew the horrible existence of the needy. She took her part, moreover, all of a sudden, with heroism. That dreadful debt must be paid. She would pay it. They dismissed their servant; they changed their lodgings; they rented a garret under the roof.

She came to know what heavy housework meant and the odious cares of the kitchen. She washed the dishes, using her rosy nails on the greasy pots and pans. She washed the dirty linen, the shirts, and the dishcloths, which she dried upon a line; she carried the slops down to the street every morning, and carried up the water, stopping for breath at every landing. And, dressed like a woman of the people, she went to the fruiterer, the grocer, the butcher, her basket on her arm, bargaining, insulted, defending her miserable money sou by sou.

Each month they had to meet some notes, renew others, obtain more time.

Her husband worked in the evening making a fair copy of some tradesman's accounts, and late at night he often copied manuscript for five sous a page.

And this life lasted for ten years. At the end of ten years they had paid everything, everything, with the rates of usury, and the accumulations of the compound interest.

Mme. Loisel looked old now. She had become the woman of impoverished households—strong and hard and rough. With frowsy hair, skirts askew, and red hands, she talked loud while washing the floor with great swishes of water. But sometimes, when her husband was at the office, she sat down near the window, and she thought of that gay evening of long ago, of that ball where she had been so beautiful and so feted.

What would have happened if she had not lost that necklace? Who knows? Who knows? How life is strange and changeful! How little a thing is needed for us to be lost or to be saved!

But, one Sunday, having gone to take a walk in the Champs Elysées to refresh herself from the labor of the week, she suddenly perceived a woman who was leading a child. It was Mme. Forestier, still young, still beautiful, still charming.

Mme. Loisel felt moved. Was she going to speak to her? Yes, certainly. And now that she had paid, she was going to tell her all about it. Why not?

She went up.

"Good-day, Jeanne."

The other, astonished to be familiarly addressed by this plain goodwife, did not recognize her at all, and stammered:

But—madam!—I do not know—You must be mistaken."

"No. I am Mathilde Loisel."

Her friend uttered a cry.

"Oh, my poor Mathilde! How you are changed!"

"Yes, I have had days hard enough, since I have seen you, days wretched enough—and that because of you!"

"Of me! How so?"

"Do you remember that diamond necklace which you lent me to wear at the ministerial ball?"

"Yes. Well?"

"Well, I lost it."

"What do you mean? You brought it back."

"I brought you back another just like it. And for this we have been ten years paying. You can understand that it was not easy for us, us who had nothing. At last it is ended, and I am very glad."

Mme. Forestier had stopped.

"You say that you bought a necklace of diamonds to replace mine?"

"Yes. You never noticed it, then! They were very like."

And she smiled with a joy which was proud and naive at once.

Mme. Forestier, strongly moved, took her two hands.

"Oh, my poor Mathilde! Why, my necklace was paste. It was worth at most five hundred francs!"

Discussion of "The Necklace"

Guy de Maupassant (1850-1893), as all the world knows, is a distinguished French novelist and short-story writer. If not the greatest, he is at least the most widely known and read of all the French writers of the short story. Most of his dozens of stories are built around an actual incident or situation from life, experienced or observed. They are narrated with deft skill by a master craftsman and are characterized by a tone of detachment, realistic detail, rapid movement, and a dramatic unfolding at the close that often gives the reader a "surprise-ending" feeling. They range from the delightfully realistic to the sordidly realistic. And they are clever without being artily contrived and clear without being shallow or obvious. Other short-story writers have considered ethical problems more profoundly, explored complex personalities more psychologically, and chronicled life more vividly than Maupassant; but few have written stories as compellingly interesting and meaningful as his. Generally he is a reporter of life rather than its interpreter, but his concern with human values is richly implied in all his writing. Without question Maupassant stands as one of the great short-story writers of all time.

Both the triumph and the limitation of many of Maupassant's short stories is that they are peculiarly French. "The Necklace" transcends national boundaries to achieve not only universal appeal but also universal meaning. It fully deserves the reputation it long ago earned as one of Maupassant's most famous and best stories.

On a first reading "The Necklace" may seem just a clever story with a surprise ending. But it is more than this, and it must be seen as more than this to be fully appreciated and fully understood. In fact, when read carefully it emerges as a story without a surprise ending at all.

"The Necklace" is above all a character study, and a study in values. When the story opens we see Mathilde Loisel as a fadingly pretty young wife—unhappy, resentful, and self-pitying. In her shallow vanity she looks back to her family with shame because they were mere clerks and to her husband with resentment because he is also a "little clerk." She "let herself be married" to him because she could do no better. But in her daydreams she yearns to escape from what she feels is her drab life to a life of gaiety and luxury. Her sour unhappiness as she feels sorry for herself is matched only by her envy as she looks at what others have that she does not.

Although she yearns for a gay social life, she complains when her husband arranges tickets to a government ball because, as she puts it, she has nothing decent to wear. And even the purchase of a new dress doesn't satisfy her, because then she remembers that she has no jewelry. Wearing flowers, as her husband suggests, would be out of the question. Obviously her concern is not for beauty but for an impression of wealth. So she borrows a diamond necklace from a wealthy acquaintance, Mme. Forestier. And on the evening of the ball she gives herself gushily to the attentions of all who will admire her until the affair ends and she must return with her drab husband to their drab marriage—and the calamitous discovery that she has lost the necklace. Then follow the ten years of drudgery in which she and her husband pay back the money borrowed to buy the duplicate necklace for Mme. Forestier.

A full appreciation of the story depends, as stated earlier, on the reader's perceiving that it does not have a surprise ending—that the disclosure at the end of the story that the diamond necklace was a cheap imitation was suggested all through the story and was, indeed, logical and probable. One may not catch the hints as he first reads the story, but he should see them as he thinks back through it. For one thing, Mme. Forestier, though developed as a somewhat materialistic person, allows Mme. Loisel to borrow the necklace with hardly a thought, and doesn't even open the jewel-case when it is returned. A woman such as Mme. Forestier is portrayed as being would be more concerned if the jewels were real. For another thing, when Mme. Loisel and her husband try to find a duplicate of the lost necklace, the jeweler whose name is in the jewel-case says that he sold Mme. Forestier only the case, not the necklace. This in itself suggests a peculiar ungenuineness. And finally, as the reader thinks through the story and on Mme. Loisel's qualities, he realizes that she is the very kind of woman who would choose the false over the true, the cheap and imitative over the valuable and genuine. External appearances mean everything to her. She is incapable of distinguishing things of true value from cheap imitations —in jewels, in clothes, in people, in ethics. For she is herself a cheap imitation of what a genuine woman should be. And thus the disclosure at the story's end, rather than being a surprising twist, is logical and almost inevitable.

How much does Mme. Loisel learn through the experience? Does she mature to a recognition of true values? Does she grow from shallowness to depth of character? We would like her to do this, but the truth is that she doesn't grow in character through the experience. In spite of Maupassant's saying (ironically?) that Mme. Loisel shouldered the burden "with heroism," she really doesn't. She hates the hard work she must do, hates doing her own housekeeping, her own shopping, and becomes an embittered, frowzy woman, still dreaming of the life that might have been. There is dignity in work and nobility in the simple life, but Mme. Loisel finds neither. She finds only an increase of bitterness and resentment and self-pity. The climaxing moment of character revelation comes when she meets Mme. Forestier on the street at the end of the story and sullenly comments on her "wretched" ten years of enslavement to debt, blaming Mme. Forestier for them— "that because of you," she says. She hasn't learned a thing. She is still cheap and shallow, just like the jewels she wore with such vanity.

Through this revealing character study the reader, especially if she is a woman, should be left with a desire to examine her own personality and character, her own sense of values. How widespread are Mme. Loisel's tendencies to regard external appearances as more important than internal worth, to worship things that glitter even though they are false, to live with envy and to work with resentment, to place value on what one can get rather than on what one can give?

Quality

by John Galsworthy

I knew him from the days of my extreme youth, because he made my father's boots; inhabiting with his elder brother two little shops let into one, in a small by-street—now no more, but then most fashionably placed in the West End.

That tenement had a certain quiet distinction; there was no sign upon its face that he made for any of the Royal Family—merely his own German name of Gessler Brothers; and in the window a few pairs of boots. I remember that it always troubled me to account for those unvarying boots in the window, for he made only what was ordered, reaching nothing down, and it seemed so inconceivable that what he made could ever have failed to fit. Had he bought them to put there? That, too, seemed inconceivable. He would never have tolerated in his house leather on which he had not worked himself. Besides, they were too beautiful—the pair of pumps, so inexpressibly slim, the patent leathers with cloth tops, making water come into one's mouth, the tall brown riding-boots with marvelous sooty glow, as if, though new, they had been worn a hundred years. Those pairs could only have been made by one who saw before him the Soul of Boot—so truly were they prototypes, incarnating the very spirit of all footwear. These thoughts, of course, came to me later, though even when I was promoted to him, at the age of perhaps fourteen, some inkling haunted me of the dignity of himself and brother. For to make boots—such boots as he made—seemed to me then, and still seems to me, mysterious and wonderful.

I remember well my shy remark, one day, while stretching out to him my youthful foot:

"Isn't it awfully hard to do, Mr. Gessler?"

And his answer, given with a sudden smile from out of the sardonic redness of his beard: "Id is an Ardt!"

Himself, he was a little as if made of leather, with his yellow crinkly face, and crinkly reddish hair and beard, and neat folds slanting down his cheeks to the corners of his mouth, and his guttural and one-toned voice; for leather is a sardonic substance, and stiff and slow of purpose. And that was the character of his face, save that his eyes, which were gray-blue, had in them the simple gravity of one secretly possessed by the Ideal. His elder brother was so very like him—though watery, paler in every way, with a great industry—that sometimes in early days I was not quite sure of him until the interview was over. Then I knew that it was he, if the words, "I will ask my brudder," had not been spoken, and that, if they had, it was the elder brother.

When one grew old and wild and ran up bills, one somehow never ran them up with Gessler Brothers. It would not have seemed becoming to go in there and stretch out one's foot to that blue iron-spectacled face, owing him for more than—say—two pairs, just the comfortable reassurance that one was still his client.

For it was not possible to go to him very often—his boots lasted terribly, having something beyond the temporary—some, as it were essence of boot stitched into them.

One went in, not as into most shops, in the mood of: "Please serve me, and let me go!" but restfully, as one enters a church; and, sitting on the single wooden chair, waited—for there was never anybody there. Soon—over the top edge of that sort of well—rather dark and smelling soothingly of leather—which formed the shop, there would be seen his face, or that of his elder brother, peering down. A guttural sound, and the tip-tap of bast slippers beating the narrow wooden stairs, and he would stand before one without coat, a little bent, in leather apron, with sleeves turned back, blinking—as if awakened from some dream of boots, or like an owl surprised in daylight and annoyed at this interruption.

And I would say: "How do you do, Mr. Gessler? Could you make me a pair of Russia leather boots?"

Without a word he would leave me, retiring whence he came, or into the other portion of the shop, and I would continue to rest in the wooden chair, inhaling the incense of this trade. Soon he would come back, holding in his thin, veined hand a piece of gold-brown leather. With eyes fixed on it, he would remark: "What a beaudiful biece!" When I, too, had admired it, he would speak again. "When do you wand dem?" And I would answer: "Oh! As soon as you conveniently can." And he would say: "Tomorrow fordnighd?" Or if he were his elder brother: "I will ask my brudder!"

Then I would murmur: "Thank you! Good-morning, Mr. Gessler." "Goot-morning!" he would reply, still looking at the leather in his hand. And as I moved to the door, I would hear the tip-tap of his bast slippers restoring him, up the stairs, to his dream of boots. But if it were some new kind of foot-gear that he had not yet made me, then indeed he would observe ceremony—divesting me of my boot and holding it long in his hand, looking at it with eyes at once critical and loving, as if recalling the glow with which he had created it, and rebuking the way in which one had disorganized this masterpiece. Then, placing my foot on a piece of paper, he would two or three times tickle the outer edges with a pencil and pass his nervous fingers over my toes, feeling himself into the heart of my requirements.

I cannot forget that day on which I had occasion to say to him: "Mr. Gessler, that last pair of town walking-boots creaked, you know."

He looked at me for a time without replying, as if expecting me to withdraw or qualify the statement, then said:

"Id shouldn'd 'ave greaked."

"It did, I'm afraid."

"You goddem wed before dey found demselves?"

"I don't think so."

At that he lowered his eyes, as if hunting for memory of those boots, and I felt sorry I had mentioned this grave thing.

"Zend dem back!" he said; "I will look at dem."

A feeling of compassion for my creaking boots surged up in me, so well could I imagine the sorrowful long curiosity of regard which he would bend on them.

"Some boods," he said slowly, "are bad from birdt. If I can do noding wid dem, I dake dem off your bill."

Once (once only) I went absent-mindedly into his shop, in a pair of boots bought in an emergency at some large firm's. He took my order without showing me any leather, and I could feel his eyes penetrating the inferior integument of my foot. At last he said:

"Dose are nod my boods."

The tone was not one of anger, nor of sorrow, not even of contempt, but there was in it something quiet that froze the blood. He put his hand down and pressed a finger on the place where the left boot, endeavoring to be fashionable, was not quite comfortable.

'Id urds you dere," he said. "Dose big virms 'ave no self-respect. Drash!" And then, as if something had given way within him he spoke long and bitterly. It was the only time I ever heard him discuss the conditions and hardships of his trade.

"Dey get id all," he said, "dey get id by adverdisement, nod by work. Dey dake it away from us, who lofe our boods. Id gomes to this—presently I haf no work. Every year id gets less—you will see." And looking at his lined face I saw things I had never noticed before, bitter things and bitter struggle—and what a lot of gray hairs there seemed suddenly in his red beard!

As best I could, I explained the circumstances of the purchase of those ill-omened boots. But his face and voice made a so deep impression that during the next few minutes I ordered many pairs!

Nemesis fell! They lasted more terribly than ever. And I was not able conscientiously to go to him for nearly two years.

When at last I went I was surprised that outside one of the two little windows of his shop another name was painted, also that of a bootmaker—making, of course, for the Royal Family. The old familiar boots, no longer in dignified isolation, were huddled in the single window. Inside, the now contracted well of the one little shop was more scented and darker than ever. And it was longer than usual, too, before a face peered down, and the tip-tap of the bast slippers began. At last he stood before me, and, gazing through those rusty iron spectacles, said:

"Mr.—, isn'd it?"

"Ah! Mr. Gessler," I stammered, "but your boots are really too good, you know! See, these are quite decent still!" And I stretched out to him my foot. He looked at it.

"Yes," he said, "beople do nod wand good boods, id seems."

To get away from his reproachful eyes and voice I hastily remarked: "What have you done to your shop?"

He answered quietly: "Id was too exbensif. Do you wand some boods?"

I ordered three pairs, though I had only wanted two, and quickly left. I had, I know not quite what feeling of being part, in his mind, of a conspiracy against him; or not perhaps so much against him as against his idea of boot. One does not, I suppose, care to feel like that; for it was again many months before my next visit to his shop, paid, I remember, with the feeling: "Oh! well, I can't leave the old boy—so here goes! Perhaps it'll be his elder brother!"

For his elder brother, I knew, had not character enough to reproach me, even dumbly.

And, to my relief, in the shop there did appear to be his elder brother, handling a piece of leather.

"Well, Mr. Gessler," I said, "how are you?"

He came close and peered at me.

"I am breddy well," he said slowly; "but my elder brudder is dead."

And I saw that it was indeed himself—but how aged and wan! And never before had I heard him mention his brother. Much shocked, I murmured: "Oh I am sorry!"

"Yes," he answered, "he was a good man, he made a good bood; but he is dead." And he touched the top of his head, where the hair had suddenly gone as thin as it had been on that of his poor brother, to indicate, I suppose, the cause of death. "He could nod get over losing de oder shop. Do you wand any boods?" And he held up the leather in his hand: "Id's a beaudiful biece."

I ordered several pairs. It was very long before they came—but they were better than ever. One simply could not wear them out. And soon after that I went abroad.

It was over a year before I was again in London. And the first shop I went to was my old friend's. I had left a man of sixty, I came back to find one of seventy-five, pinched and worn and tremulous, who genuinely, this time, did not at first know me.

"Oh! Mr. Gessler," I said, sick at heart; "how splendid your boots are! See, I've been wearing this pair nearly all the time I've been abroad; and they're not half worn out, are they?"

He looked long at my boots—a pair of Russia leather, and his face seemed to regain its steadiness. Putting his hand on my instep, he said:

"Do dey vid you here? I 'ad trouble wid dat bair, I remember."

I assured him that they had fitted beautifully.

"Do you wand any boods?" he said. "I can make dem quickly; id is a slack dime."

I answered: "Please, please! I want boots all round—every kind!"

"I vill make a vresh model. Your food must be bigger." And with utter slowness, he traced round my foot, and felt my toes, only once looking up to say:

"Did I dell you my brudder was dead?"

To watch him was quite painful, so feeble had he grown; I was glad to get away.

I had given those boots up, when one evening they came. Opening the parcel, I set the four pairs out in a row. Then one by one I tried them on. There was no doubt about it. In shape and fit, in finish and quality of leather, they were the best he had ever made me. And in the mouth of one of the town walking-boots I found his bill. The amount was the same as usual, but it gave me quite a shock. He had never before sent it in until quarter day. I flew downstairs and wrote a check, and posted it at once with my own hand.

A week later, passing the little street, I thought I would go in and tell him how splendidly the new boots fitted. But when I came to where his shop had been, his name was gone. Still there, in the window, were the slim pumps, the patent leathers with cloth tops, the sooty riding boots.

I went in, very much disturbed. In the two little shops—again made into one—was a young man with an English face.

"Mr. Gessler in?" I said.

He gave me a strange, ingratiating look.

"No, sir," he said, "no. But we can attend to anything with pleasure. We've taken the shop over. You've seen our name, no doubt, next door. We make for some very good people."

"Yes, yes," I said, "but Mr. Gessler?"

"Oh!" he answered: "dead."

"Dead! But I only received these boots from him last Wednesday week."

"Ah" he said; "a shockin' go. Poor old man starved 'imself."

"Starved?"

"Slow starvation, the doctor called it! You see he went to work in such a way! Would keep the shop on; wouldn't have a soul touch his boots except himself. When he got an order, it took him such a time. People won't wait. He lost everybody. And there he'd sit, goin' on and on—I will say that for him—not a man in London made a better boot! But look at the competition! He never advertised! Would have the best leather, too, and do it all 'imself. Well, there it is. What could you expect with his ideas?"

"But starvation—!"

"That may be a bit flowery, as the sayin' is—but I know myself he was sittin' over his boots day and night, to the very last. You see, I used to watch him. Never gave 'imself time to eat; never had a penny in the house. All went in rent and leather. How he lived so long I don't know. He regular let his fire go out. He was a character. But he made good boots."

"Yes," I said, "he made good boots."

And I turned and went out quickly, for I did not want that youth to know that I could hardly see.

Discussion of "Quality"

John Galsworthy (1867-1933) is principally known as a novelist, especially for his *Forsyte Saga* series of novels, but is also a skillful dramatist and short-story writer. In many of his works he satirizes the worldliness of the propertied middle-class society which he knew so well in his native England and throughout the western world. But sometimes he is more concerned with sympathetic portrayal than with satire, as in this story "Quality," in which he tenderly describes an old German boot-maker who is at once to be both admired and pitied—admired for what he is, and pitied for what the world does to him.

There is something fine and beautiful and sad about this story. In an age when the emphasis is too much on quantity and too little on quality, when too many people have their eyes focused on what they can get out of life rather than what they can give to life, when more and more people want more and more money for less and less work, and too much attention is given to time clocks and salary checks—in such an age this story serves as a poignant reminder that quality workmanship is both rare and valuable. Probably it is inevitable that Mr. Gessler should have perished long ago, crowded out, at least in some countries, by mass-production factories and large department stores and push-button machines. But is it inevitable that pride in workmanship should also have perished? Is there not as much need in our complex modern world for integrity and dedication in work as there ever was?

Someone long ago said—and who said it first I do not know—that he who works only with his hands is a laborer, pity him; he who works with his hands and his head is a craftsman, respect him; and he who works with his hands and his head and his heart is an artist, honor him. Carlyle said, "Two men I honor, and no third. First, the toilworn craftsman [who] . . . conquers the earth and makes her man's. . . . A second man I honor, and still more highly;

him who is seen toiling for the spiritually indispensable; not daily bread, but the bread of life." (from "Helotage")

Surely no one can read this story by Galsworthy without gaining a greater reverence for work and high-quality workmanship. There is a satisfaction in doing good work, not for praise or reward, but for integrity's sake, simply because "a thing worth doing is worth doing well." Such a story as this should make us ashamed of any work that is less than the best we are capable of doing, ashamed of any short-cut or compromise that sacrifices quality—and should make us glow with respect whenever we see work of the highest quality done for its own sake and because of the honesty of the one who does it. For shoddy work is in fact a kind of dishonesty.

Surely the First Presidency were inspired when in 1936 they warned that "the curse of idleness" should be done away with and "the evils of a dole abolished" so that "independence, industry, thrift and self-respect [might] be once more established amongst our people" and "work [might] be re-enthroned as the ruling principle" of people's lives. (Introduction, *Church Welfare Handbook*, from Conference Report, October 1936, p. 3) Such a story as Galsworthy's should help us combat idleness and encourage honest work, especially in ourselves. All of this is not, of course, to say that we should renounce progress and return to the less efficient and more painful methods of labor of our ancestors, but we should give honest work for our pay, and we should honor the workman who places quality of workmanship above all other concerns.

As a final thought, contrast the shallowness and cheapness of Mme. Loisel with the depth and genuineness of Mr. Gessler. The worth of the latter as a good example becomes all the more moving by contrast with the former as a bad example.

Three Arshins of Land

by Leo N. Tolstoi

A woman came from the city, to visit her younger sister in the country. The elder was a city merchant's wife; the younger, a country mujik's. The two sisters drank tea together and talked. The older sister began to boast—to praise up her life in the city; how she lived roomily and elegantly, and went out, and how she dressed her children, and what rich things she had to eat and drink, and how she went to drive, and to walk, and to the theater.

The younger sister felt affronted, and began to depreciate the life of the merchant, and to set forth the advantages of her own,— that of the peasant.

"I wouldn't exchange my life for yours," says she. "Granted that we live coarsely, still we don't know what fear is. You live more elegantly; but you have to sell a great deal, else you find yourselves entirely sold. And the proverb runs, 'Loss is Gain's bigger brother.' It also happens, today you're rich, but tomorrow you're a beggar. But our mujik's affairs are more reliable; the mujik's life is meager, but long; we may not be rich, but we have enough."

The elder sister began to say:

"Enough,—I should think so! So do pigs and calves! No fine dresses, no good society. How your goodman works! How you live in the dunghill! And so you will die and it will be the same thing with your children."

"Indeed," said the younger, "our affairs are all right. We live well. We truckle to no one, we stand in fear of no one. But you in the city all live in the midst of temptations; today it's all right; but tomorrow up comes some improper person, I fear, to tempt you, and everything goes to ruin. Isn't it so?"

Pakhom, the "goodman," was listening on the oven, as the women discussed.

"That's true," says he, "the veritable truth. As we peasants from childhood turn up mother earth, so folly stays in our head, and does not depart. Our one trouble is,—so little land. If I only had as much land as I wanted, I shouldn't be afraid of any one—even of the Devil."

The women drank up their tea, talked some more about dresses, put away the dishes, and went to bed.

But the Devil was sitting behind the oven; he heard everything. He was delighted because the peasant woman had induced her hus-

band to boast with her; he had boasted that, if he had land enough,
the Devil could not get him!

"All right," he thinks; "you and I'll have to fight it out. I will
give you a lot of land. I'll get you through the land."

Pakhom's neighbor was a lady who owned a little estate. She
had one hundred and twenty dessyatins.[1] For a long time she had
never harmed the peasants in any way, living in peace with them.
But lately she had installed a retired soldier as superintendent, and
he worried the peasants with fines. No matter how careful Pakhom
was, a horse would invade his neighbor's oat-field, or his cow would
stray into her garden or the calves into the pasture. There was a
fine for everything.

Pakhom paid, growled, beat his family, and in the course of
the summer laid up much sin upon his soul because of the superintendent. He found relief only by keeping his cattle in the yard.
He begrudged the fodder, but he was thus spared much anxiety.

In the winter the rumor spread that his neighbor meant to dispose
of her land and that the superintendent thought of buying it. When
the peasants heard this they were greatly troubled.

If the superintendent becomes the master, they judged, there
will be no end to the fines.

They importuned the lady to sell the land to the community
and not to the superintendent. As they promised to pay her more
than the latter, she agreed. The peasants held a meeting, then met
again, but came to no understanding. The devil sowed dissensions.
Finally they decided that each should buy land according to his
means, and the owner consented again.

When Pakhom heard that a neighboring peasant had bought
twenty dessyatins of the land, with time extension to pay one-half
of the purchase price, he became envious. "They'll sell the whole
land, and I'll go empty-handed." He consulted with his wife. "The
peasants are buying land. We must get ten dessyatins," he said.
They considered how to arrange the matter.

They had saved a hundred rubles. They sold a foal, one-half
of their beehives, hired the son out as a laborer, and thus succeeded
in scraping one-half of the money together.

Pakhom looked over a tract of land of fifteen dessyatins, with
a grove, and negotiated with his neighbor. He contracted for the
fifteen dessyatins and paid his earnest money. Then they drove to

---

[1]A dessyatin is about 2.7 acres.

the city and made out the deed. He paid one-half of the money and agreed to pay the rest in two years. Pakhom now had land.

He borrowed money from his brother-in-law, bought seed and sowed the purchased land. Everything came up beautifully. Inside of a year he was able to pay off his debts to the neighbor and to his brother-in-law. Pakhom was now a landowner in his own right. He cultivated his own ground, and cut his own pasturage. He was overjoyed. The grass had another look; different kinds of flowers seemed to bloom on it. Once upon a time this land had looked to him the same as any other, but now it was a specially blessed piece of God's earth.

Pakhom was enjoying life. Everything would be well now if the peasants only left his fields alone, if they did not let their cattle graze on his meadows. He admonished them in a friendly fashion. But they did not desist from driving their cows on his land, and at night the strangers' horses invaded his grain. Pakhom chased them and for a time did not lay it up against the peasants. Finally, however, he lost patience and made a complaint to the court. He knew very well, tho, that necessity forced the peasants to do this, not love of wrongdoing. Still, he thought, he would have to teach them a lesson, or they would graze his land bare. A good lesson might be useful.

With the help of the court he taught them more than one lesson; more than one peasant was fined. And so it happened that the peasants were in no amiable mood towards him and were eager to play tricks on him. He was soon at loggerheads with all his neighbors. His land had grown, but the confines of the community seemed all too narrow now.

One day, as he was seated at home, a traveling peasant asked for a lodging. Pakhom kept him overnight, gave him plenty of meat and drink, inquired where he came from and talked of this and that. The peasant related that he was on the way from the lower Volga region, where he had been working. Many peasants had settled there. They were received into the community and ten dessyatins were allotted to each. Beautiful land! It made the heart feel glad to see it full of sheaves. A peasant had come there naked and poor, with empty hands, and now he had fifty dessyatins under wheat. Last year he sold his one crop of wheat for five thousand rubles.

Pakhom listened with delight. He thought: why plague one-self in this crowded section, if one can live fine elsewhere? I will sell my land and property and from the proceeds I will buy land on the lower Volga and start a farm. Here in this crowded corner there is nothing but quarreling. I will go and look things over for myself.

When summer came he started on his journey. He went by boat to Samara on the Volga, then four hundred versts[1] on foot. When he arrived at his journey's end he found things even as they had been reported to him. Ten dessyatins were allotted to each person, and the mujiks were glad to receive the stranger into the community. If a man brought money with him he was welcome and could buy as much land as he pleased. Three rubles a dessyatin was the price for the best land.

When Pakhom had investigated everything, he returned home, sold his land at a profit, sold his homestead and cattle, took leave from his community, and, when the spring came around, he journeyed with his family to the new lands.

When he reached his destination with his family, Pakhom settled in a large village and registered in the community. Having treated the elders, he received his papers in good order. He had been taken into the community, and, in addition to the pasturage, land for five souls—fifty dessyatins in all—were allotted to him. He built a homestead and bought cattle. His allotment was twice as large as his former holdings. And what fertile land! He had enough of everything and could keep as many head of cattle as he wished.

In the beginning, while he was building and equipping his homestead, he was well satisfied. But after he had lived there a while he began to feel that the new lands were too narrow. The first year Pakhom sowed wheat on his allotted land. It came up bountifully, and this created a desire to have more land at his disposal. He drove over to the merchant and leased some land for a year. The seed yielded a plentiful harvest. Unfortunately the fields were quite far from the village and the gathered grain had to be carted for a distance of fifteen versts. He saw peasant traders in the neighborhood owning dairies and amassing wealth. How much better were it, thought Pakhom, to buy land instead of leasing it, and to start dairying. That would give me a well-rounded property, all in one hand.

Then he came across a peasant who owned five hundred dessyatins of land but found himself ruined and was eager to dispose of his property at a low figure. They closed a deal. Pakhom was to pay fifteen hundred rubles, one-half down, one-half later.

About this time a traveling merchant stopped at Pakhom's farm

---

[1]A verst is approximately seven-tenths of a mile.

to feed his horses. They drank tea and spoke of this and that. The merchant told him that he was on his way home from the land of the Bashkirs. He had bought land there, about five thousand dessyatins, and had paid one thousand rubles for it. Pakhom made inquiries. The merchant willingly gave information.

"Only one thing is needful," he explained, "and that is to do some favor to their chief. I distributed raiment and rugs among them, which cost me a hundred rubles, and I divided a chest of tea between them, and whoever wanted it had his fill of vodka. I got the dessyatin land for twenty copeks. Here is the deed. The land along the river and even on the steppes is wheat-growing land."

Pakhom made further inquiries.

"You couldn't walk the land through in a year," reported the merchant. "All this is Bashkir-land. The men are as simple as sheep; one could buy from them almost for nothing."

And Pakhom thought: "Why should I buy for my thousand rubles five hundred dessyatins of land and hang a debt around my neck, while for the same amount I can acquire immeasurable property."

Pakhom inquired the way to the land of the Bashkirs. As soon as he had seen the merchant off, he made ready for the journey. He left the land and the homestead in his wife's charge and took only one of his farmhands along. In a neighboring city they bought a chest of tea, other presents, and some vodka, as the merchant had instructed them.

They rode and rode. They covered five hundred versts and on the seventh day they came into the land of the Bashkirs and found everything just as the merchant had described. On the riverside and in the steppes the Bashkirs live in kibitkas. They do not plow. They eat no bread. Cows and horses graze on the steppes. Foals are tied behind the tents, and mares are taken to them twice daily. They make kumyss out of mare's milk, and the women shake the kumyss to make cheese. The men drink kumyss and tea, eat mutton, and play the flute all day long. They are all fat and merry, and idle the whole summer through. Ignorant folk, they cannot speak Russian, but they were very friendly.

When they caught sight of Pakhom, the Bashkirs left their tents and surrounded him. An interpreter was at hand, whom Pakhom informed that he had come to buy land. The Bashkirs showed their joy and led Pakhom into their good tent. They bade him sit down on a fine rug, propped him up with downy cushions and treated him to tea and kumyss. They also slaughtered a sheep and offered him meat. Pakhom fetched from his tarantass the chest of tea and other presents and distributed them among the Bashkirs. The Bashkirs were overjoyed. They talked and talked among themselves and finally they ordered the interpreter to speak.

"They want me to tell you," said the interpreter, "that they have taken a liking to you. It is our custom to favor the guest in all possible ways and to return gifts for gifts. You have given us presents, now tell us what do you like of what we have so that we may give you presents also."

"Most of all I like land," replied Pakhom. "We're crowded where I am at home and everything is already under the plow. But you have good land and plenty of it. In all my born days I have never seen land like yours."

The Bashkirs were now talking again, and all at once it looked as though they were quarrelling. Pakhom asked why they were quarrelling. The interpreter replied:

"Some of them think that the chief should be consulted, and that no agreement ought to be made without him; but the others say it can be done without the chief just as well."

While the Bashkirs were yet arguing, a man with a hat of fox fur entered the tent. Everybody stopped talking and they all rose.

"This is the chief."

Pakhom immediately produced the best sleeping robe and five pounds of tea. The chief accepted the presents and sat down in the place of honor. The Bashkirs spoke to him. He listened, smiled and addressed Pakhom in Russian.

"Well," he said, "that can be done. Help yourself, wherever it suits you. There is plenty of land."

"How can I do this, tho," thought Pakhom. "Some official confirmation is necessary. Otherwise they say today, help yourself, but afterwards they may take it away again." And he said:

"Thank you for these good words. You have plenty of land, and I need but little. Only I must know what land belongs to me. It must be measured and I need some sort of a confrmation. For God's will rules over life and death. You are good people and you give me the land; but it may happen that your children will take it away again."

The chief laughed. "Surely this can be done," he agreed. "A confirmation so strong that it cannot be made stronger."

Pakhom replied: "I heard that a merchant had been here among you. You sold him land and gave him a deed. I should like to have it the same way."

The chief immediately understood. "This too can be done," he exclaimed. "We have a writer. We will drive to the city and have the seals put on."

"We have but one price: one thousand rubles a day."

Pakhom failed to comprehend what sort of measure a day would be. "How many dessyatins will that make?"

"That we cannot figure out. For one thousand rubles we sell you as much land as you can walk around in one day. The price of one day is one thousand rubles."

Pakhom looked surprised. "One can walk around a lot of land in one day," he said.

The chief smiled. "Everything will be yours, but on one condition. If in the course of the day you do not return to the place you start from, your money is lost."

"But how can it be noted how far I have gone?"

"We will stay right at the starting point. Our lads will ride behind you. Where you command they will drive in a stake. Then we shall mark furrows from stake to stake. Choose your circle to suit yourself, only before sunset be back at the spot where you started from. All the land that you walk around shall be yours."

Pakhom assented. It was decided to start early in the morning. They conversed for a while, drank kumyss and tea and ate more mutton. When the night set in Pakhom retired to sleep and the Bashkirs dispersed. In the morning they were to meet again in order to journey to the starting point.

Pakhom could not fall asleep. He had his mind on the land. What manner of things he thought of introducing there! "A whole principality I have before me! I can easily make fifty versts in one day. The days are long now. Fifty versts encompass ten thousand dessyatins. I will have to knuckle down to no one. I'll plow as much as may suit me; the rest I'll use for a pasturage."

The whole night through he was unable to close his eyes; only towards morning he dozed restlessly. Hardly had he begun to doze when he saw a vision. He was lying in his kibitka and heard laughter outside. To see who it was that laughed he stepped out of the kibitka and found the chief of the Bashkirs. He was holding his hands to his sides and fairly shaking with laughter. Pakhom approached him in his dream to find out why he was laughing, but now, instead of the Bashkir, he saw the merchant who had come to his farm and told him of this land. Just as he wanted to ask him how long he had been there, he saw that it was no longer the merchant but the mujik who had called on him at his old homestead and told him of the lower Volga region. And now again it was no longer the mujik but the Devil himself, with horns and hoofs, and he laughed and stared at one spot. What is he looking upon? wondered Pakhom; why is he laughing? In his dream he saw a man lying outstretched, barefoot, clad only in a shirt and pair of trousers, with his face turned upward, white as a sheet. As he looked again to see what manner of man it was, he saw clearly that it was he himself.

He awoke with the horror of it. What dreadful things one sees in a dream! He looked about. It was commencing to dawn. The people must be roused. It was time to journey to the starting place.

Pakhom arose, waked his servant, who had been sleeping in the tarantass, harnessed the horses and went to wake the Bashkirs.

"It is time," he said, "to travel to the steppe."

The Bashkirs got up, assembled, and the chief came among them. Again they drank tea and wanted to treat Pakhom, but he urged them to be off.

"If we go, let it be done at once," he remarked. "It is high time."

The Bashkirs made ready, some of them on horseback, others in tarantasses. Pakhom, accompanied by his servant, drove in his own cart. They came to the steppe as the morning sun was beginning to crimson the sky, and driving over to a little hillock they gathered together. The chief came towards Pakhom and pointed with his hand to the steppes.

"All this land that you see," he said, "as far as your eye can reach, is ours. Choose to suit yourself."

Pakhom's eyes shone. In the distance he saw grass land, smooth as the palm of his hand, black as poppy seeds. In the deeper places the grass was growing shoulder high.

The chief took his fur cap and placed it in the middle of the hill.

"This is the landmark. Here place your gold. Your servant will stay here. Go from this point hence and come back again. All the land which you encompass walking is yours."

Pakhom took out the money and laid it on the cap. He took off his coat, keeping the vest on, took a bag of bread, tied a flat water bottle to his belt, pulled up his top boots and made ready to go. He hesitated for a while which direction to take. The view was everywhere enchanting. Finally he said to himself: "I'll go towards the rising sun." He faced the East and stretched himself waiting for the sun to appear above the horizon. There was not time to lose.

It is better walking in the cool of the morning. The riders took up their positions behind him. As soon as the sun was visible, he set off, followed by the men on horseback.

He walked neither briskly nor slowly. He had walked about a verst without stopping when he ordered a stake to be driven in. Once again in motion, he hastened his steps and soon ordered another stake to be put in. He looked back; the hill was still to be seen with the people on it. Looking up at the sun he figured that he had walked about five versts. It had grown warm, so he doffed his vest. Five versts further the heat began to trouble him. Another glance at the sun showed him it was time for breakfast. "I have already covered a good stretch," he thought. "Of course, there are four of these to be covered today; still it is too early to turn yet; but I'll take my boots off." He sat down, took off his boots and went on. The walking was now easier. "I can go five versts more he thought, "and then turn to the left." The further he went, the more beautiful the land grew. He walked straight ahead. As he looked again, the hill was hardly to be seen, and the people on it looked like ants.

"Now it's time to turn back," he thought. "How hot I am! I feel like having a drink." He took his bottle with water and drank while walking. Then he made them drive in another stake and turned to the left. He walked and walked; the grass was high, the sun beat down with evergrowing fierceness. Weariness now set in. A glance at the sun showed him that it was midday. "I must rest," he thought. He stopped and ate a little bread. "If I sit down to eat, I'll fall asleep." He stood for a while, caught his breath and walked on. For a time it was easy. The food had refreshed him and given him new strength. But it was too oppressively hot, and sleep threatened to overcome him. He felt exhausted. "Well," he thought, "an hour of pain for an age of joy."

In this second direction he walked nearly ten versts. He meant then to turn to the left, but lo! the section was so fine—a luxuriant dale. Pity to give it up! What a wonderful place for flax! And again he walked straight on, appropriated the dale and marked the place with a stake. Now only he made his second turning. Casting his glance at the starting point he could hardly discern any people on the hill. "Must be about fifteen versts away. I have made the two sides too long and must shorten the third. Though the property will turn out irregular in this way, what else can be done? I must turn in and walk straight toward the hill. I must hasten and guard against useless turns. I have plenty of land now." And he turned and walked straight toward the hill.

Pakhom's feet ached. He had worked them almost to a standstill. His knees were giving away. He felt like talking a rest, but he dared not. He had no time; he must be back before sunset. The sun does not wait. He ran on as though someone were driving him.

"Did I not make a mistake? Did I not try to grab too much? If I only get back in time ! It is so far off, and I am all played out. If only all my trouble and labor be not in vain! I must exert myself to the utmost."

He shivered and ran onward in a trot. His feet were bleeding now. Still he ran. He cast off his vest, the boots, the bottle, the cap. "I was too greedy! I have ruined all! I can't get back by sunset!"

It was getting worse all the time. Fear shortened his breath. He ran on. The shirt and trousers were sticking to his body, his mouth was all dried out, his bosom was heaving like the bellows in a forge, his heart was beating like a hammer, the knees felt as though they were another's and gave under him.

He hardly thought of the land now; he merely thought what to do so as not to die from exertion. Yes, he feared to die, but he could not stop. "I have run so much that if I stop now they will call me a fool."

The Bashkirs, he could hear clearly, were screaming and calling. Their noise added fuel to his burning heart. With the last effort of his strength he ran. The sun was close to the horizon, but the hill was quite near now. The Bashkirs were beckoning, calling. He saw the fur cap, saw his money in it, saw the chief squatting on the ground with his hands at his stomach. He remembered his dream. "Earth there is a-plenty," he thought, "But will God let me live thereon? Ah, I have destroyed myself." And still he kept on running.

He looked at the sun. It was large and crimson, touching the earth and beginning to sink. He reached the foot of the hill. The sun had gone down. A cry of woe escaped from his lips. He thought all was lost. But he remembered that the sun must yet be visible from a higher spot. He rushed up the hill. There was the cap. He stumbled and fell, but reached the cap with his hands. "Good lad!" exclaimed the chief. "You have gained much land."

As Pakhom's servant rushed to his side, and tried to lift him, blood was flowing from his mouth. He was dead.

The servant lamented.

The chief was still squatting on the ground, and now he began laughing loudly and holding his sides. Then he rose to his feet, threw a spade to the servant and said, "Here, dig!"

The Bashkirs all clambered to their feet and drove away. The servant remained alone with the corpse.

He dug a grave for Pakhom, the measure of his body from head to foot—three arshins[1] and no more. There he buried Pakhom.

Discussion of "Three Arshins of Land"

One of the greatest Russian writers is Leo N. Tolstoi (1828-1910), novelist, playwright, short-story writer, and essayist. His most famous work is *War and Peace,* one of the great novels of the world; but many other works by him are also well known, including *Anna Karenina* and "The Death of Ivan Ilyich." Tolstoi was of a noble and wealthy family, but in his writing he emphasized faith, love, simplicity, and the Christian brotherhood of man. Eventually, in harmony with his convictions, he renounced his material possessions and endeavored to live the simple existence of a country peasant, close to nature and to God.

"Three Arshins of Land" is a very clear and simple story, effective principally through its irony, and told principally for its message. In many ways it is, indeed, a parable—that is, a short narration which conveys a moral intention. (Its most obvious quality, in fact, is that it so completely centers attention on its ethical message that it is one-dimensional: characterization, plot, setting—everything is sacrificed to theme.)

Note that "Three Arshins of Land" is not an indictment of money or property as such, but rather of greed.

---

[1]An arshin is about two feet.

Not just money but the *love* of money is the root of evil. Note that the Devil, appearing first in one disguise and then in another, knows precisely how to tempt Pakhom, and tempts him in the area of his weakness—his lust for property. Note that the more property Pakhom gets, the more he wants; his appetite is never satisfied. Note his shift in point of view: resenting those with property when he had little, and scorning those without property when he has much. When poor, he was jealous and bitter; and when rich, he is greedy and proud. Note that, no matter how much money or property he has, he never uses it for the benefit of others, but instead just glories in it, and schemes to get more. Finally, he is so calloused in his fanatical greed that he does not even see the warning in the wild dream that comes to him. Thus his selfish lust for more than he needs destroys him. And then all he needs is a six-foot tract, which, ironically, is all he gets.

It would be a mistake, however, to see Tolstoi's theme as merely an indictment of greed. It is this, but it is more than this. By implication Tolstoi is saying that the material realm and physical possessions don't count. What counts is the moral or spiritual realm. "Choose to suit yourself," Pakhom is told—and he chooses the realm of the material, sacrificing the realm of the spiritual. "Now which realm will *you* choose?" is the moral question Tolstoi asks his readers. "The realm of the flesh or the realm of the spirit?"

The Dry Rock

by Irwin Shaw

"We're late," Helen said, as the cab stopped at a light. "We're twenty minutes late." She looked at her husband accusingly.

"All right," Fitzsimmons said. "I couldn't help it. The work was on the desk and it had to. . . ."

"This is the one dinner party of the year I didn't want to be late for," Helen said. "So naturally. . . ."

The cab started and was halfway across the street when the Ford sedan roared into it, twisting, with a crashing and scraping of metal, a high mournful scream of brakes, the tinkling of glass. The cab shook a little, then subsided.

The cabby, a little gray man, turned and looked back, worriedly. "Everybody is all right?" he asked nervously.

"Everybody is fine," Helen said bitterly, pulling at her cape to get it straight again after the jolting.

"No damage done," said Fitzsimmons, smiling reassuringly at the cabby, who looked very frightened.

"I am happy to hear that," the cabby said. He got out of his car and stood looking sadly at his fender, now thoroughly crumpled, and his headlight, now without a lens. The door of the Ford opened and its driver sprang out. He was a large young man with a light gray hat. He glanced hurriedly at the cab.

"Why don't yuh watch where yer goin'?" he asked harshly.

"The light was in my favor," said the cabby. He was a small man of fifty, in a cap and a ragged coat, and he spoke with a heavy accent. "It turned green and I started across. I would like your license, Mister."

"What for?" the man in the gray hat shouted. "Yer load's all right. Get on yer way. No harm done." He started back to his car.

The cabby gently put his hand on the young man's arm. "Excuse me, friend," he said. "It is a five-dollar job, at least. I would like to see your license."

The young man pulled his arm away, glared at the cabby. "Aaah," he said and swung. His fist made a loud surprising noise against the cabby's nose. The old man sat down slowly on the runningboard of his cab, holding his head wearily in his hands. The young man in the gray hat stood over him, bent over, fists still clenched. "Didn't I tell yuh no harm was done?" he shouted. "Why didn't yuh lissen t'me? I got a good mind to. . . ."

"Now see here," Fitzsimmons said, opening the rear door and stepping out.

"What d'you want?" The young man turned and snarled at Fitzsimmons, his fists held higher. "Who asked for you?"

"I saw the whole thing," Fitzsimmons began, "and I don't think you. . . ."

"Aaah," snarled the young man. "Dry up."

"Claude," Helen called. "Claude, keep out of this."

"Claude," the young man repeated balefully. "Dry up, Claude."

"Are you all right?" Fitzsimmons asked, bending over the cabby, who still sat reflectively on the running board, his head down, his old and swollen cap hiding his face, blood trickling down his clothes.

"I'm all right," the cabby said wearily. He stood up, looked wonderingly at the young man. "Now, my friend, you force me to make trouble. Police!" he called, loudly. "Police!"

"Say lissen," the man in the gray hat shouted. "What do yuh need to call the cops for? Hey, cut it out!"

"Police!" the old cabby shouted calmly, but with fervor deep in his voice. "Police!"

"I ought to give it to you good." The young man shook his fist under the cabby's nose. He jumped around nervously. "This is a small matter," he shouted, "nobody needs the cops!"

"Police!" called the cabby.

"Claude." Helen put her head out the window, "Let's get out of here and let the two gentlemen settle this any way they please."

"I apologize!" The young man held the cabby by his lapels with both large hands, shook him to emphasize his apology. "Excuse me. I'm sorry. Stop yelling police!"

"I'm going to have you locked up," the cabby said. He stood there, slowly drying the blood off his shabby coat with his cap. His hair was gray, but long and full, like a musician's. He had a big head for his little shoulders, and a sad, lined little face and he looked older than fifty, to Fitzsimmons, and very poor, neglected, badly nourished. "You have committed a crime," the cabby said, "and there is a punishment for it."

"Will yuh talk to him?" The young man turned savagely to Fitzsimmons. "Will yuh tell him I'm sorry?"

"It's entirely up to him," Fitzsimmons said.

"We're a half hour late," Helen announced bitterly. "The perfect dinner guest."

"It's not enough to be sorry," said the cab driver. "Police. . ."

"Say, lissen, Bud," the young man said, his voice quick and confidential, "what's yer name?"

"Leopold Tarloff," the cabby said. "I have been driving a cab on the streets of New York for twenty years and everybody thinks just because you're a cab driver they can do whatever they want to you."

"Lissen, Leopold," the young man pushed his light gray hat far back on his head. Let's be sensible. I hit yer cab. All right. I hit you. All right."

"What's all right about it?" Tarloff asked.

"What I mean is, I admit it, I confess I did it, that's what I mean. All right." The young man grabbed Tarloff's short ragged arms as he spoke intensely. "Why the fuss? It happens every day. Police are unnecessary. I'll tell yuh what I'll do with yuh, Leopold. Five dollars, yuh say, for the fender. All right. And for the bloody nose, another pound. What do yuh say? Everybody is satisfied. Yuh've made yerself a fiver on the transaction; these good people go to their party without no more delay."

Tarloff shook his arms free from the huge hands of the man in the gray hat. He put his head back and ran his fingers through his thick hair and spoke coldly. "I don't want to hear another word. I have never been so insulted in my whole life."

The young man stepped back, his arms wide, palms up wonderingly. "I insult him." He turned to Fitzsimmons. "Did you hear me insult this party?" he asked.

"Claude!" Helen called. "Are we going to sit here all night?"

"A man steps up and hits me in the nose," Tarloff said. "He thinks he makes everything all right with five dollars. He is mistaken. Not with five hundred dollars."

"How much d'yuh think a clap in the puss is worth?" the young man growled. "Who d'yuh think y'are—Joe Louis?"

"Not ten thousand dollars," Tarloff said, on the surface calm, but quivering underneath. "Not for twenty thousand dollars. My dignity."

"His dignity!" the young man whispered . . .

"What do you want to do?" Fitzsimmons asked, conscious of Helen glooming in the rear seat of the cab.

"I would like to take him to the station house and make a complaint," Tarloff said. "You would have to come with me, if you'd be so kind. What is your opinion on the matter?"

"Will yuh tell him the cops are not a necessity!" the young man said hoarsely . . .

"Claude!" called Helen.

"It's up to you," Fitzsimmons said, looking with what he hoped was an impartial judicious expression at Tarloff, hoping he wouldn't have to waste any more time. "You do what you think you ought to do."

Tarloff smiled, showing three yellow teeth in the front of his small and childlike mouth, curved and red and surprising in the lined and weatherbeaten old hackie's face. "Thank you very much," he said. "I am glad to see you agree with me."

Fitzsimmons sighed.

"Yer drivin' me crazy!" the young man shouted at Tarloff. "Yer makin' life impossible!"

"To you," Tarloff said with dignity, "I talk from now on only in a court of law. That's my last word."

The young man stood there, breathing heavily, his fists clenching and unclenching, his pale gray hat shining in the light of a street lamp. A policeman turned the corner, walking in a leisurely and abstracted manner . . .

Fitzsimmons went over to him. "Officer," he said, "there's a little job for you over here." The policeman regretfully . . . sighed and walked slowly over to where the two cars were still nestling against each other.

"What are yuh?" the young man was asking Tarloff, when Fitzsimmons came up with the policeman. "Yuh don't act like an American citizen. What are yuh?"

"I'm a Russian," Tarloff said. "But I'm in the country twenty-five years now, and I know what the rights of an individual are."

"Yeah," said the young man hopelessly. "Yeah. . ."

The Fitzsimmonses drove silently to the police station in the cab, with Tarloff driving slowly and carefully, though with hands that shook on the wheel. The policeman drove with the young man in the young man's Ford. Fitzsimmons saw the Ford stop at a cigar store and the young man jump out and go into the store into a telephone booth.

"For three months," Helen said, as they drove, "I've been trying to get Adele Lowrie to invite us to dinner. Now we've finally managed it. Perhaps we ought to call her and invite the whole party down to night court."

"It isn't night court," Fitzsimmons said patiently. "It's a police station. And I think you might take it a little better. After all, the poor old man has no one else to speak up for him."

"Leopold Tarloff," Helen said. "It sounds impossible. Leopold Tarloff. Leopold Tarloff."

They sat in silence until Tarloff stopped the cab in front of the police station and opened the door for them. The Ford with the policeman and the young man drove up right behind them and they all went in together.

There were some people up in front of the desk lieutenant, a dejected-looking man with long mustaches and a loud, blonde woman who kept saying that the man had threatened her with a baseball bat three times that evening. Two Negroes with bloody bandages around their heads were waiting too.

"It will take some time," said the policeman. "There are two cases ahead of you. My name is Kraus."

"Oh, my," said Helen.

"You'd better call Adele," Fitzsimmons said. "Tell her not to hold dinner for us.

Helen held her hand out gloomily for nickels.

"I'm sorry," Tarloff said anxiously, "to interrupt your plans for the evening."

"Perfectly all right," Fitzsimmons said, trying to screen his wife's face from Tarloff by bending over to search for the nickels in his pocket.

Helen went off, disdainfully holding her long formal skirt up with her hand, as she walked down the spit- and butt-marked corridor of the police station toward a pay telephone. Fitzsimmons reflectively watched her elegant back retreat down the hallway.

"I am tired," Tarloff said. "I think I will have to sit down, if you will excuse me." He sat on the floor, looking up with a frail apologetic smile on his red face worn by wind and rain and traffic-policemen. Fitzsimmons suddenly felt like crying, watching the old man sitting there among the spit and cigarette butts, on the floor against the wall, with his cap off and his great bush of musician's gray hair giving the lie to the tired, weathered face below it.

Four men threw open the outside doors and walked into the police station with certainty and authority. They all wore the same light-gray hats with the huge flat brims. The young man who had hit Tarloff greeted them guardedly. "I'm glad you're here, Pidgear," he said to the man who, by some subtle mixture of stance and clothing, of lift of eyebrow and droop of mouth, announced himself as leader.

They talked swiftly and quietly in a corner.

"A Russian!" Pidgear's voice rang out angrily. "There are 10,000 cab drivers in the metropolitan area, you have to pick a Russian to punch in the nose!"

"I'm excitable!" the young man yelled. "Can I help it if I'm excitable? My father was the same way; it's a family characteristic."

"Go tell that to the Russian," Pidgear said. He went over to one of the three men who had come in with him, a large man who needed a shave and whose collar was open at the throat, as though no collar could be bought large enough to go all the way around that neck. The large man nodded, went over to Tarloff, still sitting patiently against the wall.

"You speak Russian?" the man with the open collar said to Tarloff.

"Yes, sir," Tarloff said.

The large man sat down slowly beside him, gripped Tarloff's knee confidentially in his tremendous hairy hand, spoke excitedly, winningly, in Russian.

Pidgear and the young man who had hit Tarloff came over to Fitzsimmons, leaving the two other men in the gray hats, small, dark men with shining eyes, who just stood at the door and looked hotly on.

"My name is Pidgear," the man said to Fitzsimmons, who by now was impressed with the beautiful efficiency of the system that had been put into motion by the young driver of the Ford—an ob- viously legal mind like Pidgear, a man who spoke Russian, and two intense men with gray hats standing on call just to see justice done, and all collected in the space of fifteen minutes. "Alton Pid- gear," the man said, smiling professionally at Fitzsimmons. "I rep- resent Mr. Rusk."

"Yeah," said the young man.

"My name is Fitzsimmons."

"Frankly, Mr. Fitzsimmons," Pidgear said, "I would like to see you get Mr. Tarloff to call this whole thing off. It's an em- barrassing affair for all concerned; nobody stands to gain anything by pressing it.

Helen came back and Fitzsimmons saw by the expression on her face that she wasn't happy. "They're at the soup by now," she said loudly to Fitzsimmons. "Adele said for us to take all the time we want, they're getting along fine."

"Mr. Rusk is willing to make a handsome offer," Pidgear said. "Five dollars for the car, five dollars for the nose. . ."

"Go out to dinner with your husband," Helen muttered, "and you wind up in a telephone booth in a police station. 'Excuse me for being late, darling, but I'm calling from the 8th precinct, this is our night for street-fighting.' "

"Sssh, Helen, please," Fitzsimmons said. He hadn't eaten since nine that morning and his stomach was growling with hunger.

"It was all a mistake," Pidgear said smoothly. "A natural mistake. Why should the man be stubborn? He is being reimbursed for everything, isn't he? I wish you would talk to him, Mr. Fitzsimmons; we don't want to keep you from your social engagements. Undoubtedly," Pidgear said, eyeing their evening clothes respectfully, "you and the madam were going to an important dinner party. It would be too bad to spoil an important dinner party for a little thing like this. Why, this whole affair is niggling," he said, waving his hand in front of Fitzsimmons' face. "Absolutely niggling."

Fitzsimmons looked over to where Tarloff and the other Russian were sitting on the floor. From Tarloff's face and gestures, even though he was talking in deepest Russian, Fitzsimmons could tell Tarloff was still as firm as ever. Fitzsimmons looked closely at Rusk, who was standing looking at Tarloff through narrow, baleful eyes.

"Why're you so anxious?" Fitzsimmons asked.

Rusk's eyes clouded over and his throat throbbed against his collar with rage. "I don't want to appear in court!" he yelled. "I don't want the whole business to start all over again, investigation, lawyers, fingerprints . . ."

Pidgear punched him savagely in the ribs, his fist going a short distance but with great violence.

"Why don't you buy time on the National Broadcasting System?" Pidgear asked. "Make an address, coast to coast?"

Rusk glared murderously for a moment at Pidgear, then leaned over toward Fitzsimmons, pointing a large blunt finger at him. "Do I have to put my finger in your mouth?" he whispered hoarsely.

"What does he mean by that?" Helen asked loudly. "Put his finger in your mouth? Why should he put his finger in your mouth?"

Rusk looked at her with complete hatred, turned, too full for words, and stalked away, with Pidgear after him. The two little men in the gray hats watched the room without moving.

"Claude?" Helen began.

"Obviously," Fitzsimmons said, his voice low, "Mr. Rusk isn't anxious for anyone to look at his fingerprints. He's happier this way."

"You picked a fine night!" Helen shook her head sadly. "Why can't we just pick up and get out of here?"

Rusk, with Pidgear at his side, strode back. He stopped in front of the Fitzsimmonses. "I'm a family man," he said, trying to sound like one. "I ask yuh as a favor. Talk to the Russian."

"I had to go to Bergdorf Goodman," Helen said, too deep in her own troubles to bother with Rusk, "to get a gown to spend the evening in a police station. 'Mrs. Claude Fitzsimmons was lovely last night in blue velvet and silver fox at Officer Kraus's reception at the 8th Precinct. Other guests were the well-known Leopold Tarloff, and the Messrs. Pidgear and Rusk, in gray hats. Other guests included the Russian Ambassador and two leading Italian artillerymen, also in gray hats.'"

Pidgear laughed politely. "Your wife is a very witty woman," he said.

"Yes," said Fitzsimmons, wondering why he'd married her.

"Will yuh . . . ask?" Rusk demanded. "Can it hurt yuh?"

"We're willing to do our part," Pidgear said. "We even brought down a Russian to talk to him and clear up any little points in his own language. No effort is too great."

Fitzsimmons' stomach growled loudly. "Haven't eaten all day," he said, embarrassed.

"That's what happens," Pidgear said. "Naturally."

"Yeah," said Rusk.

"Perhaps I should go out and get you a malted milk," Helen suggested coldly.

Fitzsimmons went over to where Tarloff was sitting with the other Russian. The others followed him.

"Are you sure, Mr. Tarloff," Fitzsimmons said, "that you still want to prosecute?"

"Yes," Tarloff said promptly.

"Ten dollars," Rusk said. "I offer yuh ten dollars. Can a man do more?"

"Money is not the object." With his cap Tarloff patted his nose, which was still bleeding slowly and had swelled enormously, making Tarloff look lopsided and monstrous.

"What's the object?" Rusk asked.

"The object, Mr. Rusk, is principle."

"You talk to him," Rusk said to Fitzsimmons.

"All right," Officer Kraus said, "You can go up there now."

They all filed up in front of the lieutenant sitting high at his desk.

Tarloff told his story, the accident, the wanton punch in the nose.

"It's true," Pidgear said, "that there was an accident, that there was a slight scuffle after by mistake. But the man isn't hurt. A little swelling in the region of the nose. No more." He pointed dramatically to Tarloff.

"Physically," Tarloff said, clutching his cap, talking with difficulty because his nose was clogged, "physically that's true. I am not badly hurt. But in a mental sense. . ." He shrugged. "I have suffered an injury."

"Mr. Rusk is offering the amount of ten dollars." Pidgear said. "Also, he apologizes; he's sorry."

The lieutenant looked wearily down at Rusk. "Are you sorry?" he asked.

"I'm sorry," said Rusk, raising his right hand. "On the Bible I swear I'm sorry."

"Mr. Tarloff," the lieutenant said, "if you wish to press charges, there are certain steps you will have to take. A deposition will have to be taken. Have you got witnesses?"

"Here," Tarloff said with a shy smile at the Fitzsimmonses.

"They will have to be present," the lieutenant said sleepily.

"Oh . . . ," Helen said.

"A warrant will have to be sworn out, there must be a hearing at which the witnesses must also be present. . ."

"Oh . . . ," Helen said.

"Then the trial," said the lieutenant.

"Oh . . . ," Helen said loudly.

"The question is, Mr. Tarloff," said the lieutenant, yawning, "are you willing to go through all that trouble?"

"The fact is," Tarloff said unhappily, "he hit me in the head without provocation. He is guilty of a crime on my person. He insulted me. He did me an injustice. The law exists for such things. One individual is not to be hit by another individual in the streets of the city without legal punishment." Tarloff was using his hands to try to get everyone, the Fitzsimmonses, the lieutenant, Pidgear, to understand. "There is a principle. The dignity of the human body. Justice. For a bad act a man suffers. It's an important thing. . ."

"I'm excitable," Rusk shouted. "If yuh want, yuh can hit me in the head."

"That is not the idea," Tarloff said.

"The man is sorry," the lieutenant said, wiping his eyes. "He is offering you the sum of ten dollars; it will be a lot of the taxpayers' money; you are bothering these good people here who have other things to do. What is the sense in it, Mr. Tarloff?"

Tarloff scraped his feet slowly on the dirty floor, looked sadly, hopefully, at Fitzsimmons. Fitzsimmons looked at his wife, who was glaring at Tarloff, tapping her foot sharply again and again. Fitz-desk, small, in his ragged coat and wild gray hair, his little worn simmons looked back at Tarloff, standing there, before the high face twisted and grotesque with the swollen nose, his eyes lost and appealing. Fitzsimmons shrugged sadly. Tarloff drooped inside his old coat, shook his head wearily, shrugged, deserted once and for all before the lieutenant's desk, on the dry rock of principle.

"O.K.," he said.

"Here." Rusk brought the ten-dollar bill out with magical speed.

Tarloff pushed it away. "Get out of here," he said, without looking up.

No one talked all the way to Adele Lowrie's house. Tarloff opened the door and sat, looking straight ahead, while they got out. Helen went to the door of the house and rang. Silently, Fitzsimmons offered Tarloff the fare. Tarloff shook his head. "You have been very good," he said, "Forget it."

Fitzsimmons put the money away slowly.

"Claude!" Helen called. "The door's open."

Fitzsimmons hated his wife, suddenly, without turning to look at her. He put out his hand and Tarloff shook it wearily.

"I'm awfully sorry," Fitzsimmons said. "I wish I. . ."

Tarloff shrugged. "That's all right," he said. "I understand." His face, in the shabby light of the cab, worn and old and battered by the streets of the city, was a deep well of sorrow. "There is not time. Principle." He laughed, shrugged. "Today there is not time for anything."

He shifted gears and the taxi moved slowly off, its motor grinding noisily.

"Claude!" Helen called.

"Oh, shut up!" Fitzsimmons said as he turned and walked into Adele Lowrie's house.

Discussion of "The Dry Rock"

Irwin Shaw (1913-   ) was born and has spent most of his life in New York City. Very early he showed promise as a writer, and he has matured to fulfill that promise. With achievements in three genres—the drama, the short story, and the novel—he is now internationally recognized as one of America's most gifted living writers, especially in the short story. Among his many works are *The Young Lions* and *The Troubled Age* (novels), *Bury the Dead* and *The Gentle People* (plays) and four volumes of short stories: *Sailor off the Bremen, Welcome to the City, Act of Faith,* and *Mixed Company.* "The Dry Rock" is from *Welcome to the City.*

"The Dry Rock" is a very simple and yet a very powerful story. It is easy to read and understand, its characters are distinctly drawn, and its theme is explicit. In spite of these "easy" and "open" qualities, the story is not shallow or cheap. Instead, a realistic richness of detail makes it remarkably convincing, effective, and, above all, meaningful.

The best way to approach this story is to start with an examination of its characters, all sharply focused and placed in opposition to each other.

First of all there is Leopold Tarloff, the little foreign cab-driver. Not too much should be made of the fact that he is a Russian, or even that he is in an American city. The issues of the story are universal, not national. It is, however, important that we see him as a little old man, pathetically proud, who years ago came from a distant land to a strange and great city to seek his freedom and fortune. He could almost as meaningfully have been a German or a Norwegian or an Italian or an American, and the city need not be New York City, although some heightening of drama is achieved by having him emigrate from Russia, where for centuries common people have had only limited freedom, to America, which for him is a land of promise and opportunity. He has come to fulfill a great dream of freedom and individual dignity. Now, years later, he is a little old man with a small job in a great city. Neither fame nor fortune has come to him, and yet he still has what for him was always most important—his simple faith in honor and justice.

In contrast to this little cabby there is young Rusk—

arrogant, noisy, disrespectful, and crude. His rough, slangy language immediately gives him away as unrefined and coarse. Both bullying and bribing are natural to him, and he is quite willing to use whatever means is necessary to get his way.

The conflict between Mr. Fitzsimmons and his wife is almost as sharp. Fitzsimmons is moved by the plight of the old cabby and feels a strong duty to stand by him, even at the cost of a quarrel with his wife. He knows that the cabby's cause is just, and he feels a responsibility to do something for him. Mrs. Fitzsimmons, on the other hand, is as little concerned with justice as is Rusk; and her language, although more sophisticated, is just as harsh and even more nastily sarcastic. She is utterly selfish. As to principle, of course she believes in it, as long as it doesn't inconvenience her—as long as it doesn't make her late for a dinner party.

Lesser characters fill in the background: Pidgear and his aides who are determined to keep Rusk out of a lawsuit by whatever means is necessary, the policeman who doesn't want to be bothered with doing his duty, and the police lieutenant who doesn't want to waste taxpayers' money merely on a matter of principle.

And all alone is Tarloff—abandoned high and dry on the rock of principle.

It is only after Fitzsimmons yields to the pressure of expediency and shrugs Tarloff off his conscience that the old cabby wearily knows he is defeated. Even then he maintains some integrity by refusing the ten dollars.

Questions that might be discussed include the following: Why is the story called "The Dry Rock"? Do you admire Tarloff for refusing the ten dollars or do you regard him as stubborn and foolish and unrealistic? Why does Fitzsimmons "hate" his wife at the end of the story? Ironically, whom does he hate even more and why?

One value of such a story as this is that it brings

dramatically into focus the need to live by principles. In an age when convenience and rush threaten to shape all our decisions, wherever we live, we need to be reminded that there are principles of honesty and justice and freedom and purity so important that they must remain unviolated at whatever the cost. It is also important to remember that if principles are sacrificed in small situations, they will be so weakened that they will not be strong enough to stand in big situations. Such a reminder, sharply given by this story, should make any thoughtful reader forever after a little more sensitive in conscience when confronted with a situation where principle is involved. And we are confronted constantly with such situations in our daily living. How many times during the past month have you had to make a decision in which principle was in some measure involved? Did you always make the decision on the side of principle?

A Queer Heart

by Elizabeth Bowen

Mrs. Cadman got out of the bus backwards. No amount of practice ever made her more agile; the trouble she had with her big bulk amused everyone, and herself. Gripping the handles each side of the bus door so tightly that the seams of her gloves cracked, she lowered herself cautiously, like a climber, while her feet, overlapping her smart shoes, uneasily scrabbled at each step. One or two people asked why the bus made, for one passenger, such a long, dead stop. But on the whole she was famous on this line, for she was constantly in and out of town. The conductor waited behind her, smiling, holding her basket, arms wide to catch her if she should slip.

Having got safe to the ground, Mrs. Cadman shook herself like a satisfied bird. She took back her shopping basket from the conductor and gave him a smile instead. The big kind scarlet bus once more ground into movement, off up the main road hill: it made a fading blur in the premature autumn dusk. Mrs. Cadman almost waved after it, for with it went the happy part of her day. She turned down the side road that led to her gate.

A wet wind of autumn, smelling of sodden gardens, blew in her face and tilted her hat. Leaves whirled along it, and one lime leaf, as though imploring shelter, lodged in her fur collar. Every gust did more to sadden the poor trees. This was one of those roads outside growing provincial cities that still keep the rural mystery. They seem to lead into something still not known. Traffic roars past one end, but the other end is in silence: you see a wood, a spire, a haughty manor gate, or your view ends with the turn of an old wall. Here some new raw-looking villas stood with spaces between them; in the spaces were orchards and market-gardens. A glasshouse roof reflected the wet grey light; there was a shut chapel further along. And, each standing back in half an acre of ground, there were two or three stucco houses with dark windows, sombre but at the same time ornate, built years ago in this then retired spot. Dead line leaves showered over their grass plots and evergreens. Mrs. Cadman's house, Granville, was one of these: its name was engraved in scrolls over the porch. The solid house was not large, and Mrs. Cadman's daughter, Lucille, could look after it with a daily help.

The widow and her daughter lived here in the state of cheerless meekness Lucille considered suitable for them now. Mr. Cadman had liked to have everything done in style. But twelve years ago he had died, travelling on business, in a hotel up in the North. Always the gentleman, he had been glad to spare them this upset at home. He had been brought back to the Midlands for his impressive funeral, whose size showed him a popular man. How unlike Mr. Cadman was Rosa proving herself. One can be most unfriendly in one's way of dying. Ah, well, one chooses one's husband; one's sister is dealt out to one by fate.

Mrs. Cadman, thumb on the latch of her own gate, looked for a minute longer up and down the road—deeply, deeply unwilling to go in. She looked back at the corner where the bus had vanished, and an immense sigh heaved up her coat lapels and made a cotton carnation, pinned to the fur, brush a fold of her chin. Laced, hooked, buttoned so tightly into her clothes, she seemed to need to deflate herself by these sudden sighs, by yawns or by those explosions of laughter that often vexed Lucille. Through her face—embedded in fat but still very lively, as exposed, as ingenuous as a little girl's—you could see some emotional fermentation always at work in her. Her smiles were frequent, hopeful and quick. Her pitching walk was due to her tight shoes.

When she did go in, she went in with a sort of rush. She let the door bang back on the hall wall, so that the chain rattled and an outraged clatter came from the letterbox. Immediately she knew she had done wrong. Lucille, appalled, looked out of the dining-room. "Shisssssh! How can you, mother!" she said.

"Ever so sorry, dear," said Mrs. Cadman, cast down.

"She'd just dropped off," said Lucille. "After her bad night and everything. It really does seem hard."

Mrs. Cadman quite saw that it did. She glanced nervously up the stairs, then edged into the dining-room. It was not cheerful in here: a monkey puzzle, too close to the window, drank the last of the light up; the room still smelt of dinner; the fire smouldered resentfully, starved for coal. The big mahogany furniture lowered, with no shine. Mrs. Cadman, putting her basket down on the table, sent an uncertain smile across at Lucille, whose glasses blankly gleamed high up on her long face. She often asked herself where Lucille could have come from. *Could* this be the baby daughter she had borne, and tied pink bows on, and christened a pretty name? In the sun in this very bow window she had gurgled into the sweet-smelling creases of Lucille's neck—one summer lost in time.

"You *have* been an age," Lucille said.

"Well, the shops were quite busy. I never saw," she said with irrepressible pleasure, "I never *saw* so many people in town!"

Lucille, lips tighter than ever shut, was routing about, unpacking the shopping basket, handling the packages. Chemist's and grocer's parcels. Mrs. Cadman watched her with apprehension. Then Lucille pounced; she held up a small soft parcel in frivolous wrappings. "Oho," she said. "So you've been in at Babbington's?

"Well, I missed one bus, so I had to wait for the next. So I just popped in there a minute out of the cold. And, you see, I've been wanting a little scarf—"

"Little scarf!" said Lucille. "I don't know what to make of you, mother. I don't really. How *could* you, at such a time? How you ever could have the heart!" Lucille, standing the other side of the table, leaned across it, her thin weight on her knuckles. This brought her face near her mother's. "Can't you understand?" she said. "Can't you take *anything in?* The next little scarf *you'll* need to buy will be black!"

"What a thing to say!" exclaimed Mrs. Cadman, profoundly offended. "With that poor thing upstairs now, waiting to have her tea."

"Tea? She can't take her tea. Why, since this morning she can't keep a thing down."

Mrs. Cadman blenched and began unbuttoning her coat. Lucille seemed to feel that her own prestige and Aunt Rosa's entirely hung on Aunt Rosa's approaching death. You could feel that she and her aunt had thought up this plan together. These last days had been the climax of their complicity. And there was Mrs. Cadman—as ever, as usual—put in the wrong, frowned upon, out of things. Whenever Rosa arrived to stay Mrs. Cadman had no fun in her home, and now Rosa was leaving for ever it seemed worse. A perverse kick of the heart, a flicker of naughtiness, made Mrs. Cadman say: "Oh, well, while there's life there's hope."

Lucille said: "If you won't face it, you won't. But I just say it does fall heavy on me . . . . We had the vicar round here this afternoon. He was up with Aunt for a bit, then he looked in and said he did feel I needed a prayer too. He said he thought I was wonderful. He asked where you were, and he seemed to wonder you find the heart to stay out so long. I thought from his manner he wondered a good deal."

Mrs. Cadman, with an irrepressible titter, said: "Give him something to think about! Why if I'd ha' shown up that vicar'd have popped out as fast as he popped in. Thinks I'd make a mouthful of him! Why, I've made him bolt down the street. Well, well. He's not *my* idea of a vicar. When your father and I first came here we had a rural dean. Oh, he was as pleasant as anything."

Lucille, with the air of praying for Christian patience, folded
her lips. Jabbing her fingers down the inside of her waistbelt, she
more tightly tucked in her tight blouse. She liked looking like Mrs.
Noah—no, *Miss* Noah. "The doctor's not been again. We're to
let him know of any change."

"Well, let's do the best we can," said Mrs. Cadman. "But
don't keep on *talking*. You don't make things any better, keeping on
going on. My opinion is one should keep bright to the last. When
my time comes, oh, I would like a cheery face."

"It's well for you . . ." began Lucille. She bit the remark off and,
gathering up the parcels, stalked scornfully out of the dining-room.
Without comment she left exposed on the table a small carton of
goodies Mrs. Cadman had bought to cheer herself up with and had
concealed in the toe of the shopping bag. Soon, from the kitchen
came the carefully muffled noises of Lucille putting away provisions
and tearing the wrappings off the chemist's things. Mrs. Cadman,
reaching out for the carton, put a peppermint into each cheek. She,
oh so badly, wanted a cup of tea but dared not follow Lucille into
the kitchen in order to put the kettle on.

Though, after all, Granville *was* her house. . . .

You would not think it was her house—not when Rosa was
there. While Lucille and her mother were *tête à tête* Lucille's dis-
approval was at least fairly tacit. But as soon as Rosa arrived on
one of these yearly autumn visits—always choosing the season when
Mrs. Cadman felt in her least good form, the fall of the leaf—the
aunt and niece got together and found everything wrong. Their
two cold natures ran together. They found Mrs. Cadman lacking;
they forbade the affection she would have offered them. They censured her the whole time. Mrs. Cadman could date her real aliena-
tion from Lucille from the year when Rosa's visits began. During
Mr. Cadman's lifetime Rosa had never come for more than an afternoon. Mr. Cadman had been his wife's defence from her sister—
a great red kind of rumbustious fortification. He had been a man
who kept every chill wind out. Rosa, during those stilted afternoon
visits, had adequately succeeded in conveying that she found marriage *low*. She might just have suffered a pious marriage; she openly
deprecated this high living, this state of fleshly bliss. In order not to
witness it too closely she lived on in lodgings in her native town.
. . . But once widowhood left her sister exposed, Rosa started flapping round Granville like a doomed bird. She instituted these yearly
visits, which, she made plain at the same time, gave her not much
pleasure. The journey was tedious, and by breaking her habits,

leaving her lodgings, Rosa was, out of duty, putting herself about. Her joyless and intimidating visits had, therefore, only one object— to protect the interests of Lucille.

Mrs. Cadman had suspected for some time that Rosa had something the matter with her. No one looks as yellow as that for nothing. But she was not sufficiently intimate with her sister to get down to the cosy subjects of insides. This time, Rosa arrived looking worse than ever, and three days afterwards had collapsed. Lucille said now she had known her aunt was poorly. Lucille said now she had always known. "But of course you wouldn't notice, mother," she said.

Mrs. Cadman sat down by the fire and, gratefully, kicked off her tight shoes. In the warmth her plump feet uncurled, relaxed, expanded like sea-anemones. She stretched her legs out, propped her heels on the fender and wiggled her toes voluptuously. They went on wiggling of their own accord: they seemed to have an independent existence. Here, in her home, where she felt so "put wrong" and chilly, they were like ten stout confidential friends. She said, out loud: "Well, *I* don't know what I've done."

The fact was: Lucille and Rosa resented her. (She'd feel better when she had had her tea.) She should *not* have talked as she had about the vicar. But it seemed so silly, Lucille having just him. She did wish Lucille had a better time. No young man so much as paused at the gate. Lucille's aunt had wrapped her own dank virginity round her, like someone sharing a mackintosh.

Mrs. Cadman had had a good time. A real good time always lasts: you have it with all your nature and all your nature stays living with it. She had been a pretty child with long, blonde hair that her sister Rosa, who was her elder sister, used to tweak when they were alone in their room. She had grown used, in that childish attic bedroom, to Rosa's malevolent silences. Then one had grown up, full of great uppish curves. Hilda Cadman could sing. She had sung at parties and sung at charity concerts, too. She had been invited from town to town, much fêted in business society. She had sung in a dress cut low at the bosom, with a rose or carnation tucked into her hair. She had drunk port wine in great red rooms blazing with chandeliers. Mr. Cadman had whisked her away from her other gentlemen friends, and not for a moment had she regretted it. Nothing had been too good for her; she had gone on singing. She had felt warm air on her bare shoulders; she still saw the kind, flushed faces crowding round. Mr. Cadman and she belonged to the jolly set. They all thought the world of her, and she thought the world of them.

Mrs. Cadman, picking up the poker, jabbed the fire into a spurt of light. It does not do any good to sit and think in the dark.

The town was not the same now. They had all died, or lost their money, or gone. But you kept on loving the town for its dear old sake. She sometimes thought: Why not move and live at the seaside, where there would be a promenade and a band? But she knew her nature clung to the old scenes; where you had lived, you lived—your nature clung like a cat. While there was *something* to look at she was not one to repine. It kept you going to keep out and about. Things went, but then new things came in their place. You can't cure yourself of the habit of loving life. So she drank up the new pleasures—the big cafês, the barging buses, the cinemas, the shops dripping with colour, almost all built of glass. She could be perfectly happy all alone in a cafê, digging into a cream bun with a fork, the band playing, smiling faces all round. The old faces had not gone: they had dissolved, diluted into the ruddy blur through which she saw everything.

Meanwhile, Lucille was hard put to it, living her mother down. Mother looked ridiculous, always round town like that.

Mrs. Cadman heard Lucille come out of the kitchen and go up-stairs with something rattling on a tray. She waited a minute more, then sidled into the kitchen, where she cautiously started to make tea. The gas-ring, as though it were a spy of Lucille's, popped loudly when she applied the match.

"Mother, she's asking for you."

"Oh, dear—do you mean she's—?"

"She's much more herself this evening," Lucille said implacably.

Mrs. Cadman, at the kitchen table, had been stirring sugar into her third cup. She pushed her chair back, brushed crumbs from her bosom and followed Lucille like a big unhappy lamb. The light was on in the hall, but the stairs led up into shadow: she had one more start of reluctance at their foot. Autumn draughts ran about in the top story: up there the powers of darkness all seemed to mobilize. Mrs. Cadman put her hand on the banister knob. "Are you sure she *does* want to see me? Oughtn't she to stay quiet?"

"You should go when she's asking. You never know. . . ."

Breathless, breathing unevenly on the top landing, Mrs. Cadman pushed open the spare-room—that was the sickroom—door. In there—in here—the air was dead, and at first it seemed very dark. On the ceiling an oil-stove printed its flower-pattern; a hooded lamp, low down, was turned away from the bed. On that dark side of the lamp she could just distinguish Rosa, propped up, with the sheet drawn to her chin.

"Rosa?"

"Oh, it's you?"

"Yes; it's me, dear. Feeling better this evening?"

"Seemed funny, you not coming near me."

"They said for you to keep quiet."

"My own sister. . . . You never liked sickness, did you? Well, I'm going, I shan't trouble you long."

"Oh, don't talk like that!"

"I'm glad to be going. Keeping on lying here. . . . We all come to it. Oh, give over crying, Hilda. Doesn't do any good"

Mrs. Cadman sat down, to steady herself. She fumbled in her lap with her handkerchief, perpetually, clumsily knocking her elbows against the arms of the wicker chair. "It's such a shame," she said. "It's such a pity. You and me, after all . . ."

"Well, it's late for all that now. Each took our own ways." Rosa's voice went up in a sort of ghostly sharpness. "There were things that couldn't be otherwise. I've tried to do right by Lucille. Lucille's a good girl, Hilda. You should ask yourself if you've done right by her."

"Oh, for shame, Rosa," said Mrs. Cadman, turning her face through the dark towards that disembodied voice. "For shame, Rosa, even if you *are* going. You know best what's come between her and me. It's been you and her, you and her. I don't know where to turn sometimes—"

Rosa said: "You've got such a shallow heart."

"How should you know? Why, you've kept at a distance from me ever since we were tots. Oh, I know I'm a great silly, always after my fun, but I never took what was yours; I never did harm to you. I don't see what call we have got to judge each other. You didn't want my life that I've had."

Rosa's chin moved: she was lying looking up at her sister's big rippling shadow, splodged up there by the light of the low lamp. It is frightening, having your shadow watched. Mrs. Cadman said: "But what did I do to you?"

"I *could* have had a wicked heart," said Rosa. "A vain, silly heart like yours. I could have fretted, seeing you take everything. One thing, then another. But I was shown. God taught me to pity you. God taught me my lesson. . . . You wouldn't even remember that Christmas tree"

"What Christmas tree?"

"No, you wouldn't even remember. Oh, I though it was lovely.

I could have cried when they pulled the curtains open, and there it was, all blazing away with candles and silver and everything—"

"Well, isn't that funny. I—"

"No; you've had all that pleasure since. All of us older children couldn't take it in, hardly, for quite a minute or two. It didn't look real. Then I looked up, and there was a fairy doll fixed on the top, right on the top spike, fixed on to a star. I set my heart on her. She had wings and long fair hair, and she was shining away. I couldn't take my eyes off her. They cut the presents down; but she wasn't for anyone. In my childish blindness I kept praying to God. If I am not to have her, I prayed, let her stay there."

"And what did God do?" Hilda said eagerly.

"Oh, He taught me and saved me. You were a little thing in a blue sash; you piped up and asked might you have the doll."

"Fancy me! Aren't children awful!" said Mrs. Cadman. "Asking like that."

"They said: 'Make her sing for it.' They were taken with you. So you piped up again, singing. You got her, all right. I went off where they kept the coats. I've thanked God ever since for what I had to go through!" I turned my face from vanity that very night. I had been shown."

"Oh, what a shame!" said Hilda. "Oh, I think it was cruel; you poor little mite."

"No, I used to see that doll all draggled about the house till no one could bear the sight of it. I said to myself: that's how those things end. Why, I'd learnt more in one evening than you've ever learnt in your life. Oh, yes, I've watched you, Hilda. Yes, and I've pitied you."

"Well, you showed me no pity."

"You asked for no pity—all vain and set up."

"No wonder you've been against me. Fancy me not knowing. I didn't *mean* any harm—why, I was quite a little thing. I don't even remember."

"Well, you'll remember one day. When you lie as I'm lying you'll find that everything comes back. And you'll see what it adds up to."

"Well, if I do?" said Hilda. "I haven't been such a baby; I've seen things out in my own way; I've had my ups and downs. It hasn't been all jam." She got herself out of the arm-chair and came and stood uncertainly by the foot of the bed. She had a great wish to reach out and turn the hooded lamp round, so that its light could fall on her sister's face. She felt she should *see* her sister, perhaps for the first time. Inside the flat, still form did implacable disappointment, then, stay locked? She wished she could give Rosa some little present. Too late to give Rosa anything pretty now: she looked back—it had always, then, been too late? She thought: you poor queer heart; you queer heart, eating yourself out, thanking God for the pain. She thought: I did that to her; then what have I done to Lucille?

She said: "You're ever so like me, Rosa, really, aren't you? Setting our hearts on things. When you've got them you don't notice. No wonder you wanted Lucille. . . . You did ought to have had that fairy doll."

Discussion of "A Queer Heart"

Elizabeth Bowen (1899-   ) is a distinguished Anglo-Irish novelist and short-story writer. "A Queer Heart" is one of the best and most famous of her stories.

Immediately the reader is struck with how skillfully this story is written. Note, for example, its two opening sentences: "Mrs. Cadman got out of the bus backwards. No amount of practice ever made her more agile; the trouble she had with her big bulk amused everyone, and herself." The words are simple, but they tell so much. We see Mrs. Cadman not only as a very fat woman, but as a very fat woman who can laugh at herself—and this makes all the difference.

As the story develops it becomes a study in contrasts. Mrs. Hilda Cadman is fat and good-natured, talkative and fun-loving, extroverted and pleasure-seeking. Her sister Rosa is just the opposite—thin, reserved, pious, introverted, and pleasure-hating. Obviously the two sisters do not get along well. ("One chooses one's husband; one's sister is dealt out to one by fate," says Hilda.) And obviously Hilda's daughter, Lucille, is like her Aunt Rosa rather than like her mother. Indeed, Rosa has gone out of her way to alienate Lucille from her mother. And she has done a good job, for Lucille is as pious and ascetic and "sour" as Rosa herself.

At the end of the story we learn why Rosa has so deliberately influenced Lucille away from her mother. We see the resentment that has smoldered through the years in Rosa's heart because pretty Hilda was given the fairy doll from the top of the Christmas tree and Rosa had nothing.

Which of the sisters has sinned the greater? Jolly, vain, pleasure-loving Hilda, who has spent her life pursuing fun and feeding the desires of her flesh? Or cold, resentful, jealous, pleasure-denying Rosa, who has spent her life getting revenge and making a martyr of herself? That Hilda is worldly and sensuous is obvious. But is Rosa's sin any less? True, Rosa has sacrificed and suffered. But is there a kind of unselfishness so smug that it becomes selfishness, a kind of pain so self-imposed that it is enjoyed? Does righteousness turned to self-righteousness become unrighteousness? If one prides oneself too much in one's virtues, can the virtues become evils?

The final point of the story is an interesting one as it relates to the title, "A Queer Heart." Whose heart is queer? Is only one heart referred to? Now that we have finished the story and thought about it, we can make an important discovery: These sisters who were oh so different are really very much alike. Each has a queer, narrow heart; each has misunderstood the other; each has taken what the other wanted without being aware of the other's needs. Each has been basically selfish, and each has been hurt by her own selfishness.

The New Dress

by Virginia Woolf

Mabel had her first serious suspicion that something was wrong as she took her cloak off and Mrs. Barnet, while handing her the mirror and touching the brushes and thus drawing her attention, perhaps rather markedly, to all the appliances for tidying and improving hair, complexion, clothes, which existed on the dressing table, confirmed the suspicion—that it was not right, not quite right, which growing stronger as she went upstairs and springing at her with conviction as she greeted Clarissa Dalloway, she went straight to the far end of the room, to a shaded corner where a looking-glass hung and looked. No! It was not right. And at once the misery which she always tried to hide, the profound dissatisfaction—the sense she had had, ever since she was a child, of being inferior to other people—set upon her, relentlessly, remorselessly, with an intensity which she could not beat off, as she would when she woke at night at home, by reading Borrow or Scott; for, oh, these men, oh, these women, all were thinking—"What's Mabel wearing? What a fright she looks! What a hideous new dress!"— their eyelids flickering as they came up and then their lids shutting rather tight. It was her own appalling inadequacy; her cowardice; her mean, water-sprinkled blood that depressed her. And at once the whole of the room where, for ever so many hours, she had planned with the little dressmaker how it was to go, seemed sordid, repulsive; and her own drawing-room so shabby, and herself, going out, puffed up with vanity as she touched the letters on the hall table and said: "How dull!" to show off—all this now seemed unutterably silly, paltry, and provincial. All this had been absolutely destroyed, shown up, exploded, the moment she came into Mrs. Dalloway's drawing-room.

What she had thought that evening when, sitting over the teacups, Mrs. Dalloway's invitation came, was that, of course, she could not be fashionable. It was absurd to pretend to even—fashion meant cut, meant style, meant thirty guineas at least—but why not be original? Why not be herself, anyhow? And, getting up, she had taken that old fashion book of her mother's, a Paris fashion book of the time of the Empire, and had thought how much prettier, more dignified, and more womanly, they were then, and so set herself— oh, it was foolish—trying to be like them, pluming herself in fact upon being modest and old-fashioned and very charming, giving herself up, no doubt about it, to an orgy of self-love which deserved to be chastised, and so rigged herself out like this.

But she dared not look in the glass. She could not face the whole horror—the pale yellow, idiotically old-fashioned silk dress with its long skirt and its high sleeves and its waist and all the things that looked so charming in the fashion book, but not on her. not among all these ordinary people. She felt like a dressmaker's dummy standing there for young people to stick pins into.

"But, my dear, it's perfectly charming!" Rose Shaw said, looking her up and down with that little satirical pucker of the lips which she expected—Rose herself being dressed in the height of the fashion, precisely like everybody else, always.

"We are all like flies trying to crawl over the edge of the saucer," Mabel thought, and repeated the phrase as if she were crossing herself, as if she were trying to find some spell to annul this pain, to make this agony endurable. Tags of Shakespeare, lines from books she had read ages ago, suddenly came to her when she was in agony, and she repeated them over and over again. "Flies trying to crawl," she repeated. If she could say that over often enough and make herself see the flies, she would become numb, chill, frozen, dumb. Now she could see flies crawling slowly out of a saucer of milk with their wings stuck together; and she strained and strained (standing in front of the looking-glass, listening to Rose Shaw) to make herself see Rose Shaw and all the other people there as flies, trying to hoist themselves out of something, or into something, meagre, insignificant, toiling flies. But she could not see them like that, not other people. She saw herself like that—she was a fly, but the others were dragonflies, butterflies, beautiful insects, dancing, fluttering, skimming, while she alone dragged herself up out of the saucer. (Envy and spite, the most detestable of the vices, were her chief faults.)

"I feel like some dowdy, decrepit, horribly dingy old fly," she said, making Robert Haydon stop just to hear her say that, just to reassure herself by furbishing up a poor weak-kneed phrase and so showing how detached she was, how witty, that she did not feel in the least out of anything. And, of course, Robert Haydon answered something quite polite, quite insincere, which she saw through instantly, and said to herself, directly he went (again from some book), "Lies, lies, lies!" For a party makes things either much more real or much less real, she thought; she saw in a flash to the bottom of Robert Haydon's heart; she saw through everything. She saw the truth. This was true, this drawing-room, this self, and the other false. Miss Milan's little work-room was really terribly hot, stuffy, sordid. It smelt of clothes and cabbage cooking; and yet, when Miss Milan put the glass in her hand, and she looked at herself with the dress on, finished, an extraordinary bliss shot through her heart. Suffused with light, she sprang into existence. Rid of cares and wrinkles, what she had dreamed of herself was there—a beautiful woman. Just for a second (she had not dared look longer, Miss Milan wanted to know about the length of the skirt), there looked at her, framed in the scrolloping mahogany, a gray-white, mysteriously smiling, charming girl, the core of herself, the soul of herself; and it was not vanity only, not only self-love that made her think it good, tender, and true. Miss Milan said that the skirt could not well be longer; if anything the skirt, said Miss Milan, puckering her forehead, considering with all her wits about her, must be shorter; and she felt, suddenly, honestly, full of love for Miss Milan, much, much fonder of Miss Milan than of anyone in the whole world, and could have cried for pity that she should be crawling on the floor with her mouth full of pins and her face red and her eyes bulging— that one human being should be doing this for another, and she saw them all as human beings merely, and herself going off to her party, and Miss Milan pulling the cover over the canary's cage, or letting him pick a hemp-seed from between her lips, and the thought of it, of this side of human nature and its patience and its endurance and its being content with such miserable, scanty, sordid, little pleasures filled her eyes with tears.

And now the whole thing had vanished. The dress, the room, the love, the pity, the scrolloping looking-glass, and the canary's cage—all had vanished, and here she was in a corner of Mrs. Dalloway's drawing-room, suffering tortures, woken wide awake to reality.

But it was all so paltry, weak-blooded, and petty-minded to care so much at her age with two children, to be still so utterly dependent on people's opinions and not have principles or convictions, not to be able to say as other people did, "There's Shakespeare! There's death! We're all weevils in a captain's biscuit"—or whatever it was that people did say.

She faced herself straight in the glass; she pecked at her left shoulder; she issued out into the room, as if spears were thrown at her yellow dress from all sides. But instead of looking fierce or tragic, as Rose Shaw would have done—Rose would have looked like Boadicea—she looked foolish and self-conscious and simpered like a schoolgirl and slouched across the room, positively slinking, as if she were a beaten mongrel, and looked at a picture, an engraving. As if one went to a party to look at a picture! Everybody knew why she did it—it was from shame, from humiliation.

"Now the fly's in the saucer," she said to herself, "right in the middle, and can't get out, and the milk," she thought, rigidly staring at the picture, "is sticking its wings together."

"It's so old-fashioned," she said to Charles Burt, making him stop (which by itself he hated) on his way to talk to someone else.

She meant, or she tried to make herself think that she meant, that it was the picture and not her dress, that was old-fashioned. And one word of praise, one word of affection from Charles would have made all the difference to her at the moment. If he had only said, "Mabel, you're looking charming tonight!" it would have changed her life. But then she ought to have been truthful and direct. Charles said nothing of the kind, of course. He was malice itself. He always saw through one, especially if one were feeling particularly mean, paltry, or feeble-minded.

"Mabel's got a new dress!" he said, and the poor fly was absolutely shoved into the middle of the saucer. Really, he would like her to drown, she believed. He had no heart, no fundamental kindness, only a veneer of friendliness. Miss Milan was much more real, much kinder. If only one could feel that and stick to it, always. "Why," she asked herself—replying to Charles much too pertly, letting him see that she was out of temper, or "ruffled" as he called it ("Rather ruffled?" he said and went on to laugh at her with some woman over there) — "Why," she asked herself, "can't I feel one thing always, feel quite sure that Miss Milan is right, and Charles wrong and stick to it, feel sure about the canary and pity and love and not be whipped all round in a second by coming into a room full of people?" It was her odious, weak, vacillating character again, always giving at the critical moment and not being seriously interested in conchology, etymology, botany, archaeology, cutting up potatoes and watching them fructify like Mary Dennis, like Violet Searle.

Then Mrs. Holman, seeing her standing there, bore down upon her. Of course a thing like a dress was beneath Mrs. Holman's notice, with her family always tumbling downstairs or having the scarlet fever. Could Mabel tell her if Elmthorpe was ever let for August and September? Oh, it was a conversation that bored her unutterably!—it made her furious to be treated like a house agent or a messenger boy, to be made use of. Not to have value, that was it, she thought, trying to grasp something hard, something real, while she tried to answer sensibly about the bathroom and the south aspect and the hot water to the top of the house; and all the time she could see little bits of her yellow dress in the round looking-glass which made them all the size of boot-buttons or tadpoles; and it was amazing to think how much humiliation and agony and self-loathing and effort and passionate ups and downs of feeling were contained in a thing the size of a threepenny bit. And what was still odder, this thing, this Mabel Waring, was separate, quite disconnected; and though Mrs. Holman (the black button) was leaning forward and telling her how her eldest boy had strained his heart running, she could see her, too, quite detached in the looking-glass, and it was impossible that the black dot, leaning forward, gesticulating, should make the yellow dot, sitting solitary self-centred, feel what the black dot was feeling, yet they pretended.

"So impossible to keep boys quiet"—that was the kind of thing one said.

And Mrs. Holman, who could never get enough sympathy and snatched what little there was greedily, as if it were her right (but she deserved much more for there was her little girl who had come down this morning with a swollen kneejoint), took this miserable offering and looked at it suspiciously, grudgingly, as if it were a half-penny when it ought to have been a pound and put it away in her purse, must put up with it, mean and miserly though it was, times being hard, so very hard; and on she went, creaking, injured Mrs. Holman, about the girl with the swollen joints. Ah, it was tragic, this greed, this clamour of human beings, like a row of cormorants, barking and flapping their wings for sympathy—it was tragic, could one have felt it and not merely pretended to feel it!

But in her yellow dress tonight she could not wring out one drop more; she wanted it all, all for herself. She knew (she kept on looking into the glass, dipping into that dreadfully showing-up blue pool) that she was condemned, despised, left like this in a backwater, because of her being like this—a feeble, vacillating creature; and it seemed to her that the yellow dress was a penance which she had deserved, and if she had been dressed like Rose Shaw, in lovely, clinging green with a ruffle of swansdown, she would have deserved that; and she thought that there was no escape for her—none whatever. But it was not her fault altogether, after all. It was being one of a family of ten; never having money enough, always skimping and paring; and her mother carrying great cans, and the linoleum worn on the stair edges, and one sordid little domestic tragedy after another—nothing catastrophic, the sheep farm failing, but not utterly; her eldest brother marrying beneath him, but not very much—there was no romance, nothing extreme about them all. They petered out respectably in seaside resorts; every watering-place had one of her aunts even now asleep in some lodging with the front windows not quite facing the sea. That was so like them—they had to squint at things always. And she had done the same—she was just like her aunts. For all her dreams of living in India, married to some hero like Sir Henry Lawrence, some empire builder (still the sight of a native in a turban filled her with romance), she had failed utterly. She had married Hubert, with his safe, permanent underling's job in the Law Courts, and they managed tolerably in a smallish house, without proper maids, and hash when she was alone or just bread and butter, but now and then—Mrs. Holman was off, thinking her the most dried-up, unsympathetic twig she had ever met, absurdly dressed, too, and would tell everyone about Mabel's fantastic appearance—now and then, thought Mabel Waring, left alone on the blue sofa, punching the cushion in order to look occupied, for she would not join Charles Burt and Rose Shaw, chattering like magpies and perhaps laughing at her by the fireplace—now and then, there did come to her delicious moments, reading the other night in bed, for instance, or down by the sea on the sand in the sun, at Easter— let her recall it—a great tuft of pale sand-grass, standing all twisted like a shock of spears against the sky, which was blue like a smooth china egg, so firm, so hard, and then the melody of the waves— "Hush, hush," they said, and the children's shouts paddling—yes, it was a divine moment, and there she lay, she felt, in the hand of the Goddess who was the world; rather a hard-hearted, but very beautiful Goddess, a little lamb laid on the altar (one did think these silly things, and it didn't matter so long as one never said them). And also with Hubert sometimes she had quite unexpectedly— carving the mutton for Sunday lunch, for no reason, opening a letter, coming into a room—divine moments, when she said to herself (for she would never say this to anybody else), "This is it. This has happened. This is it!" And the other way about it was equally surprising—that is, when everything was arranged—music, weather, holidays, every reason for happiness was there—then nothing happened at all. One wasn't happy. It was flat, just flat, that was all.

Her wretched self again, no doubt! She had always been a fretful, weak, unsatisfactory mother, a wobbly wife, lolling about in a kind of twilight existence with nothing very clear or very bold, or more one thing than another, like all her brothers and sisters, except perhaps Herbert—they were all the same poor water-veined creatures who did nothing. Then in the midst of this creeping, crawling life suddenly she was on the crest of a wave. That wretched fly—where had she read the story that kept coming into her mind about the fly and the saucer?—struggled out. Yes, she had those moments. But now that she was forty, they might come more and more seldom. By degrees she would cease to struggle any more. But that was deplorable! That was not to be endured! That made her feel ashamed of herself!

She would go to the London Library tomorrow. She would find some wonderful helpful, astonishing book, quite by chance, a book by a clergyman, by an American no one had ever heard of; or she would walk down the strand and drop, accidentally, into a hall where a miner was telling about the life in the pit, and suddenly she would become a new person. She would be absolutely transformed. She would wear a uniform; she would be called Sister Somebody; she would never give a thought to clothes again. And forever after she would be perfectly clear about Charles Burt and Miss Milan and this room and that room; and it would be always, day after day, as if she were lying in the sun or carving the mutton. It would be it!

So she got up from the blue sofa, and the yellow button in the looking-glass got up too, and she waved her hand to Charles and Rose to show them she did not depend on them one scrap, and the yellow button moved out of the looking-glass, and all the spears were gathered into her breast as she walked towards Mrs. Dalloway and said, "Good night."

"But it's too early to go," said Mrs. Dalloway, who was always so charming.

"I'm afraid I must," said Mabel Waring. "But," she added in her weak wobbly voice which only sounded ridiculous when she tried to strengthen it, "I have enjoyed myself enormously."

"I have enjoyed myself," she said to Mr. Dalloway, whom she met on the stairs.

"Lies, lies, lies!" she said to herself, going downstairs, and "Right in the saucer!" she said to herself as she thanked Mrs. Barnet for helping her and wrapped herself, round and round and round, in the Chinese cloak she had worn these twenty years.

Discussion of "The New Dress"

One of the most gifted of English writers of prose fiction—that is, of novels and short stories—was Virginia Woolf (1882-1941). With James Joyce she formed the center of the brilliantly psychological stream-of-consciousness movement, which had as its goal to explore the processes of the human mind with all its tumbled mixture of thoughts and half thoughts, feelings and half feelings, impressions and half impressions. Among her important works are *Mrs. Dalloway, To the Lighthouse, Orlando, Jacob's Room,* and *The Waves* (all novels), plus several volumes of distinguished short stories and critical essays.

"The New Dress" is a stream-of-consciousness story. Even though it is written in the third person, it takes place entirely within the mind of Mabel Waring, letting us know her thoroughly, perhaps even more thoroughly than we know ourselves. And notice how the long, involved sentences, rambling loosely and at times almost incoherently from thought to thought, suggest the muddled state of Mabel's mind.

Having the right attitudes may not be everything in the world, but it is certainly one of the most important things. Two people can have essentially the same jobs, same incomes, same environments, same experiences—yet one will be happy and the other unhappy. The difference is attitude. Two writers can look at the same world around them with the same mixture of good and evil, of the beautiful and the ugly—yet one will react to it optimistically and the other pessimistically. The difference is again attitude. Whether we are happy or unhappy, optimistic or pessimistic, affirmative or negative, appreciative or fault-finding, pleasant or sour depends not so much on external incidents as on inner attitudes.

Unfortunately, some people are like Mabel Waring. She is painfully self-conscious and unhealthily self-pitying. In her extreme introversion she spends all of her time imagining what others are thinking about her, and generally imagining the worst. She is so concerned with herself and her appearance that she can think of nothing else, do nothing constructive. Obviously she needs to follow the advice of Christ and forget herself in the service of others, thus finding herself by losing herself; but she is so neurotic that she is ready-made for the hands of a psychiatrist. One might say that she has an extreme inferiority complex. But there is something strange about an inferiority complex: It is also a superiority complex. Mabel is so obsessed with feeling sorry for herself that she thinks other people spend their time pitying her, when the truth is that other people probably are not even aware of her much of the time. An egoist, even a self-pitying egoist, is generally deep down inside also an egotist. And so Mabel goes on year after year seeing herself as a drab fly trying to crawl over the edge of a saucer with all the beautiful butterflies looking on and scorning her.

If one has tendencies to be like Mabel, great strength of will is necessary to throw off the self-pity and develop a healthy attitude toward oneself and one's environment. But it can be done. The first step is to recognize the tendencies, and the second step is to exert the constant will-power necessary to overcome them. One purpose for including "The New Dress" in this book is that seeing the unwholesome qualities in Mabel may help to detect them in oneself if they are present.

Birthday Party

by Katharine Brush

They were a couple in their late thirties, and they looked unmistakably married. They sat on the banquette opposite us in a little narrow restaurant, having dinner. The man had a round, self-satisfied face, with glasses on it; the woman was fadingly pretty, in a big hat. There was nothing conspicuous about them, nothing particularly noticeable, until the end of their meal, when it suddenly became obvious that this was an Occasion—in fact, the husband's birthday, and the wife had planned a little surprise for him.

It arrived, in the form of a small but glossy birthday cake, with one pink candle burning in the center. The headwaiter brought it in and placed it before the husband, and meanwhile the violin-and-piano orchestra played "Happy Birthday to You" and the wife beamed with shy pride over her little surprise, and such few people as there were in the restaurant tried to help out with a pattering of applause. It became clear at once that help was needed, because the husband was not pleased. Instead he was hotly embarrassed, and indignant at his wife for embarrassing him.

You looked at him and you saw this and you thought, "Oh, now, don't *be* like that!" But he was like that, and as soon as the little cake had been deposited on the table, and the orchestra had finished the birthday piece, and the general attention had shifted from the man and the woman, I saw him say something to her under his breath—some punishing thing, quick and curt and unkind. I couldn't bear to look at the woman then, so I stared at my plate and waited for quite a long time. Not long enough, though. She was still crying when I finally glanced over there again. Crying quietly and heartbrokenly and hopelessly, all to herself, under the gay big brim of her best hat.

Discussion of "Birthday Party"

Katharine Brush (1902-   ) is an American journalist, novelist, and short-story writer. Although her work is popular, it is also of excellent quality, as the preceding story shows.

"Birthday Party" is a very short short-story, but a whole drama of life is compressed into its three little paragraphs. The two qualities that have always characterized short stories—brevity and unity—are seen here in exaggeration: the goal of a short-story writer having always been to use words economically and to make them all pertain to a central theme or mood or character portrayal. Note how precisely each word is chosen in this story, as precisely as if it were a lyric poem.

The scene presented is not pretty. Obviously the marriage has gone sour and neither husband nor wife is happy, at least not this day. It is as if the skin of life had been peeled back exposing the raw sore of a marriage failure, or at least a nasty marriage quarrel.

The most interesting point for discussion is to see how the author has in a few deft phrases suggested the source of the marriage problem. Note how basically different the husband and wife are. The "fadingly pretty" woman apparently is sentimental, romantic, nostalgically looking to the past and trying to hold on to the romance that is also fading. The husband is brusque and practical. But is the problem simply that they are different?

Who is the villain of the little story? That the husband is cruel is obvious. He deliberately says cutting words to his wife, deliberately hurts her. Such action is, of course, inexcusably mean and crude—especially since he knows that his wife has tried to do something sweet for him.

But is the wife also at fault? Obviously the husband is unfeeling towards his wife's wishes and needs. Is she also unfeeling towards his? If she really loved and understood him, if she really thought of him and not of herself, would she plan a public party for his birthday? Wouldn't she know that such a party would embarrass him? Wouldn't she realize that he would be annoyed by a public display of personal sentiment?

Looked at this way, both husband and wife are exposed as at fault. Each is guilty of thinking mostly of himself. Neither loves as one should love in marriage, unselfishly placing the desires and needs of the marriage partner ahead of one's own desires and needs. Unselfish understanding is essential for happiness in marriage, and selfish lack of understanding dooms a marriage to unhappiness—especially when there is little effort to achieve understanding or to overcome selfishness.

The Bear

by William Faulkner

He was ten. But it had already begun, long before that day
when at last he wrote his age in two figures and he saw for the
first time the camp where his father and Major de Spain and old
General Compson and the others spent two weeks each November
and two weeks again each June. He had already inherited then, without ever having seen it, the tremendous bear with one trap-ruined
foot which, in an area almost a hundred miles deep, had earned
itself a name, a definite designation like a living man.

He had listened to it for years: the long legend of corn-cribs
rifled, of shotes and grown pigs and even calves carried bodily into
the woods and devoured, of traps and deadfalls overthrown and
dogs mangled and slain, and shotgun and even rifle charges delivered
at point-blank range and with no more effect than so many peas
blown through a tube by a boy—a corridor of wreckage and destruction beginning back before he was born, through which sped,
not fast but rather with the ruthless and irresistible deliberation of
a locomotive, the shaggy tremendous shape.

It ran in his knowledge before he ever saw it. It looked and
towered in his dreams before he even saw the unaxed woods where
it left its crooked print, shaggy, huge, red-eyed, not malevolent but
just big—too big for the dogs which tried to bay it, for the horses
which tried to ride it down, for the men and the bullets they fired
into it, too big for the very country which was its constricting scope.
He seemed to see it entire with a child's complete divination before
he ever laid eyes on either—the doomed wilderness whose edges
were being constantly and punily gnawed at by men with axes and
plows who feared it because it was wilderness, men myriad and
nameless even to one another in the land where the old bear had
earned a name, through which ran not even a mortal animal but an
anachronism, indomitable and invincible, out of an old dead time, a
phantom, epitome and apotheosis of the old wild life at which the
puny humans swarmed and hacked in a fury of abhorrence and fear,
like pygmies about the ankles of a drowsing elephant: the old bear
solitary, indomitable and alone, widowered, childless, and absolved
of mortality—old Priam reft of his old wife and having outlived all
his sons.

Until he was ten, each November he would watch the wagon
containing the dogs and the bedding and food and guns and his
father and Tennie's Jim, the Negro, and Sam Fathers, the Indian,

son of a slave woman and a Chickasaw chief, depart on the road to town, to Jefferson, where Major de Spain and the others would join them. To the boy, at seven, eight, and nine, they were not going into the Big Bottom to hunt bear and deer, but to keep yearly rendezvous with the bear which they did not even intend to kill. Two weeks later they would return, with no trophy, no head and skin. He had not expected it. He had not even been afraid it would be in the wagon. He believed that even after he was ten and his father would let him go too, for those two weeks in November, he would merely make another one, along with his father and Major de Spain and General Compson and the others, the dogs which feared to bay it and the rifles and shotguns which failed even to bleed it, in the yearly pageant of the old bear's furious immortality.

Then he heard the dogs. It was in the second week of his first time in the camp. He stood with Sam Fathers against a big oak beside the faint crossing where they had stood each dawn for nine days now, hearing the dogs. He had heard them once before, one morning last week—a murmur, sourceless, echoing through the wet woods, swelling presently into separate voices which he could recognize and call by name. He had raised and cocked the gun as Sam told him and stood motionless again while the uproar, the invisible course, swept up and past and faded; it seemed to him that he could actually see the deer, the buck, blond, smoke-colored, elongated with speed, fleeing, vanishing, the woods, the gray solitude, still ringing even when the cries of the dogs had died away.

"Now let the hammers down," Sam said.

"You knew they were not coming here too," he said.

"Yes," Sam said. "I want you to learn how to do when you didn't shoot. It's after the chance for the bear or the deer has done already come and gone that men and dogs get killed."

"Anyway," he said, "it was just a deer."

Then on the tenth morning he heard the dogs again. And he readied the too-long, too-heavy gun as Sam had taught him, before Sam even spoke. But this time it was no deer, no ringing chorus of dogs running strong on a free scent, but a moiling yapping an octave too high, with something more than indecision and even abjectness in it, not even moving very fast, taking a long time to pass completely out of hearing, leaving then somewhere in the air that echo, thin, slightly hysterical, abject, almost grieving, with no sense of a fleeing, unseen, smoke-colored, grass-eating shape ahead of it, and Sam, who had taught him first of all to cock the gun and take position where he could see everywhere and then never move again, had himself moved up beside him; he could hear Sam breathing at his shoulder, and he could see the arched curve of the old man's inhaling nostrils.

"Hah," Sam said. "Not even running. Walking."

"Old Ben!" the boy said. "But up here!" he cried. "Way up here!"

"He do it every year," Sam said. "Once. Maybe to see who in camp this time, if he can shoot or not. Whether we got the dog yet that can bay and hold him. He'll take them to the river, then he'll send them back home. We may as well go back too; see how they look when they come back to camp."

When they reached the camp the hounds were already there, ten of them crouching back under the kitchen, the boy and Sam squatting to peer back into the obscurity where they had huddled, quiet, the eyes luminous, glowing at them and vanishing, and no sound, only that effluvium of something more than dog, stronger than dog and not just animal, just beast, because still there had been nothing in front of that abject and almost painful yapping save the solitude, the wilderness, so that when the eleventh hound came in at noon and with all the others watching—even old Uncle Ash, who called himself first a cook—Sam daubed the tattered ear and the raked shoulder with turpentine and axle grease, to the boy it was still no living creature, but the wilderness which, leaning for the moment down, had patted lightly once the hound's temerity.

"Just like a man," Sam said. "Just like folks. Put off as long as she could having to be brave, knowing all the time that sooner or later she would have to be brave to keep on living with herself, and knowing all the time beforehand what was going to happen to her when she done it."

That afternoon, himself on the one-eyed wagon mule which did not mind the smell of blood nor, as they told him, of bear, and with Sam on the other one, they rode for more than three hours through the rapid, shortening winter day. They followed no path, no trail even that he could see; almost at once they were in a country which he had never seen before. Then he knew why Sam had made him ride the mule which would not spook. The sound one stopped short and tried to whirl and bolt even as Sam got down, blowing its breath, jerking and wrenching at the rein, while Sam held it, coaxing it forward with his voice, since he could not risk tying it, drawing it forward while the boy got down from the marred one.

Then, standing beside Sam in the gloom of the dying afternoon, he looked down at the rotted over-turned log, gutted and scored with claw marks and, in the wet earth beside it, the print of the enormous warped two-toed foot. He knew now what he had smelled when he peered under the kitchen where the dogs huddled. He realized for the first time that the bear which had run in his listening and loomed in his dreams since before he could remember to the contrary, and which, therefore, must have existed in the listening and dreams of his father and Major de Spain and even old General Compson, too, before they began to remember in their turn, was a mortal animal, and that if they had departed for the camp each November without any actual hope of bringing its trophy back, it was not because it could not be slain, but because so far they had had no actual hope to.

"Tomorrow," he said.

"We'll try tomorrow," Sam said. "We ain't got the dog yet."

"We've got eleven. They ran him this morning."

"It won't need but one," Sam said. "He ain't here. Maybe he ain't nowhere. The only other way will be for him to run by accident over somebody that has a gun."

"That wouldn't be me," the boy said. "It will be Walter or Major or—"

"It might," Sam said. "You watch close in the morning. Because he's smart. That's how come he has lived this long. If he gets hemmed up and has to pick out somebody to run over, he will pick out you."

"How?" the boy said. "How will he know—" He ceased. "You mean he already knows me, that I ain't never been here before, ain't had time to find out yet whether I—" He ceased again, looking at Sam, the old man whose face revealed nothing until it smiled. He said humbly, not even amazed, "It was me he was watching. I don't reckon he did need to come but once."

The next morning they left the camp three hours before daylight. They rode this time because it was too far to walk, even the dogs in the wagon; again the first gray light found him in a place which he had never seen before, where Sam had placed him and told him to stay and then departed. With the gun which was too big for him, which did not even belong to him, but to Major de Spain, and which he had fired only once—at a stump on the first day, to learn the recoil and how to reload it—he stood against a gum tree beside a little bayou whose black still water crept without movement out of a canebrake and crossed a small clearing and into cane again, where, invisible, a bird—the big woodpecker called Lord-to-God by Negroes—clattered at a dead limb.

It was a stand like any other, dissimilar only in incidentals to the one where he had stood each morning for ten days; a territory new to him, yet no less familiar than that other one which, after almost two weeks, he had come to believe he knew a little—the same solitude, the same loneliness through which human beings had merely passed without altering it, leaving no mark, no scar, which looked exactly as it must have looked when the first ancestor of Sam Fathers' Chickasaw predecessors crept into it and looked about, club or stone ax or bone arrow drawn and poised; different only because, squatting at the edge of the kitchen, he smelled the hounds huddled and cringing beneath it and saw the raked ear and shoulder of the one who, Sam said, had had to be brave once in order to live with herself, and saw yesterday in the earth beside the gutted log the print of the living foot.

He heard no dogs at all. He never did hear them. He only heard the drumming of the woodpecker stop short off and knew that the bear was looking at him. He never saw it. He did not know whether it was in front of him or behind him. He did not move, holding the useless gun, which he had not even had warning to cock and which even now he did not cock, tasting in his saliva that taint as of brass which he knew now because he had smelled it when he peered under the kitchen at the huddled dogs.

Then it was gone. As abruptly as it had ceased, the woodpecker's dry, monotonous clatter set up again, and after a while he even believed he could hear the dogs—a murmur, scarce a sound even, which he had probably been hearing for some time before he even remarked it, drifting into hearing and then out again, dying away. They came nowhere near him. If it was a bear they ran, it was another bear. It was Sam himself who came out of the cane and crossed the bayou, followed by the injured bitch of yesterday. She was almost at heel, like a bird dog, making no sound. She came and crouched against his leg, trembling, staring off into the cane.

"I didn't see him," he said. "I didn't Sam!"

"I know it," Sam said. "He done the looking. You didn't hear him neither, did you?"

"No," the boy said. "I—"

"He's smart," Sam said. "Too smart." He looked down at the hound, trembling faintly and steadily against the boy's knee. From the raked shoulder a few drops of fresh blood oozed and clung. "Too big. We ain't got the dog yet. But maybe someday. Maybe not next time. But someday."

So I must see him, he thought. *I must look at him.* Otherwise, it seemed to him that it would go on like this forever, as it had gone on with his father and Major de Spain, who was older than his father, and even with old General Compson, who had been old enough to be a brigade commander in 1865. Otherwise, it would go on so forever, next time and next time, after and after and after. It seemed to him that he could never see the two of them, himself and the bear, shadowy in the limbo from which time emerged, becoming time; the old bear absolved of mortality and himself partaking, sharing a little of it, enough of it. And he knew now what he had smelled in the huddled dogs and tasted in his saliva. He recognized fear. *So I will have to see him,* he thought, without dread or even hope. *I will have to look at him.*

It was in June of the next year. He was eleven. They were in camp again, celebrating Major de Spain's and General Compson's birthdays. Although the one had been born in September and the other in the depth of winter and in another decade, they met for two weeks to fish and shoot squirrels and turkey and run coons and wildcats with the dogs at night. That is, he and Boon Hoggenbeck and the Negroes fished and shot squirrels and ran the coons and cats, because the proved hunters, not only Major de Spain and Old General Compson, who spent those two weeks sitting in a rocking chair before a tremendous iron pot of Brunswick stew, stirring and tasting, with old Ash to quarrel with about how he was making it and Tennie's Jim to pour whiskey from the demijohn into the tin dipper from which he drank it, but even the boy's father and Walter Ewell, who were still young enough, scorned such, other than shooting the wild gobblers with pistols for wagers on their marksmanship.

Or, that is, his father and the others believed he was hunting squirrels. Until the third day, he thought that Sam Fathers believed that too. Each morning he would leave the camp right after breakfast. He had his own gun now, a Christmas present. He went back to the tree beside the bayou where he had stood that morning. Using the compass which old General Compson had given him, he ranged from that point; he was teaching himself to be a better-than-fair woodsman without knowing he was doing it. On the second day he even found the gutted log where he had first seen the crooked print. It was almost completely crumbled now, healing with unbelievable speed, a passionate and almost visible relinquishment, back into the earth from which the tree had grown.

He ranged the summer woods now, green with gloom; if anything, actually dimmer than in November's gray dissolution, where, even at noon, the sun fell only in intermittent dappling upon the earth, which never completely dried out and which crawled with snakes—moccasins and water snakes and rattlers, themselves the color of the dappling gloom, so that he would not always see them until they moved, returning later and later, first day, second day, passing in the twilight of the third evening the little log pen enclosing the log stable where Sam was putting up the horses for the night.

"You ain't looked right yet," Sam said.

He stopped. For a moment he didn't answer. Then he said, peacefully in a peaceful rushing burst as when a boy's miniature dam in a little brook gives way, "All right. But how? I went to the bayou. I even found that log again. I—"

"I reckon that was all right. Likely he's been watching you. You never saw his foot?"

"I," the boy said—"I didn't—I never thought—"

"It's the gun," Sam said. He stood beside the fence motionless— the old man, the Indian, in the battered faded overalls and the five-cent straw hat which in the negro's race had been the badge of his enslavement and was now the regalia of his freedom. The camp— the clearing, the house, the barn and its tiny lot with which Major de Spain in his turn had scratched punily and evanescently at the wilderness—faded in the dusk, back into the immemorial darkness of the woods. *The gun,* the boy thought. *The gun.*

"Be scared," Sam said. "You can't help that. But don't be afraid. Ain't nothing in the woods going to hurt you unless you corner it, or it smells that you are afraid. A bear or a deer, too, has got to be scared of a coward the same as a brave man has got to be."

The gun, the boy thought.

"You will have to choose," Sam said.

He left the camp before daylight, long before Uncle Ash would wake in his quilts on the kitchen floor and start the fire for breakfast. He had only the compass and a stick for snakes. He could go almost a mile before he would begin to need the compass. He sat on a log, the invisible compass in his invisible hand, while the secret night sounds, fallen still at his movements, scurried again and then ceased for good, and the owls ceased and gave over to the waking of day birds, and he could see the compass. Then he went fast yet still quietly; he was becoming better and better as a woodsman, still without having yet realized it.

He jumped a doe and a fawn at sunrise, walked them out of the bed, close enough to see them—the crash of undergrowth, the white scut, the fawn scudding behind her faster than he had believed it could run. He was hunting right, upwind, as Sam had taught him;

not that it mattered now. He had left the gun; of his own will and relinquishment he had accepted not a gambit, not a choice, but a condition in which not only the bear's heretofore inviolable anonymity but all the old rules and balances of hunter and hunted had been abrogated. He would not even be afraid, not even in the moment when the fear would take him completely—blood, skin, bowels, bones, memory from the long time before it became his memory—all save that thin, clear, immortal lucidity which alone differed him from this bear and from all the other bear and deer he would ever kill in the humility and pride of his skill and endurance, to which Sam had spoken when he leaned in the twilight on the lot fence yesterday.

By noon he was far beyond the little bayou, farther into the new and alien country than he had ever been. He was traveling now only by the old, heavy, biscuit-thick silver watch which had belonged to his grandfather. When he stopped at last, it was for the first time since he had risen from the log at dawn when he could see the compass. It was far enough. He had left the camp nine hours ago; nine hours from now, dark would have already been an hour old. But he didn't think that. He thought, *All right. Yes. But what?* and stood for a moment, alien and small in the green and topless solitude, answering his own question before it had formed and ceased. It was the watch, the compass, the stick—the three lifeless mechanicals with which for nine hours he had fended the wilderness off; he hung the watch and compass carefully on a bush and leaned the stick beside them and relinquished completely to it.

He had not been going very fast for the last two or three hours. He went no faster now, since distance would not matter even if he could have gone fast. And he was trying to keep a bearing on the tree where he had left the compass, trying to complete a circle which would bring him back to it or at least intersect itself, since direction would not matter now either. But the tree was not there, and he did as Sam had schooled him—made the next circle in the opposite direction, so that the two patterns would bisect somewhere, but crossing no print of his own feet, finding the tree at last, but in the wrong place—no bush, no compass, no watch—and the tree not even the tree, because there was a down log beside it and he did what Sam Fathers had told him was the next thing and the last.

As he sat down on the log he saw the crooked print—the warped, tremendous, two-toed indentation which, even as he watched it, filled with water. As he looked up, the wilderness coalesced, solidified—the glade, the tree he sought, the bush, the watch and the compass glinting where a ray of sunshine touched them. Then he saw the bear. It did not emerge, appear; it was just there immobile, solid, fixed in the hot dappling of the green and windless noon, not as big as he had dreamed it, but as big as he had expected it, bigger, dimensionless, against the dappled obscurity, looking at him where he sat quietly on the log and looked back at it.

Then it moved. It made no sound. It did not hurry. It crossed the glade, walking for an instant into the full glare of the sun; when it reached the other side it stopped again and looked back at him across one shoulder while his quiet breathing inhaled and exhaled three times.

Then it was gone. It didn't walk into the woods, the undergrowth. It faded, sank back into the wilderness as he had watched a fish, a huge old bass, sink and vanish into the dark depths of its pool without even any movement of its fins.

He thought, *It will be next fall.* But it was not next fall, nor the next nor the next. He was fourteen then. He had killed his buck, and Sam Fathers had marked his face with the hot blood, and in the next year he had killed a bear. But even before that accolade he had become as competent in the woods as many grown men with the same experience; by his fourteenth year he was a better woodsman than most grown men with more. There was no territory within thirty miles of the camp that he did not know—bayou, ridge, brake, landmark, tree and path. He could have led anyone to any point in it, without deviation, and brought them out again. He knew the game trails that even Sam Fathers did not know; in his thirteenth year he found a buck's bedding place, and unbeknown to his father he borrowed Walter Ewell's rifle and lay in wait at dawn and killed the buck when it walked back to the bed, as Sam had told him how the old Chickasaw fathers did.

But not the old bear, although by now he knew its footprints better than he did his own, and not only the crooked one. He could see any one of the three sound ones and distinguish it from any other, and not only by its size. There were other bears within these thirty miles which left tracks almost as large, but this was more than that. If Sam Fathers had been his mentor and the back-yard rabbits and squirrels at home his kindergarten, then the wilderness the old bear ran was his college, the old male bear itself, so long unwifed and childless as to have become its own ungendered progenitor, was his alma mater. But he never saw it.

He could find the crooked print now almost whenever he liked, fifteen or ten or five miles, or sometimes nearer the camp than that. Twice while on stand during the three years he heard the dogs strike its trail by accident; on the second time they jumped it seemingly, the voices high, abject, almost human in hysteria, as on that first morning two years ago. But not the bear itself. He would remember that noon three years ago, the glade, himself and the bear fixed during that moment in the windless and dappled blaze, and it would seem to him that it had never happened, that he had dreamed that too. But it had happened. They had looked at each other, they had emerged from the wilderness old as earth, synchronized to the instant by something more than the blood that moved the flesh and bones, which bore them, and touched, pledged something, affirmed, something more lasting than the frail web of bones and flesh which any accident could obliterate.

Then he saw it again. Because of the very fact that he thought of nothing else, he had forgotten to look for it. He was still hunting with Walter Ewell's rifle. He saw it cross the end of a long blow-down, a corridor where a tornado had swept, rushing through rather than over the tangle of trunks and branches as a locomotive would have, faster than he had ever believed it could move, almost as fast as a deer even, because a deer would have spent most of that time in the air, faster than he could bring the rifle sights up with it. And now he knew what had been wrong during all the three years. He sat on a log, shaking and trembling as if he had never seen the woods before nor anything that ran them, wondering with incredulous amazement how he could have forgotten the very thing which Sam Fathers had told him and which the bear itself had proved the next day and had now returned after three years to reaffirm.

And now he knew what Sam Fathers had meant about the right dog, a dog in which size would mean less than nothing. So when he returned alone in April—school was out then, so that the sons of farmers could help with the land's planting, and at last his father had granted him permission, on his promise to be back in four days— he had the dog. It was his own, a mongrel of the sort called by Negroes a fyce, a ratter, itself not much bigger than a rat and possessing that bravery which had long since stopped being courage and had become foolhardiness.

It did not take four days. Alone again, he found the trail on the first morning. It was not a stalk; it was an ambush. He timed the meeting almost as if it were an appointment with a human being. Himself holding the fyce muffled in a feed sack and Sam Fathers with two of the hounds on a piece of a plowline rope, they lay down wind of the trail at dawn of the second morning. They were so close that the bear turned without even running, as if in surprised amazement at the shrill and frantic uproar of the released fyce, turning at bay against the trunk of a tree, on its hind feet; it seemed to the boy that it would never stop rising, taller and taller, and even the two hounds seemed to take a desperate and despairing courage from the fyce, following it as it went in.

Then he realized that the fyce was actually not going to stop. He flung, threw the gun away, and ran; when he overtook and grasped the frantically pin-wheeling little dog, it seemed to him that he was directly under the bear.

He could smell it, strong and hot and rank. Sprawling, he looked up to where it loomed and towered over him like a cloudburst and colored like a thunderclap, quite familiar, peacefully and even lucidly familiar, until he remembered: This was the way he had used to dream about it. Then it was gone. He didn't see it go. He knelt, holding the frantic fyce with both hands, hearing the abashed wailing of the hounds drawing farther and farther away, until Sam came up. He carried the gun. He laid it down quietly beside the boy and stood looking down at him.

"You've done seed him twice now with a gun in your hands," he said. "This time you couldn't have missed him."

The boy rose. He still held the fyce. Even in his arms and clear of the ground, it yapped frantically, straining and surging after the fading uproar of the two hounds like a tangle of wire springs. He was panting a little, but he was neither shaking nor trembling now.

"Neither could you!" he said. "You had the gun! Neither did you!"

"And you didn't shoot," his father said. "How close were you?"

"I don't know, sir," he said. "There was a big wood tick inside his right leg. I saw that. But I didn't have the gun then."

"But you didn't shoot when you had the gun," his father said. "Why?"

But he didn't answer, and his father didn't wait for him to, rising and crossing the room, across the pelt of the bear which the boy had killed two years ago and the larger one which his father had killed before he was born, to the bookcase beneath the mounted head of the boy's first buck. It was the room which his father called his office, from which all the plantation business was transacted; in it for the fourteen years of his life he had heard the best of all talking. Major de Spain would be there and sometimes old General Compson, and Walter Ewell and Boon Hoggenback and Sam Fathers and Tennie's Jim, too, were hunters, knew the woods and what ran them.

He would hear it, not talking himself but listening—the wilderness, the big woods, bigger and older than any recorded document

of white man fatuous enough to believe he had bought any fragment
of it or Indian ruthless enough to pretend that any fragment of it
had been his to convey. It was of the men, not white nor black nor
red, but men, hunters with the will and hardihood to endure and the
humility and skill to survive, and the dogs and the bear and deer
juxtaposed and reliefed against it, ordered and compelled by and
within the wilderness in the ancient and unremitting contest by the
ancient and immitigable rules which voided all regrets and brooked
no quarter, the voices quiet and weighty and deliberate for retro-
spection and recollection and exact remembering, while he squatted
in the blazing firelight as Tennie's Jim squatted, who stirred only
to put more wood on the fire and to pass the bottle from one glass
to another. Because the bottle was always present, so that after a
while it seemed to him that those fierce instants of heart and
brain and courage and wiliness and speed were concentrated and
distilled into that brown liquor which not women, not boys and
children, but only hunters drank, drinking not of the blood they had
spilled but some condensation of the wild immortal spirit, drinking
it moderately, humbly even, not with the pagan's base hope of ac-
quiring the virtues of cunning and strength and speed, but in salute
to them.

His father returned with a book and sat down again and opened
it. "Listen," he said. He read the five stanzas aloud, his voice quiet
and deliberate in the room where there was no fire now because it
was already spring. Then he looked up. The boy watched him. "All
right," his father said. "Listen." He read again, but only the second
stanza this time, to the end of it, the last two lines, and closed the
book and put it on the table beside him. "She cannot fade, though
thou hast not thy bliss, forever wilt thou love, and she be fair,"
he said.

"He's talking about a girl," the boy said.

"He had to talk about something," his father said. Then he said,
"He was talking about truth. Truth doesn't change. Truth is one
thing. It covers all things which touch the heart—honor and pride
and pity and justice and courage and love. Do you see now?"

He didn't know. Somehow it was simpler than that. There was
an old bear, fierce and ruthless, not merely just to stay alive, but
with the fierce pride of liberty and freedom, proud enough of the
liberty and freedom to see it threatened without fear or even alarm;
nay, who at times even seemed deliberately to put that freedom and
liberty in jeopardy in order to savor them, to remind his old strong
bones and flesh to keep supple and quick to defend and preserve
them. There was an old man, son of a Negro slave and an Indian

king, inheritor on the one side of the long chronicle of a people who had learned humility through suffering, and pride through the endurance which survived the suffering and injustice, and on the other side, the chronicle of a people even longer in the land than the first, yet who no longer existed in the land at all save in the solitary brotherhood of an old Negro's alien blood and the wild and invincible spirit of an old bear. There was a boy who wished to learn humility and pride in order to become skillful and worthy in the woods, who suddenly found himself becoming so skillful so rapidly that he feared he would never become worthy because he had not learned humility and pride, although he had tried to, until one day and as suddenly he discovered that an old man who could not have defined either had led him, as though by the hand, to that point where an old bear and a little mongrel of a dog showed him that, by possessing one thing other, he would possess them both.

And a little dog, nameless and mongrel and manyfathered, grown, yet weighing less than six pounds, saying as if to itself, "I can't be dangerous, because there's nothing much smaller than I am; I can't be fierce, because they would call it just a noise; I can't be humble, because I'm already too close to the ground to genuflect; I can't be proud, because I wouldn't be near enough to it for anyone to know who was casting the shadow, and I don't even know that I'm not going to heaven, because they have already decided that I don't possess an immortal soul. So all I can be is brave. But it's all right. I can be that, even if they still call it just noise."

That was all. It was simple, much simpler than somebody talking in a book about youth and a girl he would never need to grieve over, because he could never approach any nearer her and would never have to get any farther away. He had heard about a bear, and finally got big enough to trail it, and he trailed it four years and at last met it with a gun in his hands and he didn't shoot. Because a little dog— But he could have shot long before the little dog covered the twenty yards to where the bear waited, and Sam Fathers could have shot at any time during that interminable minute while Old Ben stood on his hind feet over them. He stopped. His father was watching him gravely across the spring-rife twilight of the room; when he spoke, his words were as quiet as the twilight, too, not loud, because they did not need to be because they would last. "Courage, and honor, and pride," his father said, "and pity, and love of justice and of liberty. They all touch the heart, and what the heart holds to becomes truth, as far as we know the truth. Do you see now?"

Sam, and Old Ben, and Nip, he thought. And himself too. He had been all right too. His father had said so. "Yes, sir," he said.

Discussion of "The Bear"

Perhaps no other 20th century American novelist and short-story writer seems so assured of permanent recognition as a truly great writer as does William Faulkner (1897-1962), author of *The Sound and the Fury, As I Lay Dying,* and a dozen other novels plus several volumes of short stories. Climaxed by the Nobel Prize for Literature in 1949, Faulkner is probably more praised than read, and more read than understood. But he is sufficiently praised, read, and understood by discriminating readers to assure his position as the finest American writer of prose fiction of the past half century.

Mostly Faulkner wrote about the U.S. Southland, exploring its problems of adjustment following the great Civil War. But in a larger sense his stories depict the world in miniature, a huge saga of the whole human race in defeat and triumph, represented through the myriad characters of mythical Yoknapatawpha County in rural Mississippi.

Many readers, lost in the tangled darkness of Faulkner's incidents or frightened by the extravagant complexities of his style, have failed to see the great affirmation of his writing, but it is there. An unfaltering belief in the dignity of man and his ultimate victory over his environment permeates everything that Faulkner wrote, as evidenced by these words in his Nobel Prize Acceptance Speech:

I decline to accept the end of man. It is easy enough to say that man is immortal simply because he will endure. . . . I believe that man will not merely endure: he will prevail. He is immortal, not because he alone among creatures has an inexhaustible voice, but because he has a soul, a spirit capable of compassion and sacrifice and endurance.

"The Bear," which is Faulkner's most famous and finest short story,[1] achieves its place as one of the greatest

---

[1]Actually he wrote "The Bear" in two versions—a long one and a short one. It is the short and less complicated version that is printed and discussed in this book.

stories of the English language partly because of its magnificent prose style. Note such sentences as the two following from early in the story, describing the bear:

It looked and towered in his dreams before he even saw the unaxed
woods where it left its crooked print, shaggy, huge, red-eyed, not
malevolent but just big—too big for the dogs which tried to bay it,
for the horses which tried to ride it down, for the men and the bullets
they fired into it, too big for the very country which was its constricting scope. He seemed to see it entire with a child's complete divination before he ever laid eyes on either—the doomed wilderness whose
edges were being constantly and punily gnawed at by men with axes
and plows who feared it because it was wilderness, men myriad and
nameless even to one another in the land where the old bear had
earned a name, through which ran not even a mortal animal but an
anachronism, indomitable and invincible, out of an old dead time, a
phantom, epitome and apotheosis of the old wild life at which the
puny humans swarmed and hacked in a fury of abhorrence and fear,
like pygmies about the ankles of a drowsing elephant: the old bear
solitary, indomitable and alone, widowered, childless, and absolved of
mortality—old Priam reft of his old wife and having outlived all
his sons.

This is symphonic prose in its most brilliant luxury. Not
even Joseph Conrad or Thomas Wolfe could write prose
in the grand manner better than this, and most writers
could not even approach it.

But the greatness of the story goes far beyond its
prose style. It has a greatness in meaning fully matching
its triumph in language.

The story begins with a ten-year-old boy already
steeped in the lore of the wilderness. He comes from a
family of skilled hunters who respect the untamed power
of the forest and who have special respect for the mightiest
of all the forest creatures, a great shaggy bear with a
crooked foot. The dream of the family is to track and shoot
this huge bear, whose power and majesty the boy feels
years before he ever sees it.

In his first encounter with the bear when he is ten
years old the boy does not even see it or hear it. He senses

its presence, knows that it is looking at him, studying him, and tastes the brassy feel of fear; but he does not even catch a glimpse of its form:

> He heard no dogs at all. He never did hear them. He only heard the drumming of the woodpecker stop short off and knew that the bear was looking at him. He never saw it. He did not know whether it was in front of him or behind him. He did not move, holding the useless gun, which he had not even had warning to cock and which even now he did not cock, tasting in his saliva that taint as of brass which he knew now because he had smelled it when he peered under the kitchen at the huddled dogs. Then it was gone.

A year later, when the boy is eleven, he has his second encounter with the bear, and sees it for the first time. To do so he must prove himself worthy. From his father and others of his family the boy has learned much about the wilderness, and especially from Sam Fathers, the half-Indian and half-Negro who is the wisest wilderness hunter of them all. But the boy must learn also from trial and error, and from instinct. Before the bear will allow itself to be seen, the boy must discard not only his gun but also his watch, compass, and walking stick. He must prove that he is not afraid, partly because the bear knows that a frightened person with a gun in his hands is dangerous, and partly because only through a display of courage can the boy prove his worthiness to meet the bear, both of them naked in the wilderness. He must come to the bear on even terms, having discarded all the artificial tools of "civilization." Then—and only then—will the bear expose himself to the boy. The moment is a momentous one, heightened by the sense of the bear's immediacy through the footprint filling with water even before the bear is seen:

> As he sat down on the log he saw the crooked print—the warped, tremendous, two-toed indentation which, even as he watched it, filled with water. As he looked up, the wilderness coalesced, solidified—the glade, the tree he sought, the bush, the watch and the compass glinting where a ray of sunshine touched them. Then he saw the bear. It did not emerge, appear; it was just there, immobile,

solid, fixed in the hot dappling of the green and windless noon, not as big as he had dreamed it, but as big as he had expected it, bigger, dimensionless, against the dappled obscurity, looking at him where he sat quietly on the log and looked back at it.

Then it moved. It made no sound. It did not hurry. It crossed the glade, walking for an instant into the full glare of the sun; when it reached the other side it stopped again and looked back at him across one shoulder while his quiet breathing inhaled and exhaled three times.

Then it was gone. It didn't walk into the woods, the undergrowth. It faded, sank back into the wilderness as he had watched a fish, a huge old bass, sink and vanish into the dark depths of its pool without even any movement of its fins.

Three years pass before the boy again sees the bear. He is now fourteen. And he now knows all that Sam Fathers has to teach him about the wilderness. Anything more that he learns must be learned by himself.

Then he saw it again. . . . He saw it cross the end of a long blowdown, a corridor where a tornado had swept, rushing through rather than over the tangle of trunks and branches as a locomotive would have, faster than he had ever believed it could move, almost as fast as a deer even, because a deer would have spent most of that time in the air, faster than he could bring the rifle sights up with it.

Shaking and trembling from the terrifying yet magnificent incident of this second sighting, the boy remembers all that Sam has told him about fear and courage, all that he himself has experienced during his years of exploring the forest. And when he comes back a few months later for what he knows is to be his most momentous encounter with the bear, he has what he knows is the "right" dog—a little mongrel fyce "itself not much bigger than a rat and possessing that bravery which had long since stopped being courage and had become foolhardiness."

This encounter is the climax of all the years of stalking and waiting:

He timed the meeting almost as if it were an appointment with a human being. Himself holding the fyce muffled in a feed sack and Sam Fathers with two of the hounds on a piece of a plowline rope, they lay down wind of the trail at dawn of the second morning. They were so close that the bear turned without even running, as if in surprised amazement at the shrill and frantic uproar of the released fyce, turning at bay against the trunk of a tree, on its hind feet; it seemed to the boy that it would never stop rising, taller and taller, and even the two hounds seemed to take a desperate and despairing courage from the fyce, following it as it went in.

Terrified in concern for the safety of the yipping little fyce, the boy flings his gun aside and runs to rescue the dog. Meanwhile, the great bear lumbers away, but not until after the boy has come so close that he can see a big wood tick inside its right hind leg.

At this point the action in the story ends. The rest of it is conversation—conversation between the boy and his father. They are in a room in their home, and they are talking about their hunting experiences, and about a poem read by the father to his son out of a book. The father reminds the boy that he didn't shoot the bear when he twice had a chance even though shooting it was the great dream and goal of the boy's life. "Why?" asks the father. The boy doesn't quite know why, at least not yet—but the reader does. And in answering this question we are plunged to the very heart of the story in meaning.

If the boy had shot the bear he would have killed the most magnificent thing in his life. The bear had become to him a symbol of the majesty of the untamed wilderness. It represented all that was beautiful and powerful and magnificently free. To destroy it would be to destroy the dream of his life. Moreover, he didn't need to kill it. He had proved his courage to meet it on equal terms, and he now even had the strength and control to meet it with a gun in his hands and not shoot.

And what about the poem? Some of you will recognize from the lines quoted by the father ("She cannot fade, though thou hast not thy bliss, for ever wilt thou love, and she be fair") that it is Keats's "Ode on a Grecian Urn."[1]

---

[1] See pp. 21-24 for a discussion of this poem.

As the father says, the poem is about truth, as its famous closing lines epitomize:

> Beauty is truth, truth beauty—that is all
> Ye know on earth, and all ye need to know.

In the words of the father, "Truth doesn't change. Truth is one thing. It covers all things which touch the heart— honor and pride and pity and justice and courage and love." "Do you see now?" asks the father. "Yes, sir," answers the boy—and the story ends.

What does the boy see? What finally, is the story all about? It is about beauty and truth, courage and fear, pride and humility, freedom and bondage. But what are these? Mere abstract nouns. And abstract nouns, contrasted with concrete nouns, have no dimensional existence. Concrete nouns such as "chair" or "cow" or "girl" or "pencil" literally exist in the realm of the senses. We can see and touch them. But abstract nouns exist only as concepts in the mind. They are mere words, mere puffs of air. They cannot be sensed — indeed, they have no meaning — until, like the artistic beauty of the urn in Keats's poem, they are experienced. Then they become meaningful. *This* is what the story is all about. The boy had heard the words "courage," "fear," "pride," "humility," etc.; but they were meaningless to him until *through experience* he came to know them. Thus, with the wilderness as his school, and the bear and Sam Fathers as his teachers, the boy *through experience*, and through meditating on his experiences, changes from immaturity to the wisdom of maturity.

By implication, Faulkner is saying, there is no way to mature except through the growth of experience. And through the growth of experience we learn that humility is power and that fear destroys life whereas courage saves it.

The Portable Phonograph

by Walter Van Tilburg Clark

The red sunset with narrow, black cloud strips like threats across it, lay on the curved horizon of the prairie. The air was still and cold, and in it settled the mute darkness and greater cold of night. High in the air there was wind, for through the veil of the dusk the clouds could be seen gliding rapidly south and changing shapes. A queer sensation of torment, of two-sided, unpredictable nature, arose from the stillness of the earth air beneath the violence of the upper air. Out of the sunset, through the dead, matted grass and isolated weed stalks of the prairie, crept the narrow and deeply rutted remains of a road. In the road, in places, there were crusts of shallow, brittle ice. There were little islands of an old oiled pavement in the road too, but most of it was mud, now frozen rigid. The frozen mud still bore the toothed impress of great tanks, and a wanderer on the neighboring undulations might have stumbled, in this light, into large, partially filled-in and weed-grown cavities, their banks channelled and beginning to spread into badlands. These pits were such as might have been made by falling meteors, but they were not. They were the scars of gigantic bombs, their rawness already made a little natural by rain, seed, and time. Along the road, there were rakish remnants of fence. There was also just visible, one portion of tangled and multiple barbed wire still erect, behind which was a shelving ditch with small caves, now very quiet and empty, at intervals in its back wall. Otherwise there was no structure or remnant of a structure visible over the dome of the darkling earth, but only, in sheltered hollows, the darker shadows of young trees trying again.

Under the wuthering arch of the high wind a V of wild geese fled south. The rush of their pinions sounded briefly, and the faint, plaintive notes of their expeditionary talk. Then they left a still greater vacancy. There was the smell and expectation of snow, as there is likely to be when the wild geese fly south. From the remote distance, towards the red sky, came faintly the protracted howl and quick yap-yap of a prairie wolf.

North of the road, perhaps a hundred yards, lay the parallel and deeply intrenched course of a small creek, lined with leafless alders and willows. The creek was already silent under ice. Into the bank above it was dug a sort of cell, with a single opening, like a reflection or a deception of the imagination. The light came from the chary burning of four blocks of poorly aged peat, which gave off a petty warmth and much acrid smoke. But the precious remnants of wood, old fence posts and timbers from the long-deserted dugouts, had to be saved for the real cold, for the time when a man's breath blew white, the moisture in his nostrils stiffened at once when he stepped out, and the expansive blizzards paraded for days over the vast open, swirling and settling and thickening, till the dawn of the cleared day when the sky was thin blue-green and the terrible cold, in which a man could not live for three hours unwarmed, lay over the uniformly drifted swell of the plain.

Around the smoldering peat, four men were seated crosslegged. Behind them, traversed by their shadows, was the earth bench, with two old and dirty army blankets, where the owner of the cell slept. In a niche in the opposite wall were a few tin utensils which caught the glint of the coals. The host was rewrapping in a piece of daubed burlap four fine, leatherbound books. He worked slowly and very carefully, and at last tied the bundle securely with a piece of grass-woven cord. The other three looked intently upon the process, as if a great significance lay in it. As the host tied the cord, he spoke. He was an old man, his long, matted beard and hair gray to nearly white. The shadows made his brows and cheekbones appear gnarled, his eyes and cheeks deeply sunken. His big hands, rough with frost and swollen by rheumatism, were awkward but gentle at their task. He was like a prehistoric priest performing a fateful ceremonial rite. Also his voice had in it a suitable quality of deep, reverent despair, yet perhaps at the moment, a sharpness of selfish satisfaction.

"When I perceived what was happening," he said, "I told myself, 'It is the end. I cannot take much; I will take these.'

"Perhaps I was impractical," he continued. "But for myself, I do not regret, and what do we know of those who will come after us? We are the doddering remnant of a race of mechanical fools. I have saved what I love; the soul of what was good in us is here; perhaps the new ones will make a strong enough beginning not to fall behind when they become clever."

He rose with slow pain and placed the wrapped volumes in the niche with his utensils. The others watched him with the same ritualistic gaze.

"Shakespeare, the Bible, *Moby Dick, The Divine Comedy,*" one of them said softly. "You might have done worse, much worse."

"You will have a little soul left until you die," said another harshly. "That is more than is true of us. My brain becomes thick, like my hands." He held the big, battered hands, with their black nails, in the glow to be seen.

"I want paper to write on," he said. "And there is none."

"The fourth man said nothing. He sat in the shadow farthest from the fire, and sometimes his body jerked in its rags from the cold. Although he was still young, he was sick and coughed often. Writing implied a greater future than he now felt able to consider.

The old man seated himself laboriously, and reached out, groaning at the movement, to put another block of peat on the fire. With bowed heads and averted eyes, his three guests acknowledged his magnanimity.

"We thank you, Doctor Jenkins, for the reading," said the man who had named the books.

They seemed then to be waiting for something. Doctor Jenkins understood, but was loath to comply. In an ordinary moment he would have said nothing. But the words of *The Tempest*, which he had been reading, and the religious attention of the three made this an unusual occasion.

"You wish to hear the phonograph," he said grudgingly.

The two middle-aged men stared into the fire, unable to formulate and expose the enormity of their desire.

The young man, however, said anxiously, between suppressed coughs, "Oh, please," like an excited child.

The old man rose again in his difficult way, and went to the back of the cell. He returned and placed tenderly upon the packed floor, where the firelight might fall upon it, an old portable phonograph in a black case. He smoothed the top with his hand, and then opened it. The lovely green-felt-covered disk became visible.

"I have been using thorns as needles," he said. "But tonight, because we have a musician among us"—he bent his head to the young man, almost invisible in the shadow—"I will use a steel needle. There are only three left."

The two middle-aged men stared at him in speechless adoration. The one with the big hands, who wanted to write, moved his lips, but the whisper was not audible.

"Oh, don't!" cried the young man, as if he were hurt. "The thorns will do beautifully."

"No," the old man said. "I have become accustomed to the thorns, but they are not really good. For you, my young friend, we will have good music tonight."

"After all," he added generously, and beginning to wind the phonograph, which creaked, "they can't last forever."

"No, nor we," the man who needed to write said harshly. "The needle, by all means."

"Oh, thanks," said the young man. "Thanks," he said again

in a low, excited voice, and then stifled his coughing with a bowed head.

"The records, though," said the old man when he had finished winding, "are a different matter. Already they are very worn. I do not play them more than once a week. One, once a week, that is what I allow myself.

"More than a week I cannot stand it; not to hear them," he apologized.

"No, how could you?" cried the young man. "And with them here like this."

"A man can stand anything," said the man who wanted to write, in his harsh, antagonistic voice.

"Please, the music," said the young man.

"Only the one," said the old man. "In the long run, we will remember more that way."

He had a dozen records with luxuriant gold and red seals. Even in that light the others could see that the threads of the records were becoming worn. Slowly he read out the titles and the tremendous dead names of the composers and the artists and the orchestras. The three worked upon the names in their minds, carefully. It was difficult to select from such a wealth what they would at once most like to remember. Finally, the man who wanted to write named Gershwin's "New York."

"Oh, no," cried the sick young man, and then could say nothing more because he had to cough. The others understood him, and the harsh man withdrew his selection and waited for the musician to choose.

The musician begged Doctor Jenkins to read the titles again, very slowly, so that he could remember the sounds. While they were read, he lay back against the wall, his eyes closed, his thin, horny hand pulling at his light beard, and listened to the voices and the orchestras and the single instruments in his mind.

When the reading was done he spoke despairingly. "I have forgotten," he complained; "I cannot hear them clearly.

"There are things missing," he explained.

"I know," said Doctor Jenkins. "I thought that I knew all of Shelley by heart. I should have brought Shelley."

"That's more soul than we can use," said the harsh man. *"Moby Dick* is better.

"We can understand that," he emphasized.

The Doctor nodded.

"Still," said the man who had admired the books, "we need the absolute if we are to keep a grasp on anything.

"Anything but these sticks and peat clods and rabbit snares," he said bitterly.

"Shelley desired an ultimate absolute," said the harsh man. "It's too much," he said. "It's no good; no earthly good."

The musician selected a Debussy nocturne. The others considered and approved. They rose to their knees to watch the Doctor prepare for the playing, so that they appeared to be actually in an attitude of worship. The peat glow showed the thinness of their bearded faces, and the deep lines in them, and revealed the condition of their garments. The other two continued to kneel as the old man carefully lowered the needle onto the spinning disk but the musician suddenly drew back against the wall again, with his knees up, and buried his face in his hands.

At the first notes of the piano the listeners were startled. They stared at each other. Even the musician lifted his head in amazement, but then quickly bowed it again, strainingly, as if he were suffering from a pain he might not be able to endure. They were all listening deeply, without movement. The wet, blue-green notes tinkled forth from the old machine, and were individual, delectable presences in the cell. The individual, delectable presences swept into a sudden tide of unbearably beautiful dissonance, and then continued fully the swelling and ebbing of that tide, the dissonant inpourings, and the resolutions, and the diminishments, and the little, quiet wavelets of interlude lapping between. Every sound was piercing and singularly sweet. In all the men except the musician, there occurred rapid sequences of tragically heightened recollection. He heard nothing but what was there. At the final, whispering disappearance, but moving quietly so that the others would not hear him and look at him, he let his head fall back in agony, as if it were drawn there by the hair, and clenched the fingers of one hand over his teeth. He sat that way while the others were silent, and until they began to breathe again normally. His drawn-up legs were trembling violently.

Quickly Doctor Jenkins lifted the needle off, to save it and not to spoil the recollection with scraping. When he had stopped the whirling of the sacred disk, he courteously left the phonograph open and by the fire, in sight.

The others, however, understood. The musician rose last, but then abruptly, and went quickly out at the door without saying anything. The others stopped at the door and gave their thanks in low voices. The Doctor nodded magnificently.

"Come again," he invited, "in a week. We will have the 'New York.'"

When the two had gone together, out towards the rimed road, he stood in the entrance, peering and listening. At first, there was only the resonant boom of the wind overhead, and then far over the dome of the dead, dark plain, the wolf cry lamenting. In the rifts of clouds the Doctor saw four stars flying. It impressed the Doctor that one of them had just been obscured by the beginning of a flying cloud at the very moment he heard what he had been listening for, a sound of suppressed coughing. It was not near-by, however. He believed that down against the pale alders he could see the moving shadow.

With nervous hands he lowered the piece of canvas which served as his door, and pegged it at the bottom. Then quickly and quietly, looking at the piece of canvas frequently, he slipped the records into the case, snapped the lid shut, and carried the phonograph to his couch. There, pausing often to stare at the canvas and listen, he dug earth from the wall and disclosed a piece of board. Behind this there was a deep hole in the wall, into which he put the phonograph. After a moment's consideration, he went over and reached down his bundle of books and inserted it also. Then, guardedly, he once more sealed up the hole with the board and the earth. He also changed his blankets, and the grass-stuffed sack which served as a pillow, so that he could lie facing the entrance. After carefully placing two more blocks of peat upon the fire, he stood for a long time watching the stretched canvas, but it seemed to billow naturally with the first gusts of a lowering wind. At last he prayed, and got in under his blankets, and closed his smoke-smarting eyes. On the inside of the bed, next the wall, he could feel with his hand the comfortable piece of lead pipe.

Discussion of "The Portable Phonograph"

Walter Van Tilburg Clark (1909-   ), contemporary American novelist and short-story writer, has been especially effective in combining a dramatically sharp literary style with the exploring of complicated moral issues. One of his strongest and most hauntingly meaningful stories is "The Portable Phonograph."

The plot of this story is very simple: Four men are struggling to survive in a cold prairie-land that bears obvious scars of a terribly destructive war a few years earlier. The men have reverted to a primitive existence, living in separate caves warmed by peat fires. Occasionally they meet to talk and listen to music on an old portable phonograph. Apparently they are the only survivors of a war that has destroyed all other human life, at least so far as they are aware. A detailed account is given of one gathering of the four men during which they talk about a few works of literature saved by one of them from the destroyed past, are much moved by listening to a Debussy nocturne on the phonograph, and separate into the night. The owner of the few books and the phonograph goes to bed after hiding the items away in a deep hole in the cave wall. And there, with a "comfortable piece of lead pipe" in his hand for protection, the story ends.

Setting is extremely important in this story. In fact, until the reader has determined where and when the story takes place he will not fully comprehend its meaning. The author does not identify the setting, but with some careful thinking we can figure it out. First of all, we know that it is in the northern hemisphere because the geese are flying south with the oncoming winter; they would be flying north if they were in the southern hemisphere. More particularly, the prairie-land is in an area that becomes bitter cold in mid-winter, with "expansive blizzards" swirling for days over the vast open "badlands," over which fly wild geese, and in which prairie wolves howl. A few years earlier this open land had been part of a civilized nation, evidenced by the remnants of a paved road crossing the area. More abundant are the reminders that a terrible war has been fought in the region, not just bombs dropped from airplanes or shot from rockets, but dugouts and barbed-wire entanglements indicating that the war has been hand-fought, apparently to total destruction.

Where are to be found open badlands such as these with geese and prairie wolves, and where and when was a war such as this fought? In western or central Europe? In the vast and cold steppes of Russia? Yes, perhaps. But details don't quite seem to fit. The dugouts and barbed-wire entanglements might suggest World War I, but a perceptive reader knows that this couldn't be because of the reference to Gershwin, who composed his music in the 1920's and 1930's. Except for the fact that there has been no recent war in America, an American reader would probably feel that the story has an American setting. The four men seem American, or at least English-American. Dr. Jenkins is an American-sounding name, *Moby Dick* is an American novel, Gershwin is an American composer, and the men's reaction to the comment on Gershwin's "New York" seems an American reaction. Also, in the northern United States and in Canada there are vast, cold open-lands such as described in the story. But what about the war? Well, what about the war? Is it a war of the past? Or is it a war of the future—World War III, that has totally destroyed civilization, that has come to America and destroyed it? As soon as one recognizes that it *is* a war of the future, the American setting becomes entirely plausible, say in the area of Montana or the Dakotas or Minnesota. A reader may wonder about the peat, but a check of geography books indicates that there are peat beds in America's central northern plains, not now commercially productive, but there nevertheless.

Why place the story in this north-central part of the U.S.? Why not, for example, in New York City or Washington, D.C., or San Francisco where a more awful description of ruined cities and killed masses of people might be suggested? Was the north-central region chosen simply to give an area of coldness and desolation? Or was it chosen to suggest that the destruction of American civilization has been complete, that the war has come to the very heart-land of America and destroyed everything so far as these four survivors know except themselves? As Dr. Jenkins says, they are "the doddering remnant of a race of mechanical fools," by which he means not the American race but the human race.

So much for plot and setting. What about characterization? Of the four men, we know Dr. Jenkins best, and he is the only one whose name we know. He is described as old, probably in his sixties or seventies, not yet feeble but starting to weaken physically. Obviously he was an educated professional man, but apparently a university professor rather than a medical doctor—probably a professor of English. Only an English professor would be likely to know Shelley by heart! He loves the four books and the few music records he saved when he fled the awful devastation of war, and he hungers for the civilization that is gone.

We know the tense young musician next best. Apparently tuberculosis is weakening his fragile body: he coughs often. And we sense the subjective intensity with which he suffers the deprivations thrust upon the four men.

The bitter would-be writer with the big hands we also see vividly. The author of the story once commented in an essay that originally this man was depicted as a sculptor. Hence the big hands. But he was changed to a writer because he is intended to represent embittered frustration and despair, partly because he has a terrible urge to write but no paper to write on. If he had been left a sculptor he would not have been so frustrated because clay for sculpturing would have been available.

Of the fourth man we know only that he is middle-aged. He is intentionally left vague and unidentified. He represents nameless humanity, the masses suffering in a kind of apathetic and numb silence.

Setting, plot, characterization—all are important in this story. But more important even than these, and growing out of these, is theme (central idea, message). As in most high-quality works of literature, the theme is not explicitly stated but is implicitly suggested throughout the story. This "suggesting" of the meaning rather than openly stating it is not done to hide anything from the reader or to befuddle him but is done because a good writer knows that a story's theme will be more meaningful to the reader if he is actively involved in creating it through thoughtful response.

Actually two themes are developed in this story—a primary one and a significant secondary one. The secondary theme is simply the basic need in humanity for beauty, for culture. Even in their primitive struggle to survive these four men hunger for an interchange of ideas, for literature, for music—hunger so intensely that they make a kind of ritual of coming together from time to time to worship beauty. In all human beings, regardless of how they live, there is a craving for things of beauty and of the spirit as intense as the cravings of the flesh. (Incidentally, note the extraordinary excellence of the description of the music of Debussy near the end of the story.)

But there is in the story also a more central and more specific theme. Here are four men who are the only survivors of a terrible war that, at least so far as they know, has destroyed all other human life in the world. They are "the doddering remnant of a race of mechanical fools," a civilization so "advanced" scientifically that it created weapons of war powerful enough to destroy the human race, yet a "civilization" so spiritually and morally weak, so foolish that it used its scientific marvels to annihilate itself. Surely the few who survived this awful destruction should have learned a terrible lesson. We would expect the four men to unite in a harmonious effort to save each other and their few treasured belongings. But do they? Instead they are still suspicious and jealous and selfishly possessive. They are little nations at war with each other. The young musician is ready to kill to get what he wants and doesn't have. And Dr. Jenkins is ready to kill to keep what he now has and so suspiciously guards. He is willing to share his treasured possessions only on his own terms, and he is going to see that if he dies they will be hidden where no one else can find them. As human beings they haven't learned a thing. They still place their confidence in the "comfortable" power of the lead pipe as a means of survival.

In a way, though to say so runs the risk of spoiling the story as a work of art, this story is an upside-down sermon, a dramatic plea for understanding, trust, cooperation, and unselfishness in human relations. It is an implied but eloquent assertion that the only way humanity can survive is through unselfish cooperation, and that the "lead pipe" philosophy of survival through placing trust in weapons of destruction leads inevitably not to survival but to death — of nations as of individuals.

Note in the story, especially in its closing paragraphs, the hollowness of the religion practiced by these men. Dr. Jenkins is described as "like a prehistoric priest" as he prepares the phonograph for playing, and the others watch with a "ritualistic gaze." Later they are described as appearing to be "actually in an attitude of worship" as they listen to the Debussy nocturne coming from the "sacred disk" of the phonograph. And at the very end Dr. Jenkins prays before going to bed with the un-Christian lead pipe in his hand. But the prayer is only a mechanical habit. It has no meaning for him, except perhaps a kind of frightened and selfish plea for protection against those he ought to love and trust. For all of them religion has become merely a meaningless ritual. They are completely lacking in the kind of vibrant faith that could enrich their lives and save them from each other.

So examined this is an excellent and powerful story — both dramatically and thematically. Only one thing would make it better. A fifth character is needed—a beautiful girl whom they could love and over whom they could quarrel. Shall we make her blonde or brunette? I am not, of course, serious. Aside from distorting the message of the story and making it a little trite and corny, why would adding a girl spoil it? The obvious answer is that it would destroy the atmosphere of hopelessness in the story on which its power depends. If there were a woman in it, there might be a future. Instead there are only four suspicious men—and this is the end!

The Pardoner's Tale

by Geoffrey Chaucer

Modernized by J. U. Nicolson

In Flanders, once, there was a company
Of young companions given to folly,
Riot and gambling, brothels and taverns;
And, to the music of harps, lutes, gitterns,
They danced and played at dice both day and night,
And ate also and drank beyond their might,
Whereby they made the devil's sacrifice
Within that devil's temple, wicked wise,
By superfluity both vile and vain.
So damnable their oaths and so profane   10
That it was terrible to hear them swear;
Our Blessed Saviour's Body did they tear;
They thought the Jews had rent Him not enough;
And each of them at others' sins would laugh.
Then entered dancing-girls of ill repute,
Graceful and slim, and girls who peddled fruit,
Harpers and bawds and women selling cake,
Who do their office for the Devil's sake,
To kindle and blow the fire of lechery,
Which is so closely joined with gluttony;   20
I call on holy writ, now, to witness
That lust is in all wine and drunkenness.
    Lo, how the drunken Lot unnaturally
Lay with his daughters two, unwittingly;
So drunk he was he knew not what he wrought.
    Herod, as in his story's clearly taught,
When full of wine and merry at a feast,
Sitting at table idly gave behest
To slay John Baptist, who was all guiltless.
    Seneca says a good word too, doubtless;   30
He says there is no difference he can find
Between a man that's quite out of his mind
And one that's drunken, save perhaps in this
That when a wretch in madness fallen is,
The state lasts longer than does drunkenness.
O gluttony, full of all wickedness,

O first cause of confusion to us all,
Beginning of damnation and our fall,
Till Christ redeemed us with His blood again!
Behold how dearly, to be brief and plain,   40
Was purchased this accursed villainy;
Corrupt was all this world with gluttony!
   Adam our father, and his wife also,
From Paradise to labour and to woe
Were driven for that vice, no doubt; indeed
The while that Adam fasted, as I read,
He was in Paradise; but then when he
Ate of the fruit forbidden of the tree,
Anon he was cast out to woe and pain.
O gluttony, of you we may complain!   50
Oh, knew a man how many maladies
Follow on excess and on gluttonies,
Surely he would be then more moderate
In diet, and at table more sedate.

.   .   .   .

   A lecherous thing is wine, and drunkenness
Is full of striving and of wretchedness
O drunken man, disfigured is your face,
Sour is your breath, foul are you to embrace,   90
And through your drunken nose there comes a sound
As if you snored out "Samson, Samson" round;
And yet God knows that Samson drank no wine.
You fall down just as if you were stuck swine;
Your tongue is loose, your honest care obscure;
For drunkenness is very sepulture
Of any mind a man may chance to own.
In whom strong drink has domination shown
He can no counsel keep for any dread.

.   .   .   .

   But hearken, masters, one word more I pray:
The greatest deeds of all, I'm bold to say,
Of victories in the old testament,
Through the True God, Who is omnipotent,
Were gained by abstinence and after prayer: 115
Look in the Bible, you may learn this there.

.   .   .   .

   And now that I have told of gluttony,
I'll take up gambling, showing you thereby

The curse of chance, and all its evils treat;
From it proceeds false swearing and deceit,   130
Blaspheming, murder, and—what's more—the waste
Of time and money; add to which, debased
And shamed and lost to honour quite is he,
Who once a common gambler's known to be.
And ever the higher one is of estate,
The more he's held disgraced and desolate.
And if a prince plays similar hazardry
In all his government and policy,
He loses in the estimate of men
His good repute, and finds it not again.   140

.   .   .   .

    Now will I speak of oaths both false and great
A word or two, whereof the old books treat.
Great swearing is a thing abominable,
And vain oaths yet more reprehensible.   170
The High God did forbid swearing at all,
As witness Matthew; but in especial
Of swearing says the holy Jeremiah,
"Thou shalt not swear in vain, to be a liar,
But swear in judgment and in righteousness";
But idle swearing is a wickedness.
Behold, in the first table of the Law,
That should be honoured as High God's, sans flaw,
This second one of His commandments plain:
"Thou shalt not take the Lord God's name in vain."   180
Nay, sooner He forbids us such swearing
Than homicide or many a wicked thing;
I say that, as to order, thus it stands;
'Tis known by him who His will understands
That the great second law of God is that.
Moreover, I will tell you full and flat,
That retribution will not quit his house
Who in his swearing is too outrageous.

.   .   .   .

Now for the love of Christ, Who for us died,
Forgo this swearing oaths, both great and small;
But, sirs, now will I tell to you my tale.
    Now these three roisterers, whereof I tell,
Long before prime was rung by any bell,   200

Were sitting in a tavern for to drink;
And as they sat they heard a small bell clink
Before a corpse being carried to his grave;
Whereat one of them called unto his knave:
"Go run," said he, "and ask them civilly
What corpse it is that's just now passing by,
And see that you report the man's name well."
  "Sir," said the boy, "it needs not that they tell.
I learned it, ere you came here, full two hours;
He was, by gad, an old comrade of yours;   210
And he was slain, all suddenly, last night,
When drunk, as he sat on his bench upright;
An unseen thief, called Death, came stalking by,
Who hereabouts makes all the people die,
And with his spear he clove his heart in two
And went his way and made no more ado.
He's slain a thousand with this pestilence;
And, master, ere you come in his presence,
It seems to me to be right necessary
To be forewarned of such an adversary: 220
Be ready to meet him for evermore.
My mother taught me this, I say no more."
    "By holy Mary," said the innkeeper,
"The boy speaks truth, for Death has slain, this year,
A mile or more hence, in a large village,
Both man and woman, child and hind and page.
I think his habitation must be there;
To be advised of him great wisdom 'twere,
Before he did a man some dishonour."
    "Yea, by God's arms!" exclaimed this roisterer,   230
"Is it such peril, then, this Death to meet?
I'll seek him in the road and in the street,
As I now vow to God's own noble bones!
Hear, comrades, we're of one mind, as each owns;
Let each of us hold up his hand to other
And each of us become the other's brother,
And we three will go slay this traitor Death;
He shall be slain who's stopped so many a breath,
By God's great dignity, ere it be night."
    Together did these three their pledges plight   240
To live and die, each of them for the other,
As if he were his very own blood brother.

And up they started, drunken, in this rage,
And forth they went, and towards that village
Whereof the innkeeper had told before.
And so, with many a grisly oath, they swore
And Jesus' blessed body once more rent—
"Death shall be dead if we find where he went."
    When they had gone not fully half a mile,
Just as they would have trodden over a stile,   250
An old man, and a poor, with them did meet.
This ancient man full meekly them did greet,
And said thus: "Now, lords, God keep you and see!"
    The one that was most insolent of these three
Replied to him: "What? Churl of evil grace,
Why are you all wrapped up except your face?
Why do you live so long in so great age?"
    This ancient man looked upon his visage
And thus replied: "Because I cannot find
A man, nay, though I walked from here to Ind.   260
Either in town or country who'll engage
To give his youth in barter for my age;
And therefore must I keep my old age still,
As long a time as it shall be God's will.
Not even Death, alas! my life will take;
Thus restless I my wretched way must make,
And on the ground, which is my mother's gate,
I knock with my staff early, aye, and late,
And cry: 'O my dear mother, let me in!
Lo, how I'm wasted, flesh and blood and skin!   270
Alas! When shall my bones come to their rest?
Mother, with you fain would I change my chest,
That in my chamber so long time has been,
Aye! For a haircloth rag to wrap me in!'
But yet to me she will not show that grace,
And thus all pale and withered is my face.
    "But, sirs, in you it is no courtesy
To speak to an old man despitefully,
Unless in word he trespass or in deed.
In holy writ you may, yourselves, well read   280
'Before an old man, hoar upon the head,
You should arise.' Which I advise you read,
Nor to an old man any injury do
More than you would that men should do to you

In age, if you so long time shall abide;
And God be with you, whether you walk or ride.
I must pass on now where I have to go."
   "Nay, ancient churl, by God it sha'n't be so,"
Cried out this other hazarder, anon;
"You sha'n't depart so easily, by Saint John!   290
You spoke just now of that same traitor Death,
Who in this country stops our good friends' breath
Hear my true word, since you are his own spy,
Tell where he is or you shall rue it, aye
By God and by the holy Sacrament!
Indeed you must be, with Death, intent
To slay all us young people, you false thief."
   "Now, sirs," said he, "if you're so keen, in brief,
To find out Death, turn up this crooked way,
For in that grove I left him, by my fay,   300
Under a tree, and there he will abide;
Nor for your boasts will he a moment hide.
See you that oak? Right there you shall him find.
God save you, Who redeemed all humankind,
And mend your ways!"—thus said this ancient man.
   And every one of these three roisterers ran
Till he came to that tree; and there they found,
Of florins of fine gold, new-minted, round,
Well-nigh eight bushels full, or so they thought.
No longer, then, after this Death they sought,   310
But each of them so glad was of that sight,
Because the florins were so fair and bright,
That down they all sat by this precious hoard.
The worst of them was first to speak a word.
   "Brothers," said he, "take heed to what I say!
My wits are keen, although I mock and play.
This treasure here Fortune to us has given
That mirth and jollity our lives may liven,
And easily as it's come, so will we spend.
Eh! By God's precious dignity! Who'd pretend   320
Today, that we should have so fair a grace?
But might this gold be carried from this place
Home to my house, or if you will, to yours—
For well we know that all this gold is ours—
Then were we all in high felicity.
But certainly by day this may not be;

For men would say that we were robbers strong,
And we'd, for our own treasure, hang ere long.
This treasurer must be carried home by night
All prudently and slyly, out of sight.   330
So I propose that cuts among us all
Be drawn, and let's see where the cut will fall;
And he that gets the short cut, blithe of heart
Shall run to town at once, and to the mart,
And fetch us bread and wine here, privately.
And two of us shall guard, right cunningly,
This treasure well; and if he does not tarry,
When it is night we'll all the treasure carry
Where, by agreement, we may think it best."
    That one of them the cuts brought in his fist   340
And bade them draw to see where it might fall;
And it fell on the youngest of them all;
And so, forth toward the town he went anon.
And just as soon as he had turned and gone,
That one of them spoke thus unto the other:
    "You know well that you are my own sworn brother,
So to your profit I will speak anon.
You know well how our comrade is just gone;
And here is gold, and that in great plenty,
That's to be parted here among us three.   350
Nevertheless, if I can shape it so
That it be parted only by us two,
Shall I not do a turn that is friendly?"
    The other said: "Well, now, how can that be?
He knows well that the gold is with us two.
What shall we say to him? What shall we do?"
    "Shall it be secret?" asked the first rogue, then,
"And I will tell you in eight words, or ten,
What we must do, and how bring it about."
    "Agreed," replied the other, "Never doubt,   360
That, on my word, I nothing will betray."
    "Now," said the first, "we're two, and I dare say
The two of us are stronger than is one.
Watch when he sits, and soon as that is done
Arise and make as if with him to play;
And I will thrust him through the two sides, yea,
The while you romp with him as in a game,
And with your dagger see you do the same;

And then shall all this gold divided be,
My right dear friend, just between you and me;   370
Then may we both our every wish fulfill
And play at dice all at our own sweet will."
And thus agreed were these two rogues, that day,
To slay the third, as you have heard me say.
    This youngest rogue who'd gone into the town,
Often in fancy rolled he up and down
The beauty of those florins new and bright.
"O Lord," thought he, "if so be that I might
Have all this treasure to myself alone,
There is no man who lives beneath the throne   380
Of God that should be then so merry as I"
    And at the last the Fiend, our enemy,
Put in his thought that he should poison buy
With which he might kill both his fellows; aye,
The Devil found him in such wicked state,
He had full leave his grief to consummate;
For it was utterly the man's intent
To kill them both and never to repent.
And on he strode, no longer would he tarry,
Into the town, to an apothecary,   390
And prayed of him that he'd prepare and sell
Some poison for his rats, and some as well
For a polecat that in his yard had lain,
The which, he said, his capons there had slain,
And fain he was to rid him, if he might,
Of vermin that thus damaged him by night.
    The apothecary said: "And you shall have
A thing of which, so God my spirit save,
In all this world there is no live creature
That's eaten or has drunk of this mixture   400
As much as equals but a grain of wheat,
That shall not sudden death thereafter meet;
Yea, die he shall, and in a shorter while
Than you require to walk but one short mile;
This poison is so violent and strong."
    This wicked man the poison took along
With him boxed up, and then he straightway ran
Into the street adjoining, to a man,
And of him borrowed generous bottles three;
And into two his poison then poured he;   410

The third one he kept clean for his own drink.
For all that night he was resolved to swink
In carrying the florins from that place.
And when this roisterer, with evil grace,
Had filled with wine his mighty bottles three,
Then to his comrades forth again went he.
    What is the need to tell about it more?
For just as they had planned his death before,
Just so they murdered him, and that anon.
And when the thing was done, then spoke the one: 420
"Now let us sit and drink and so be merry,
And afterward we will his body bury."
    And as he spoke, one bottle of the three
He took wherein the poison chanced to be
And drank and gave his comrade drink also,
For which, and that anon, lay dead these two.
    I feel quite sure that Doctor Avicena
Within the sections of his *Canon* never
Set down more certain signs of poisoning
Than showed these wretches two at their ending.   430
Thus ended these two homicides in woe;
Died thus the treacherous poisoner also.
    O cursed sin, full of abominableness!
O treacherous homicide! O wickedness!
O gluttony, lechery, and hazardry!
O blasphemer of Christ with villainy,
And with great oaths, habitual for pride!
Alas! Mankind, how may this thing betide
That to thy dear Creator, Who thee wrought,
And with His precious blood salvation bought,   440
Thou art so false and so unkind, alas!
    Now, good men, God forgive you each trespass,
And keep you from the sin of avarice.
My holy pardon cures and will suffice,
So that it brings me gold, or silver brings,
Or else, I care not—brooches, spoons or rings.
Bow down your heads before this holy bull!
Come up, you wives, and offer of your wool!
Your names I'll enter on my roll, anon,
And into Heaven's bliss you'll go, each one.   450
For I'll absolve you, by my special power,
You that make offering, as clean this hour
As you were born.

Discussion of "The Pardoner's Tale"

Geoffrey Chaucer (1343?-1400) is the greatest English poet before Shakespeare and one of the greatest writers at the dawn of the European Renaissance. Now, despite the more than 500 years that separate him from us and despite the fact that he wrote in a medieval form of English so different from modern English that special training is needed to read it, he still stands as one of the great poets of the world, by many regarded as next to Shakespeare among English poets.

Above all the rest of Chaucer's poems stand two great works: *"Troilus and Criseyde,* one of the subtlest and most poignantly tragic studies of human emotions in all the world's literature, and *The Canterbury Tales,* the richest unified collection of narrative poems in English.

In the frame-story of *The Canterbury Tales* are some twenty-four narratives, plus the general Prologue and several dozen other prologues, epilogues, and interludes connecting the narratives. In the Prologue Chaucer tells how a group of pilgrims planning a pilgrimage to a religious shrine decide to entertain themselves by telling stories to each other. The pilgrims are a motley group of devout and worldly, rich and poor, refined and crude people, and they tell stories suited to their natures, interrupted by various quarrels and other incidents realistic to such a group. The whole thing is written by Chaucer with such psychological brilliance and such artistic excellence that all readers respond to it as clearly a masterpiece, rich in human relations, realism, and comedy. In a sense it is a little library of masterpieces, because every type of verse fiction popular in the Middle Ages is illustrated by one or another of the tales, and done better by Chaucer than by any of his contemporaries. The romance, the fabliau, the fable, the saint's legend, the exemplary anecdote—all are there, each brilliantly colored by the genius of Chaucer's individuality. The variety of the achievement almost staggers the imagination.

"The Pardoner's Tale" is an exemplary anecdote, a story told to teach a moral lesson. It is narrated by the Pardoner, a professional religionist who is himself more worldly than genuinely devout. But the story he tells has a powerful message echoing through the ages.

The version printed in this book is in modernized English, and for this there must be an apology. Anyone familiar with the melodious flexibility of Chaucer's English knows that his poetry is better as he wrote it than any modernization of it could be. But unfortunately, special study is required to read the original version, as the following sampling from the beginning of "The Pardoner's Tale" will show:

> In Flaundres whilom was a compaignye
> Of yonge folk that haunteden folye,
> As riot, hasard, stywes, and tavernes,
> Where as with harpes, lutes, and gyternes,
> They daunce and pleyen at dees bothe day and nyght,
> And eten also and drynken over hir myght,
> Thurgh which they doon the devel sacrifise
> Withinne that develes temple, in cursed wise,
> By superfluytee abhomynable.

Even though the modernized version, by J. U. Nicolson, is not so good as the original, the story is strong enough that it will communicate impressively. And its message will be as meaningful to a modern reader as it has been to readers of other centuries for more than 500 years.

In the first section of 22 lines the Pardoner tells how in Flanders there was once a group of wild young men who idled their time in gambling, drinking, swearing, having affairs with girls, and committing all manner of other sins. Then in lines 23-126 (part of which is omitted here) he interrupts his story to preach a sermon against the evil of drunkenness and gluttony, against gambling in lines 127-166 (with part again omitted), and against swearing in lines 167-198 (again part omitted).

In line 199 the Pardoner returns to his tale of the three

young roisterers, telling how (lines 199-248) they were sitting in a tavern one evening when they were upset at seeing a dead friend carried by on his way to burial. In their half-drunken condition the three pledged to be life-and-death comrades to each other and further pledged to seek out Death and slay him. On the way to find Death they meet an old man (lines 249-305) who is feebly stumbling along, yearning to die, and with his staff tapping Mother Earth to let him in. The old man says that not even Death will take him, and when the three drunken young men rudely taunt the old man he consents to tell them where they can find Death. "Just go under the big oak in that grove of trees and there you will find him," he says.

Instead of Death they find eight bushels of gold coins under the oak. And so gluttonous are they at this "good fortune" that they forget their quest for Death and decide to spend the treasure in lusty living (lines 306-339). But they are afraid to take the money to town in daylight, so they draw cuts to see which one shall go to town for food and wine.

The lot falls on the youngest, who leaves for town, and in his absence the two other rogues treacherously agree that they will murder the one when he returns and then divide the treasure two ways instead of three (lines 340-374). Meanwhile (lines 375-416), the youngest also gluttonously schemes how he can get all the treasure for himself and arranges to take poison wine back to kill them with, buying the poison from an apothecary for some "rats and a polecat."

Both plans work beautifully. The two rogues stab to death the third with their daggers—and celebrate their good fortune by swigging the poison wine (lines 417-432). Thus all three find Death under the oak tree as the old man had predicted.

"The Pardoner's Tale" ends (lines 433-506, partly omitted here) with the Pardoner further sermonizing against sin and trying to sell relics and pardons to the pilgrims, also with a quarrel that develops between the Pardoner and the Host.

Much of the appeal of the tale to one who reads it in full context is in the relationship between the tale and the worldly Pardoner who tells it. But in the abbreviated form here given the story will appeal principally as an ironic and vigorous old classic exposing the evils of drunkenness and gluttony. He who seeks after the lusts of the mortal flesh will find only self-destruction.

Two Poems by Robert Burns

Greatest of the Scottish poets and, if one can judge by the frequency of references to him, President David O. McKay's favorite poet is Robert Burns (1759-1796). Although his personal life was rather loose and undisciplined, Burns in his poetry was an idealist with strong faith in the goodness of God and the potential goodness of man. He triumphs as a great poet in two kinds of poems especially— first, beautiful lyrics of love and friendship (such as "Mary Morison," "John Anderson, My Jo," "My Luv Is Like a Red, Red Rose," "Auld Lang Syne," "Sweet Afton," "To Highland Mary," etc.); and second, delightful satires attractively mixing humor with stinging criticism (such as "The Holy Fair," "To a Louse," "Holy Willie's Prayer," "Address to the Deil," "Address to the Unco Guid," etc.). He also wrote some very good narrative poems, such as "The Cotter's Saturday Night" and "Tam o' Shanter"; but he is at his best in songs and satires. He is also at his best in the Scottish dialect that was his native tongue.

Burns had a rare gift for saying things in quotable phrases, as all the world knows. It was Burns in "To a Mouse" who said,

> The best laid schemes o' mice an' men
> Gang aft a-gley,
> An' lea'e us nought but grief an' pain
> For promis'd joy.

It was also Burns who in "To a Louse" said,

> O wad some pow'r the giftie gie us
> To see oursels as others see us!
> It wad frae mony a blunder free us,
> An' foolish notion.

And these are only two of many passages that are known the world over.

We now turn to two poems by Burns that are especially concerned with good and bad attitudes.

A Man's a Man for A' That

by Robert Burns

Is there for honest poverty,
    That hings his head, an' a' that?
The coward slave, we pass him by—
    We dare be poor for a' that!
For a' that, an' a' that,
    Our toils obscure, an' a' that,
The rank is but the guinea's stamp;
    The man's the gowd[1] for a' that.

What though on hamely fare we dine,
    Wear hoddin grey[2] an' a' that?
Gie fools their silks, and knaves their wine—
    A man's a man for a' that!
For a' that, an' a' that,
    Their tinsel show, an' a' that,
The honest man, tho' e'er sae poor,
    Is king o' men for a that.

Ye see yon birkie,[3] ca'd 'a lord.'
    Wha struts, an' stares, an' a' that?
Tho' hundreds worship at his word
    He's but a cuif[4] for a' that:
For a' that, an' a' that,
    His ribband, star, an' a' that,
The man o' independent mind,
    He looks an' laughs at a' that.

A prince can mak a belted knight,
    A marquis, duke, an' a' that;
But an honest man's aboon his might—
    Guid faith, he mauna fa'[5] that
For a' that, an' a' that,
    Their dignities, an' a' that.
The pith o' sense, an' pride o' worth,
    Are higher rank than a' that.

[1] gold
[2] coarse woolen cloth
[3] conceited fellow
[4] blockhead
[5] claim

Then let us pray that come it may,
    As come it will for a' that,
That Sense and Worth o'er a' the earth,
    Shall bear the gree[1] an' a' that;
For a' that, an' a' that,
    It's comin yet for a' that,
That man to man, the world o'er,
    Shall brithers be for a' that!

Discussion of "A Man's a Man for A' That"

"A Man's a Man for A' That" is a positive poem. In it Burns proclaims the dignity of common man and denounces whatever pretenses or artificialities destroy his dignity. Honesty, independence of mind, the brotherhood of man—these are the things that matter. Costly clothes, social position, fancy titles — these are mere decorations that hide what is genuine. "The honest man, however so poor, is king of men," is the central idea of the poem.

---

[1]prize

Address to the Unco Guid
or
The Rigidly Righteous

by Robert Burns

A ye wha are sae guid yoursel,
    Sae pious and sae holy,
Ye've nought to do but mark and tell
    Your Neebours' fauts and folly!
Whase life is like a weel-gaun[1] mill,
    Supply'd wi' store o' water,
The heaped happer's[2] ebbing still,
    And still the clap[3] plays clatter.

Hear me, ye venerable Core,[4]
    As counsel for poor mortals,
That frequent pass douce[5] Wisdom's door
    For glaikit[6] Folly's portals;
I, for their thoughtless, careless sakes
    Would here propone[7] defences,
Their donsie[8] tricks, their black mistakes,
    Their failings and mischances.

Ye see your state wi' theirs compar'd,
    And shudder at the niffer,[9]
But cast a moment's fair regard
    What maks the mighty differ;[10]
Discount what scant occasion gave,
    That purity ye pride in,
And (what's aft[11] mair than a' the lave[12])
    Your better art o' hiding.

[1]well-going
[2]hopper
[3]clapper
[4]company
[5]sober
[6]giddy
[7]put forward
[8]restless
[9]exchange
[10]difference
[11]often
[12]rest

Think, when your castigated pulse
    Gies now and then a wallop,
What ragings must his veins convulse,
    That still eternal gallop:
Wi' wind and tide fair i' your tails,
    Right on ye scud your sea-way;
But, in the teeth o' baith[1] to sail,
    It makes an unco[2] leeway.

See Social-life and Glee sit down,
    All joyous and unthinking,
Till, quite transmugrify'd,[3] they're grown
    Debauchery and Drinking:
O would they stay to calculate
    Th' eternal consequences;
Or—your more dreaded hell to state—
    Damnation of expenses!

Ye high, exalted, virtuous Dames,
    Ty'd up in godly laces,
Before ye gie poor *Frailty* names,
    Suppose a change o' cases;
A dear-lov'd lad, convenience snug,
    A treacherous inclination—
But, let me whisper i' your lug,[4]
    Ye're aiblins[5] nae temptation.

Then gently scan your brother Man,
    Still gentler sister Woman;
Tho' they may gang a kennin[6] wrang,
    To step aside is human:
One point must still be greatly dark,
    The moving *Why* they do it;
And just as lamely can ye mark,
    How far perhaps they rue it.

---

[1]both
[2]wonderful
[3]transformed
[4]ear
[5]perhaps
[6]trifle

Who made the heart, 'tis *He* alone
        Decidedly can try us,
He knows each chord its various tone,
        Each spring its various bias:
Then at the balance let's be mute,
        We never can adjust it;
What's *done* we partly may compute,
        But know not what's *resisted*.

Discussion of "Address to the Unco Guid or the Rigidly Righteous"

"Address to the Unco Guid or the Rigidly Righteous" is a satire, humorous yet serious, addressed by Burns to those people who regard themselves as very good, very pious, very holy and who spend their time talking about their neighbors' faults and follies. I should like to speak, says Burns, in defense of all the poor mortals who often act unwisely and make mistakes. You look at them, he continues, and shudder at how weak and sinful they are compared with your strength and purity. But is the difference that great? Are you flawless—or just better at hiding? Also, you may now be grown up and beyond the temptations that "galloped" in your veins when you were young, but have you forgotten? Besides, maybe you're not any temptation. Therefore, look gently on men, and even more gently on women. Although they may go a little wrong, do not condemn them. Above all, consider not merely *what* they have done but *why*. God alone has the power to look into a human heart to judge actions and motives and regrets. He alone knows not only what one has done and why but what one has resisted doing and why. Man's responsibility is to forgive; only God, and His specially appointed representatives, have authority to judge.

All of this is what the poem says. But the poem is better than the paraphrase, as poems always are.

The World Is Too Much With Us

by William Wordsworth

The world is too much with us; late and soon,
Getting and spending, we lay waste our powers;
Little we see in nature that is ours;
We have given our hearts away, a sordid boon!
The sea that bares her bosom to the moon;
The winds that will be howling at all hours,
And are up-gathered now like sleeping flowers;
For this, for everything, we are out of tune;
It moves us not.—Great God! I'd rather be
A Pagan suckled in a creed outworn;
So might I, standing on this pleasant lea,
Have glimpses that would make me less forlorn;
Have sight of Proteus rising from the sea;
Or hear old Triton blow his wreathed horn.

Discussion of "The World Is Too Much With Us"

William Wordsworth[1] was a champion of ethics and spirituality. He feared materialism and hated selfishness. In a mood of high indignation he wrote several memorable sonnets[2] attacking selfishness and the pursuit of wrong goals. The best known and most powerful of these is the famous attack on worldly materialism, which begins:

The world is too much with us; late and soon,
Getting and spending, we lay waste our powers.

For Wordsworth knew, as few men have known, that most of the evils in the world stem from the mind of man ("Much

---

[1]For a general discussion of Wordsworth's life and works, see pp. 53-70.
[2]Wordsworth was one of the great sonnet writers of the world. Altogether he wrote more than 500 sonnets, including about 50 of the finest sonnets of the English language.

it grieved my heart to think what man has made of man"[1]),
and he likewise knew that the solution to these evils must
come from within, from the very heart of man, a great outpouring of unselfish love:

> Love, now a universal birth,
> From heart to heart is stealing,
> From earth to man, from man to earth;
> —It is the hour of feeling.[2]

He knew that sometimes out of grief and difficulty comes
wisdom ("a deep distress hath humanized my soul"[3]), that
to do evil is worse than to endure evil,[4] that the greatest,
most unselfish love is love of that which seems not to deserve love,[5] that the sweetest moment of life is that filled
with genuine repentance,[6] and that the greatest source of
strength is the inner resource of the immortal human spirit
in harmony with God's teachings.[7] And so in this "The
World Is Too Much With Us" sonnet Wordsworth cries
out that he would rather be a pagan than a materialist who
worships worldly possessions and misses the values of
beauty and spirituality. Wordsworth would agree with
Matthew Arnold, who later said that "perfection . . . consists in becoming something rather than in having something."[8]

---

[1]See the poem "Lines Written in Early Spring."
[2]See the poem "To My Sister."
[3]See the poem "Elegiac Stanzas Suggested by a Picture of Peele Castle."
[4]See stanza 56 of "Guilt and Sorrow."
[5]See the poem "The Idiot Boy."
[6]See Part III of the poem "Peter Bell."
[7]See the poem "Resolution and Independence."
[8]Matthew Arnold in "Sweetness and Light" from *Culture and Anarchy.*

Ozymandias

by Percy Bysshe Shelley

I met a traveller from an antique land
Who said: Two vast and trunkless legs of stone
Stand in the desert. Near them, on the sand,
Half sunk, a shattered visage lies, whose frown,
And wrinkled lip, and sneer of cold command,
Tell that its sculptor well those passions read
Which yet survive, stamped on these lifeless things,
The hand that mocked them and the heart that fed:
And on the pedestal these words appear:
"My name is Ozymandias, king of kings:
Look on my works, ye Mighty, and despair!"
Nothing besides remains. Round the decay
Of that colossal wreck, boundless and bare
The lone and level sands stretch far away.

Discussion of "Ozymandias"

Percy Bysshe Shelley (1792-1822) was the next to youngest of the six lyric geniuses (Blake, Wordsworth, Coleridge, Byron, Shelley, and Keats) who crowned the movement of English romanticism in the early nineteenth century. Independent, fiery, and idealistic, Shelley saw poetry as the hope of the world that would ultimately lift mankind to universal freedom through universal love. His masterpiece dramatizing this faith is *Prometheus Unbound*. And in dozens of shorter poems he explores facets of his views.

Ozymandias was the Greek name for the Egyptian King Rameses II (1292-1225 B.C.), one of the pyramid builders. He was one of the mightiest of the Egyptian rulers, and his statue was reputed to be the largest in all Egypt.

One word lifts "Ozymandias" from being merely a good little poem to being a truly excellent and powerful one. That word is *despair*. We feel in this word all of the arrogance of Ozymandias as he taunts the people of the world to feel their littleness by looking upon his statue and being reminded of his power. We also feel the irony of the taunt as the crumbling statue and bare sands mock the empty words and remind us that all worldly things, however mighty, dwindle to nothingness with the passing years.

(A comment on line 8 may help in reading the poem: "The hand" that mocked Ozymandias's passions is that of the sculptor, and "the heart" that fed his passions is Ozymandias's own.)

Abou Ben Adhem

by Leigh Hunt

Abou Ben Adhem, may his tribe increase!
Awoke one night from a deep dream of peace,
And saw, within the moonlight in his room,
Making it rich, and like a lily in bloom,
An angel writing in a book of gold: —

Exceeding peace had made Ben Adhem bold,
And to the presence in the room he said,
'What writest thou?'—The vision raised its head,
And with a look made of all sweet accord,
Answered, 'The names of those who love the Lord.'
'And is mine one?' said Abou. 'Nay, not so,'
Replied the angel. Abou spoke more low,
But cheerly still; and said, 'I pray thee then,
Write me as one that loves his fellow-men.'

The angel wrote, and vanished. The next night
It came again with a great wakening light,
And showed the names whom love of God had blessed,
And lo! Ben Adhem's name led all the rest.

Discussion of "Abou Ben Adhem"

Leight Hunt (1784-1859) is an important second-level English poet and critic of the Romantic Age. "Abou Ben Adhem" is his most famous poem. Its message, stressing the importance of unselfish brotherly love, is clear and explicit. The only comment needed is to say that the line "Write me as one that loves his fellow-men" is inscribed on Hunt's grave.

Two Poems by Robert Browning

As stated earlier in this book, men of literature have been as forthright in denouncing self-righteousness and hypocrisy and in defending genuine righteousness and sincerity as have men of religion. One of the most forthright was Robert Browning (1812-1889),[1] whose "Johannes Agricola in Meditation" and "Soliloquy of the Spanish Cloister" are unforgettable portraits of evil men disguised as righteous men. These poems should not be read as criticisms of any particular religion but rather of self-righteousness and hypocrisy in general. (For contrasting portraits by Browning of sincere and dominantly good men, see "Rabbi Ben Ezra" on pp. 461-68 and "A Grammarian's Funeral" on pp. 73-79.)

---

[1]For an introductory discussion of Browning and some comments on his life and work as a whole, see pp. 71-73.

Johannes Agricola in Meditation

by Robert Browning

There's heaven above, and night by night
  I look right through its gorgeous roof;
No suns and moons though e'er so bright
  Avail to stop me; splendor-proof
  I keep the broods of stars aloof.   5
For I intend to get to God,
  For 'tis to God I speed so fast,
For in God's breast, my own abode,
  Those shoals of dazzling glory, passed,
  I lay my spirit down at last.   10
I lie where I have always lain,
  God smiles as he has always smiled;
Ere suns and moons could wax and wane,
  Ere stars were thundergirt, or piled
  The heavens, God thought on me his child;   15
Ordained a life for me, arrayed
  Its circumstances every one
To the minutest; aye, God said
  This head this hand should rest upon
  Thus, ere he fashioned star or sun.   20
And having thus created me,
  Thus rooted me, he bade me grow,
Guiltless forever, like a tree
  That buds and blooms, nor seeks to know
  The law by which it prospers so.   25
But sure that thought and word and deed
  All go to swell his love for me,
Me, made because that love had need
  Of something irreversibly
  Pledged solely its content to be.   30
Yes, yes, a tree which must ascend,
  No poison-gourd foredoomed to stoop!
I have God's warrant, could I blend
  All hideous sins, as in a cup,
  To drink the mingled venoms up;   35
Secure my nature will convert
  The draft to blossoming gladness fast;
While sweet dews turn to the gourd's hurt,
  And bloat, and while they bloat it, blast,
  As from the first its lot was cast.   40

For as I lie, smiled on, full-fed
   By unexhausted power to bless,
I gaze below on hell's fierce bed,
   And those its waves of flame oppress,
   Swarming in ghastly wretchedness;   45
Whose life on earth aspired to be
   One altar-smoke, so pure!—to win
If not love like God's love for me,
   At least to keep his anger in;
   And all their striving turned to sin.   50
Priest, doctor, hermit, monk grown white
   With prayer, the broken-hearted nun,
The martyr, the wan acolyte,[1]
   The incense-swinging child—undone
   Before God fashioned star or sun!   55
God, whom I praise; how could I praise,
   If such as I might understand,
Make out and reckon on his ways,
   And bargain for his love, and stand,
   Paying a price, at his right hand?   60

Discussion of "Johannes Agricola in Meditation"

Johannes Agricola was a German reformer of the 16th century who headed a religious sect which held that faith only is necessary to salvation; morality and good works, according to this group, do not aid one towards salvation. God chooses to save some and damn others, and people can do nothing to alter the will of God. Those who are saved are saved, and those who are damned are damned, irrespective of how good or bad the people may live.

As the leader of this sect, Johannes holds an extreme position. In his monstrous conceit he believes that God has planned every minutest detail of his life and predestined him

----

[1]*Acolyte* is one who carries the wine, the water, and the lights at the Mass.

to salvation, "guiltless forever." So self-righteous is Johannes that he thinks all vices (all "hideous sins") become virtues when performed by him, and all virtues are a waste of time when performed by others.

The poem should be read not merely as an individual portrait of Johannes Agricola but as a satire against pride and self-righteousness wherever they may be found. Browning believed just as strongly as do members of the L.D.S. Church that faith without works is dead and that an individual has the responsibility through an exercise of will power to work out his own salvation. He also believed, as do Latter-day Saints, that through faith and righteousness we can know God. Johannes rationalized that we can no more know God than we can "bargain for his love."

To understand what Browning believed, all we need do is turn Johannes's beliefs upside down. As a satire, this poem exposes the exact opposite of what Browning—and Latter-day Saint readers—recognize as the true principles of Christianity.

Soliloquy of the Spanish Cloister

by Robert Browning

Gr-r-r—there go, my heart's abhorrence!
   Water your damned flower-pots, do!
If hate killed men, Brother Lawrence,
   God's blood, would not mine kill you!
What? your myrtle-bush wants trimming?   5
   Oh, that rose has prior claims—
Needs its leaden vase filled brimming?
   Hell dry you up with its flames!

At the meal we sit together:
   Salve tibi! I must hear[1]   10
Wise talk of the kind of weather,
   Sort of season, time of year:
Not a plenteous cork-crop; scarcely
   Dare we hope oak-galls, I doubt;[2]
What's the Latin name for "parsley"?   15
   What's the Greek name for Swine's Snout?

Whew! We'll have our platter burnished,
   Laid with care on our own shelf!
With a fire-new spoon we're furnished,
   And a goblet for ourself,   20
Rinsed like something sacrificial
   Ere 'tis fit to touch our chaps—
Marked with L for our initial!
   (He-he! There his lily snaps!)

Saint, forsooth While brown Dolores   25
   Squats outside the Convent bank
With Sanchicha, telling stories,
   Steeping tresses in the tank,
Blue-black, lustrous, thick like horsehairs
   —Can't I see his dead eye glow,   30
Bright as 'twere a Barbary corsair's?[3]
   (That is, if he'd let it show!)

---

[1]*Salve tibi* translated is hail to thee.
  [2]*Oak-galls* are swellings on oak leaves, a very rich source of tannic acid widely used by the monks in making black ink.
  [3]*Barbary corsair* was a Turkish or Saracen pirate from Barbary, which is one of the countries on the north coast of Africa.

When he finishes refection,[1]
    Knife and fork he never lays
Cross-wise, to my recollection,   35
    As do I, in Jesu's praise
I the Trinity illustrate,
    Drinking watered orange-pulp—
In three sips the Arian frustrate;[2]
    While he drains his at one gulp.   40

Oh, those melons! If he's able
    We're to have a feast! so nice!
One goes to the Abbot's table,
    All of us get each a slice.
How go on your flowers? None double?   45
    Not one fruit-sort can you spy?
Strange!—And I, too, at such trouble
    Keep them close-nipped on the sly!

There's a great text in Galatians,[3]
    Once you trip on it, entails   50
Twenty-nine distinct damnations,
    One sure, if another fails:
If I trip him just a-dying,
    Sure of heaven as sure can be,
Spin him round and send him flying   55
    Off to hell, a Manichee?[4]

Or, my scrofulous French novel
    On gray paper with blunt type!
Simply glance at it, you grovel
    Hand and foot in Belial's gripe;[5]   60
If I double down its pages
    At the woeful sixteenth print,
When he gathers his greengages,
    Ope a sieve and slip it in 't?

---

[1]*Refection* means eating.

[2]Arian means a follower of Arius, a fourth-century priest who held that Christ is not the Eternal Son of God, and who denied the Trinity.

[3]*Text in Galatians* probably refers to *Galatians*, 5:19-21, which enumerates seventeen "works of the flesh" and states that "they which do such things shall not inherit the kingdom of God."

[4]*Manichee* means a believer in the doctrines of Manichaeus, a Persian of the third century, who held that man's body is the product of evil and his soul the product of good.

[5]*Belial's* means the devil's.

Or, there's Satan!—one might venture   65
  Pledge one's soul to him, yet leave
Such a flaw in the indenture
  As he'd miss till, past retrieve,
Blasted lay that rose-acacia
  We're so proud of! *Hy, Zy, Hine*[1] . . .   70
'St, there's Vespers! *Plena gratia,*
  Ave, Virgo! Gr-r-r— you swine![2]

Discussion of "Soliloquy of the Spanish Cloister"

Even more vivid as poetry and as satire than "Johannes Agricola" is "Soliloquy of the Spanish Cloister." Again, the poem should not be read as an indictment of a particular religious organization or of monks but of self-righteous hypocrisy wherever it may be found. The speaker of the poem is simply an extreme example.

In the first stanza we find the speaker (whose name is not given) looking from a cloister (monastery) window down upon a fellow monk, Brother Lawrence, as he works in his garden. Obviously the speaker hates Brother Lawrence, with nasty venom spilling over in every word he utters. (Note that this is a "soliloquy" — that is, the speaker just sort of mutters aloud to himself all the thoughts of the poem.)

In the second stanza the speaker recalls his meals with Brother Lawrence and all the detestable small talk that goes on about the weather, etc. Obviously Brother Lawrence is a simple, good man, and the speaker is all the more contemptible to us as readers because he does not appreciate the goodness of Brother Lawrence.

---

[1] *Hy, Zy, Hine* represent sounds made by the vesper bells.
[2] *Plena . . . Virgo* means Hail, Virgin, full of grace (a form of prayer used when the vesper bell sounds).

In the third stanza the speaker mocks all of Brother Lawrence's actions during a meal—and then laughs gleefully when one of Brother Lawrence's lilies breaks. Note the scorn in the speaker's voice as he uses "we" and "our" in referring to Brother Lawrence.

Throughout the fourth stanza the speaker accuses Brother Lawrence of lusting after two girls who can be seen nearby. But who is doing the lusting? It is the speaker who sensually sees the hair of one of the girls as "lustrous, blue-black, thick like horsehairs." He obviously imputes his own sensuality to Lawrence.

The fifth stanza further exposes the shallowness of the speaker's views. He drinks "watered orange-pulp in three sips" in a superstitious belief that this eating of tasteless food in a ritualistic manner will please God. He also, after finishing "refection" (that is, a meal), lays his knife and fork crosswise in another ritualistic act. Obviously he believes that such rituals make him more religious than Brother Lawrence, who simply eats his food.

The speaker is revealed at his very meanest in the sixth stanza, first because he jealously complains that Brother Lawrence plans to give a whole melon to the Abbot and only a slice to the other monks, and second (the nastiest act of all) because he sneeringly delights in remembering that he has nipped the buds off Brother Lawrence's plants to keep them from flowering.

The seventh stanza suggests that the speaker deep down in his consciousness is aware that Brother Lawrence is entitled to salvation and will have to be "tricked" into hell, which the speaker is quite ready to do.

In the eighth stanza the speaker conjectures that if he can put a vulgar French novel opened at its most indecent page at a spot where Lawrence will see it when he gathers his greengage plums, he will surely be lured into damnation because the novel is so indecent that if you merely glance at it you will grovel hand and foot in the grip of the devil.

But note what this stanza reveals about the speaker. Whose novel is it? And who has its very worst page memorized?

As the "soliloquy" ends in its ninth stanza the speaker, sort of like Faust, wonders if he might make a bargain with the devil over the soul of Brother Lawrence. And while he is musing on this, the vesper bells, represented in the sounds "Hy, Zy, Hine," call the monks to evening prayer. Mechanically, ritualistically he starts to recite a prayer to the Virgin Mary ("Plena gratia, ave, virgo"). But even in the middle of the prayer his venomous hatred for Brother Lawrence spills over as the prayer is interrupted with the nasty comment "Gr-r-r—you swine!"

This is as vivid a portrait of self-righteousness, hypocisy, lust, hate, and just downright meanness as Browning or any other poet ever composed. It describes everything that Browning detested in religious attitude and surface ritualism and, by implication, suggests his admiration for sincerity, honesty, brotherly love, simplicity, and just plain goodness.

Two Poems with Contrasting Attitudes

"Miniver Cheevy" by Edwin Arlington Robinson (1869-1935), a major American poet, and "Opportunity" by Edward Rowland Sill (1841-1887), another American poet, provide a significant study in contrasting attitudes.

Miniver, like Mabel in Virginia Woolf's "The New Dress,"[1] feels sorry for himself. He looks at his life and thinks how drab it is, all the time wishing that he had lived in ancient days of adventure and heroism. But the reader easily knows that Miniver would be unhappy no matter when he lived, or where. For him, the grass always looks greener on the other side of the fence. And so in his weakness he runs away from the challenge of reality to an escapist world of daydreams and drinking, just as some people in real life do.

The young prince in "Opportunity" shows a courageously optimistic attitude, literally seizing the best tool available to meet—and win—the challenge of the day. The poem is a dramatization of President Hugh B. Brown's observation that, according to God's plan, we grow through the challenge of opposition. Most readers will recognize the lines President Brown has made famous, called "Answer to Prayer," author unknown:

> We ask for strength and God gives us
>   difficulties which make us strong.
> We pray for wisdom and God sends us problems,
>   the solution of which develops wisdom.
> We plead for prosperity and God gives us
>   brain and brawn to work.
> We plead for courage and God gives us
>   dangers to overcome.
> We ask for favors—God gives us opportunities.
>   —This is the answer.

---

[1] See pp. 167-75.

Miniver Cheevy

by Edwin Arlington Robinson

Miniver Cheevy, child of scorn,
    Grew lean while he assailed the seasons;
He wept that he was ever born,
    And he had reasons.

Miniver loved the days of old
    When swords were bright and steeds were prancing;
The vision of a warrior bold
    Would set him dancing.

Miniver sighed for what was not,
    And dreamed, and rested from his labors;
He dreamed of Thebes and Camelot,
    And Priam's neighbors.

Miniver mourned the ripe renown
    That made so many a name so fragrant;
He mourned Romance, now on the town,
    And Art, a vagrant.

Miniver loved the Medici,
    Albeit he had never seen one;
He would have sinned incessantly
    Could he have been one.

Miniver cursed the commonplace
    And eyed a khaki suit with loathing;
He missed the medieval grace
    Of iron clothing.

Miniver scorned the gold he sought,
    But sore annoyed was he without it;
Miniver thought, and thought, and thought,
    And thought about it.

Miniver Cheevy, born too late,
    Scratched his head and kept on thinking;
Miniver coughed, and called it fate,
    And kept on drinking.

Opportunity

by Edward Rowland Sill

This I beheld, or dreamed it in a dream:
There spread a cloud of dust along a plain;
And underneath the cloud, or in it, raged
A furious battle, and men yelled, and swords
Shocked upon swords and shields. A prince's banner
Wavered, then staggered backward, hemmed by foes.
A craven hung along the battle's edge
And thought, "Had I a sword of keener steel—
That blue blade that the king's son bears—but this
Blunt thing—!" He snapt and flung it from his **hand**,
And, lowering, crept away and left the field.
Then came the king's son, wounded, sore bestead,
And weaponless, and saw the broken sword,
Hilt-buried in the dry and trodden sand,
And ran and snatched it, and with battle-shout
Lifted afresh, he hewed his enemy down,
And saved a great cause that heroic day.

A Christmas Carol

by Charles Dickens

Stave One: Marley's Ghost

Marley was dead, to begin with. There is no doubt whatever about that. The register of his burial was signed by the clergyman, the clerk, the undertaker, and the chief mourner. Scrooge signed it. And Scrooge's name was good upon 'Change for anything he chose to put his hand to.

Old Marley was as dead as a doornail.

Scrooge knew he was dead? Of course he did. How could it be otherwise? Scrooge and he were partners for I don't know how many years. Scrooge was his sole executor, his sole administrator, his sole assign, his sole residuary legatee, his sole friend, his sole mourner.

Scrooge never painted out old Marley's name, however. There it yet stood, years afterward, above the warehouse door—Scrooge and Marley. The firm was known as Scrooge and Marley. Sometimes people new to the business called Scrooge Scrooge, and sometimes Marley. He answered to both names. It was all the same to him.

Oh! But he was a tight-fisted hand at the grindstone, was Scrooge! a squeezing, wrenching, grasping, scraping, clutching, covetous old sinner! External heat and cold had little influence on him. No warmth could warm, no cold could chill him. No wind that blew was bitterer than he, no falling snow was more intent upon its purpose, no pelting rain less open to entreaty. Foul weather didn't know where to have him. The heaviest rain and snow and hail and sleet could boast of the advantage over him in only one respect—they often "came down" handsomely, and Scrooge never did.

Nobody ever stopped him in the street to say, with gladsome looks, "My dear Scrooge, how are you? When will you come to see me?" No beggars implored him to bestow a trifle, no children asked him what it was o'clock, no man or woman ever once in all his life inquired the way to such and such a place of Scrooge. Even the blind men's dogs appeared to know him; and when they saw him coming on, would tug their owners into doorways and up courts; and then would wag their tails as though they said, "No eye at all is better than evil eye, dark master!"

But what did Scrooge care! It was the very thing he liked. To edge his way along the crowded paths of life, warning all human sympathy to keep its distance, was what the knowing ones call "nuts" to Scrooge.

Once upon a time—of all the good days in the year, upon a Christmas eve—old Scrooge sat busy in his counting-house. It was cold, bleak, biting, foggy weather; and the city clocks had only just gone three, but it was quite dark already.

The door of Scrooge's counting-house was open, that he might keep his eye upon his clerk, who, in a dismal little cell beyond, a sort of tank, was copying letters. Scrooge had a very small fire, but the clerk's fire was so very much smaller that it looked like one coal. But he couldn't replenish it, for Scrooge kept the coal-box in his own room; and so surely as the clerk came in with the shovel the master predicted that it would be necessary for them to part. Wherefore the clerk put on his white comforter, and tried to warm himself at the candle; in which effort, not being a man of a strong imagination, he failed.

"A merry Christmas, uncle! God save you!" cried a cheerful voice. It was the voice of Scrooge's nephew, who came upon him so quickly that this was the first intimation Scrooge had of his approach.

"Bah!" said Scrooge; "humbug!"

"Christmas a humbug, uncle! You don't mean that, I am sure?"

"I do. Out upon merry Christmas! What's Christmas-time to you but a time for paying bills without money; a time for finding yourself a year older, and not an hour richer; a time for balancing your books and having every item in 'em through a round dozen of months presented dead against you? If I had my will, every idiot who goes about with 'Merry Christmas' on his lips should be boiled with his own pudding, and buried with a stake of holly through his heart! He should!"

"Uncle!"

"Nephew, keep Christmas in your own way, and let me keep it in mine."

"Keep it! But you don't keep it."

"Let me leave it alone, then. Much good may it do you! Much good it has ever done you!"

"There are many things from which I might have derived good, by which I have not profited, I dare say, Christmas among the rest. But I am sure I have always thought of Christmas-time, when it has come round—apart from the veneration due to its sacred origin, if anything belonging to it *can* be apart from that— as a good time; a kind, forgiving, charitable, pleasant time; the only time I know of, in the long calendar of the year, when men and women seem by one consent to open their shut-up hearts freely, and to think of people below them as if they really were fellow travelers to the grave, and not another race of creatures bound on other journeys. And therefore, uncle, though it has never put a scrap of gold or silver in my pocket, I believe that it *has* done me good, and *will* do me good; and I say, God bless it!"

The clerk in the tank involuntarily applauded.

"Let me hear another sound from *you*," said Scrooge, "and you'll keep your Christmas by losing your situation! You're quite a powerful speaker, sir," he added, turning to his nephew. "I wonder you don't go into Parliament."

"Don't be angry, uncle. Come! Dine with us to-morrow."

Scrooge said that he would see him—yes, indeed he did. He went the whole length of the expression, and said that he would see him in that extremity first.

"But why?" cried Scrooge's nephew. "Why?"

"Why did you get married?"

"Because I fell in love."

"Because you fell in love!" growled Scrooge, as if that were the only one thing in the world more ridiculous than a merry Christmas. "Good afternoon!"

"Nay, uncle, but you never came to see me before that happened. Why give it as a reason for not coming now?"

"Good afternoon."

"I want nothing from you; I ask nothing of you; why cannot we be friends?"

"Good afternoon."

"I am sorry, with all my heart, to find you so resolute. We have never had any quarrel, to which I have been a party. But I have made the trial in homage to Christmas, and I'll keep my Christmas humor to the last. So A Merry Christmas, uncle!"

"Good afternoon."

"And A Happy New Year!"

"Good afternoon."

His nephew left the room without an angry word, notwithstanding. The clerk, in letting Scrooge's nephew out, had let two other people in. They were portly gentlemen, pleasant to behold, and now stood, with their hats off, in Scrooge's office. They had books and papers in their hands, and bowed to him.

"Scrooge and Marley's, I believe?" said one of the gentlemen, referring to his list. "Have I the pleasure of addressing Mr. Scrooge, or Mr. Marley?"

"Mr. Marley has been dead these seven years. He died seven years ago, this very night."

"At this festive season of the year, Mr. Scrooge," said the gentleman, taking up a pen, "it is more than usually desirable that we should make some slight provision for the poor and destitute, who suffer greatly at the present time. Many thousands are in want of common necessaries; hundreds of thousands are in want of common comforts, sir."

"Are there no prisons?"

"Plenty of prisons. But under the impression that they scarcely furnish Christian cheer of mind or body to the unoffending multitude, a few of us are endeavoring to raise a fund to buy the poor some meat and drink, and means of warmth. We choose this time, because it is a time of all others when Want is keenly felt and Abundance rejoices. What shall I put you down for?"

"Nothing!"

"You wish to be anonymous?"

"I wish to be left alone. Since you ask me what I wish, gentlemen, that is my answer. I don't make merry myself at Christmas, and I can't afford to make idle people merry. I help to support the prisons and the workhouses—they cost enough—and those who are badly off must go there."

"Many can't go there; and many would rather die."

"If they would rather die, they had better do it, and decrease the surplus population."

At length the hour of shutting up the counting-house arrived. With an ill will Scrooge, dismounting from his stool, tacitly admitted the fact to the expectant clerk in the Tank, who instantly snuffed his candle out, and put on his hat.

"You'll want all day to-morrow, I suppose?"

"If quite convenient, sir."

"It's not convenient, and it's not fair. If I was to stop half a crown for it, you'd think yourself mightily ill-used, I'll be bound?"

"Yes, sir."

"And yet you don't think *me* ill-used, when I pay a day's wages for no work."

"It's only once a year, sir."

"A poor excuse for picking a man's pocket every twenty-fifth of December! But I suppose you must have the whole day. Be here all the earlier *next* morning."

The clerk promised that he would; and Scrooge walked out with a growl. The office was closed in a twinkling, and the clerk, with the long ends of his white comforter dangling below his waist (for he boasted no great-coat), went down a slide, at the end of a lane of boys, twenty times, in honor of its being Christmas eve, and than ran home as hard as he could pelt, to play at blind man's bluff.

Scrooge took his melancholy dinner in his usual melancholy tavern; and having read all the newspapers, and beguiled the rest of the evening with his banker's book, went home to bed. He lived in chambers which had once belonged to his deceased partner. They were a gloomy suite of rooms, in a lowering pile of building up a yard. The building was old enough now, and dreary enough; for nobody lived in it but Scrooge, the other rooms being all let out as offices.

Now it is a fact, that there was nothing at all particular about the knocker on the door of this house, except that it was very large; also, that Scrooge had seen it, night and morning, during his whole residence in that place; also, that Scrooge had as little of what is called fancy about him as any man in the city of London. And yet Scrooge, having his key in the lock of the door, saw in the knocker, without its undergoing any intermediate process of change, not a knocker, but Marley's face.

Marley's face, with a dismal light about it, like a bad lobster in a dark cellar. It was not angry or ferocious, but it looked at Scrooge as Marley used to look—with ghostly spectacles turned up upon its ghostly forehead.

As Scrooge looked fixedly at this phenomenon, it was a knocker again. He said, "Pooh, pooh!" and closed the door with a bang.

The sound resounded through the house like thunder. Every room above, and every cask in the wine-merchant's cellars below, appeared to have a separate peal of echoes of its own. Scrooge was not a man to be frightened by echoes. He fastened the door, and walked across the hall, and up the stairs. Slowly, too, trimming his candle as he went.

Up Scrooge went, not caring a button for its being very dark. Darkness is cheap, and Scrooge liked it. But before he shut his heavy door, he walked through his rooms to see that all was right. He had just enough recollection of the face to desire to do that.

Sitting-room, bedroom, lumber-room, all as they should be. Nobody under the table, nobody under the sofa; a small fire in the grate; spoon and basin ready; and the little saucepan of gruel (Scrooge had a cold in his head) upon the hob. Nobody under his bed; nobody in the closet; nobody in his dressing-gown, which was hanging up in a suspicious attitude against the wall. Lumber-room as usual. Old fire-guard, old shoes, two fish-baskets, washing-stand on three legs, and a poker.

Quite satisfied, he closed his door, and locked himself in; doublelocked himself in, which was not his custom. Thus secured against surprise, he took off his cravat, put on his dressing-gown and slippers and his nightcap, and sat down before the very low fire to take his gruel.

As he threw his head back in the chair, his glance happened to rest upon a bell, a disused bell, that hung in the room, and communicated, for some purpose now forgotten, with a chamber in the highest story of the building. It was with great astonishment, and with a strange, inexplicable dread, that as he looked, he saw this bell begin to swing. Soon it rang out loudly, and so did every bell in the house.

This was succeeded by a clanking noise, deep down below, as if some person were dragging a heavy chain over the casks in the wine-merchant's cellar.

Then he heard the noise much louder, on the floors below; then coming up the stairs; then coming straight toward his door.

It came on through the heavy door, and a specter passed into the room before his eyes. And upon its coming in, the dying flame leaped up, as though it cried, "I know him! Marley's ghost!"

The same face, the very same. Marley in his pigtail, usual waistcoat, tights, and boots. His body was transparent; so that Scrooge, observing him, and looking through his waistcoat, could see the two buttons on his coat behind.

Scrooge had often heard it said that Marley had no bowels, but he had never believed it until now.

No, nor did he believe it even now. Though he looked the fantom through and through, and saw it standing before him—though he felt the chilling influence of its death-cold eyes, and noticed the very texture of the folded kerchief bound about its head and chin—he was still incredulous.

"How now!" said Scrooge, caustic and cold as ever. "What do you want with me?"

"Much!"—Marley's voice, no doubt about it.

"Who are you?"

"Ask me who I *was*."

"Who *were* you, then?"

"In life I was your partner, Jacob Marley."

"Can you—can you sit down?"

"I can."

"Do it, then."

Scrooge asked the question because he didn't know whether a ghost so transparent might find himself in a condition to take a chair; and felt that, in the event of its being impossible, it might involve the necessity of an embarrassing explanation. But the ghost sat down on the opposite side of the fireplace, as if he were quite used to it.

"You don't believe in me."

"I don't."

"What evidence would you have of my reality beyond that of your senses?"

"I don't know."

"Why do you doubt your senses?"

"Because a little thing affects them. A slight disorder of the stomach makes them cheats. You may be an undigested bit of beef, a blot of mustard, a crumb of cheese, a fragment of an under-done potato. There's more of gravy than of grave about you, whatever you are!"

Scrooge was not much in the habit of cracking jokes, nor did he feel in his heart by any means waggish then. The truth is, that he tried to be smart, as a means of distracting his own attention, and keeping down his horror.

But how much greater was his horror when, the fantom taking off the bandage around its head, as if it were too warm to wear indoors, its lower jaw dropped down upon its breast!

"Mercy! Dreadful apparition, why do you trouble me? Why do spirits walk the earth, and why do they come to me?"

"It is required of every man, that the spirit within him should walk abroad among his fellow men, and travel far and wide; and if that spirit goes not forth in life, it is condemned to do so after death. I cannot tell you all I would. A very little more is per-mitted to me. I cannot rest, I cannot stay, I cannot linger any-where. My spirit never walked beyond our counting-house—mark me!— in life my spirit never roved beyond the narrow limits of our money-changing hole; and weary journeys lie before me!"

"Seven years dead, and traveling all the time? You travel fast?"

"On the wings of the wind."

"You might have got over a great quantity of ground in seven years."

"O blind man, blind man! not to know that ages of incessant labor by immortal creatures for this earth must pass into eternity before the good of which it is susceptible is all developed. Not to know that any Christian spirit working kindly in its little sphere, whatever it may be, will find its mortal life too short for its vast means of usefulness. Not to know that no space of regret can make amends for one life's opportunities misused! Yet I was like this man; I once was like this man!"

"But you were always a good man of business, Jacob," faltered Scrooge, who now began to apply this to himself.

"Business!" cried the Ghost, wringing his hands again. "Mankind was my business. The common welfare was my business; charity, mercy, forbearance, benevolence, were all my business. The dealings of my trade were but a drop of water in the comprehensive ocean of my business."

Scrooge was very much dismayed to hear the specter going on at this rate, and began to quake exceedingly.

"Hear me! My time is nearly gone."

"I will. But don't be hard upon me! Don't be flowery, Jacob! Pray!"

"I am here to-night to warn you that you have yet a chance and hope of escaping my fate. A chance and a hope of my procuring, Ebenezer."

"You were always a good friend to me. Thank'ee!"

"You will be haunted by Three Spirits."

"Is that the chance and hope you mentioned, Jacob? I--I think I'd rather not."

"Without their visits you cannot hope to shun the path I tread. Expect the first to-morrow night, when the bell tolls One. Expect the second on the next night at the same hour. The third, upon the next night, when the last stroke of Twelve has ceased to vibrate. Look to see me no more; and look that, for your own sake, you remember what has passed between us!"

It walked backward from him; and at every step it took, the window raised itself a little, so that, when the apparition reached it, it was wide open.

Scrooge closed the window, and examined the door by which the Ghost had entered. It was double-locked, as he had locked it with his own hands, and the bolts were undisturbed. Scrooge tried to say "Humbug!" but stopped at the first syllable. And being, from the emotion he had undergone, or the fatigues of the day, or his glimpse of the invisible world, or the dull conversation of the Ghost, or the lateness of the hour, much in need of repose, he went straight to bed, without undressing, and fell asleep on the instant.

Stave Two: The First of the Three Spirits

When Scrooge awoke it was so dark that, looking out of bed, he could scarcely distinguish the transparent window from the opaque walls of his chamber, until suddenly the church clock tolled a deep, dull, hollow, melancholy ONE.

Light flashed up in the room upon the instant, and the curtains of his bed were drawn aside by a strange figure—like a child: yet not so like a child as like an old man, viewed through some supernatural medium, which gave him the appearance of having receded from the view, and being diminished to a child's proportions. Its hair, which hung about its neck and down its back, was white as if with age; and yet the face had not a wrinkle in it, and the tenderest bloom was on the skin. It held a branch of fresh green holly in its hand; and, in singular contradiction of that wintry emblem, had its dress trimmed with summer flowers. But the strangest thing about it was, that from the crown of its head there sprung a bright clear jet of light, by which all this was visible; and which was doubtless the occasion of its using, in its duller moments, a great extinguisher for a cap, which it now held under its arm.

"Are you the Spirit, sir, whose coming was foretold to me?"

"I am!"

"Who and what are you?"

"I am the Ghost of Christmas Past."

"Long past?"

"No. Your past. The things that you will see with me are shadows of the things that have been; they will have no consciousness of us."

Scrooge then made bold to inquire what business brought him there.

"Your welfare. Rise, and walk with me!"

It would have been in vain for Scrooge to plead that the weather and the hour were not adapted to pedestrian purposes; that the bed was warm, and the thermometer a long way below freezing; that he was clad but lightly in his slippers, dressing-gown, and nightcap; and that he had a cold upon him at that time. The grasp, though gentle as a woman's hand, was not to be resisted. He rose; but, finding that the Spirit made toward the window, clasped its robe in supplication.

"I am a mortal, and liable to fall."

"Bear but a touch of my hand *there*," said the Spirit, laying it upon his heart, "and you shall be upheld in more than this!"

As the words were spoken, they passed through the wall, and

stood in the busy thoroughfares of a city. It was made plain enough by the dressing of the shops that here, too, it was Christmas-time.

The Ghost stopped at a certain warehouse door, and asked Scrooge if he knew it.

"Know it? Was I apprenticed here!"

They went in. At sight of an old gentleman in a Welsh wig, sitting behind such a high desk that, if he had been two inches taller, he must have knocked his head against the ceiling, Scrooge cried in great excitement, "Why, it's old Fezziwig! Bless his heart, it's Fezziwig, alive again!"

Old Fezziwig laid down his pen, and looked up at the clock, which pointed to the hour of seven. He rubbed his hands; adjusted his capacious waistcoat; laughed all over himself, from his shoes to his organ of benevolence; and called out in a comfortable, oily, rich, fat, jovial voice, "Yo ho, there! Ebenezer! Dick!"

A living and moving picture of Scrooge's former self, a young man, came briskly in, accompanied by his fellow 'prentice.

"Dick Wilkins, to be sure!" said Scrooge to the Ghost. "My old fellow 'prentice, bless me, yes. There he is. He was very much attached to me, was Dick. Poor Dick! Dear, dear!"

"Yo ho, my boys!" said Fezziwig. No more work to-night. Christmas eve, Dick. Christmas, Ebenezer! Let's have the shutters up before a man can say Jack Robinson! Clear away, my lads, and let's have lots of room here!"

Clear away! There was nothing they wouldn't have cleared away, or couldn't have cleared away, with old Fezziwig looking on. It was done in a minute. Every movable was packed off, as if it were dismissed from public life forevermore; the floor was swept and watered, the lamps were trimmed, fuel was heaped upon the fire; and the warehouse was as snug and warm and dry and bright a ballroom as you would desire to see upon a winter's night.

In came a fiddler with a music-book, and went up to the lofty desk, and made an orchestra of it, and tuned like fifty stomachaches. In came Mrs. Fezziwig, one vast substantial smile. In came three Miss Fezziwigs beaming and lovable. In came the six young followers whose hearts they broke. In came all the young men and women employed in the business. In came the housemaid, with her cousin the baker. In came the cook, with her brother's particular friend the milkman.

In they all came one after another; some shyly, some boldly, some gracefully, some awkwardly, some pushing, some pulling; in they all came, anyhow and everyhow. Away they all went, twenty couples at once; hands half round and back again the other way;

down the middle and up again; round and round in various stages of affectionate grouping; old top couple always turning up in the wrong place; new top couple starting off again, as soon as they got there; all top couples at last, and not a bottom one to help them. When this result was brought about, old Fezziwig, clapping his hands to stop the dance, cried out, "Well done!" and the fiddler plunged his hot face into a pot of porter especially provided for that purpose.

There were more dances, and there were forfeits, and more dances, and there was cake, and there was negus, and there was a great piece of Cold Roast, and there was a great piece of Cold Boiled, and there were mince-pies and plenty of beer. But the great effect of the evening came after the Roast and Boiled, when the fiddler struck up "Sir Roger de Coverley." Then old Fezziwig stood out to dance with Mrs. Fezziwig. Top couple too; with a good stiff piece of work cut out for them; three or four and twenty pairs of partners; people who were not to be trifled with; people who *would* dance, and had no notion of walking.

But if they had been twice as many—four times—old Fezziwig would have been a match for them, and so would Mrs. Fezziwig. As to *her*, she was worthy to be his partner in every sense of the term. A positive light appeared to issue from Fezziwig's calves. They shone in every part of the dance. You couldn't have predicted, at any given time, what would become of 'em next. And when old Fezziwig and Mrs. Fezziwig had gone all through the dance—advance and retire, turn your partner, bow and courtesy, corkscrew, thread the needle, and back again to your place—Fezziwig "cut" —cut so deftly, that he appeared to wink with his legs.

When the clock struck eleven this domestic ball broke up. Mr. and Mrs. Fezziwig took their stations, one on either side the door, and, shaking hands with every person individually as he or she went out, wished him or her a Merry Christmas. When everybody had retired but the two 'prentices, they did the same to them; and thus the cheerful voices died away, and the lads were left to their beds, which were under a counter in the back shop.

"A small matter," said the Ghost, "to make these silly folks so full of gratitude. He has spent but a few pounds of your mortal money—three or four perhaps. Is that so much that he deserves this praise?"

"It isn't that," said Scrooge, heated by the remark, and speaking unconsciously like his former, not his latter self—"It isn't that, Spirit. He has the power to render us happy or unhappy; to make our service light or burdensome, a pleasure or a toil. Say that his power lies in words and looks; in things so slight and insignificant that it is impossible to add and count 'em up: what then? The happiness he gives is quite as great as if it cost a fortune."

He felt the Spirit's glance, and stopped.

"What is the matter?"

"Nothing particular."

"Something I think."

"No, no. I should like to be able to say a word or two to my clerk just now. That's all."

"My time grows short," observed the Spirit. "Quick!"

This was not addressed to Scrooge, or to any one whom he could see, but it produced an immediate effect. For again he saw himself. He was older now; a man in the prime of life.

He was not alone, but sat by the side of a fair young girl in a black dress, in whose eyes there were tears.

"It matters little," she said softly to Scrooge's former self. "To you, very little. Another idol has displaced me; and if it can comfort you in time to come, as I would have tried to do, I have no just cause to grieve."

"What Idol has displaced you?"

"A golden one. You fear the world too much. I have seen your nobler aspirations fall off one by one, until the master-passion, Gain, engrosses you. Have I not?"

"What then? Even if I have grown so much wiser, what then? I am not changed toward you. Have I ever sought release from our engagement?"

"In words, no. Never."

"In what, then?"

"In a changed nature; in an altered spirit; in another atmosphere of life; another Hope as its great end. If you were free to-day, to-morrow, yesterday, can even I believe that you would choose a dowerless girl; or, choosing her, do I not know that your repentance and regret would surely follow? I do; and I release you. With a full heart, for the love of him you once were."

"Spirit! remove me from this place."

"I told you these were shadows of the things that have been," said the Ghost. That they are what they are, do not blame me!"

"Remove me!" Scrooge exclaimed. "I cannot bear it! Leave me! Take me back. Haunt me no longer!"

As he struggled with the Spirit he was conscious of being exhausted, and overcome by an irresistible drowsiness; and further, of being in his own bedroom. He had barely time to reel to bed before he sank into a heavy sleep.

Stave Three: The Second of the Three Spirits

Scrooge awoke in his own bedroom. There was no doubt about that. But it and his own adjoining sitting-room, into which he shuffled in his slippers, attracted by a great light there, had undergone a surprising transformation. The walls and ceiling were so hung with living green, that it looked a perfect grove. The leaves of holly, mistletoe, and ivy reflected back the light, as if so many little mirrors had been scattered there; and such a mighty blaze went roaring up the chimney, as that petrifaction of a hearth had never known in Scrooge's time, or Marley's, or for many and many a winter season gone.

Heaped upon the floor, to form a kind of throne, were turkeys, geese, game, brawn, great joints of meat, sucking-pigs, long wreaths of sausages, mince-pies, plum-puddings, barrels of oysters, red-hot chestnuts, cherry-cheeked apples, juicy oranges, luscious pears, immense twelfth-cakes, and great bowls of punch. In easy state upon this couch there sat a Giant glorious to see; who bore a glowing torch, in shape not unlike Plenty's horn, and who raised it high to shed its light on Scrooge as he came peeping round the door.

"Come in; come in! and know me better, man! I am the Ghost of Christmas Present. Look upon me! You have never seen the like of me before!"

"Never."

"Have never walked forth with the younger members of my family; meaning (for I am very young) my elder brothers born in these later years?" pursued the Fantom.

"I don't think I have, I am afraid I have not. Have you had many brothers, Spirit?"

"More than eighteen hundred."

"A tremendous family to provide for! Spirit, conduct me where you will. I went forth last night on compulsion, and I learned a lesson which is working now. To-night, if you have aught to teach me, let me profit by it."

"Touch my robe!"

Scrooge did as he was told, and held it fast.

The room and its contents all vanished instantly, and they stood in the city streets upon a snowy Christmas morning.

Scrooge and the Ghost passed on, invisible, straight to Scrooge's clerk's; and on the threshold of the door the Spirit smiled, and stopped to bless Bob Cratchit's dwelling with the sprinklings of his torch. Think of that! Bob had but fifteen "Bob" a week himself; he pocketed on Saturdays but fifteen copies of his Christian name;

and yet the Ghost of Christmas Present blessed his four-roomed house!

Then up rose Mrs. Cratchit, Cratchit's wife, dressed out but poorly in a twice-turned gown, but brave in ribbons, which are cheap and make a goodly show for sixpence; and she laid the cloth, assisted by Belinda Cratchit, second of her daughters, also brave in ribbon; while Master Peter Cratchit plunged a fork into the saucepan of potatoes, and, getting the corners of his monstrous shirt-collar (Bob's private property, conferred upon his son and heir in honor of the day) into his mouth, rejoiced to find himself so gallantly attired, and yearned to show his linen in the fashionable Parks.

And now two smaller Cratchits, boy and girl, came tearing in, screaming that outside the baker's they had smelled the goose, and known it for their own; and basking in luxurious thoughts of sage and onion, these young Cratchits danced about the table, and exalted Master Peter Cratchit to the skies, while he (not proud, although his collars nearly choked him) blew the fire, until the slow potatoes, bubbling up, knocked loudly at the saucepan-lid to be let out and peeled.

"What has ever got your precious father, then?" said Mrs. Cratchit. "And your brother Tiny Tim? And Martha warn't as late last Christmas day by half an hour!"

"Here's Martha, mother!" said a girl, appearing as she spoke.

"Here's Martha, mother!" cried the two young Cratchits. "Hurrah! There's *such* a goose, Martha!"

"Why, bless your heart alive, my dear, how late you are!" said Mrs. Cratchit, kissing her a dozen times, and taking off her shawl and bonnet for her.

"We'd a deal of work to finish up last night," replied the girl, "and had to clear away this morning, mother!"

"Well! Never mind so long as you are come," said Mrs. Cratchit. "Sit ye down before the fire, my dear, and have a warm, Lord bless ye!"

"No, no! There's father coming," cried the two young Cratchits, who were everywhere at once. "Hide, Martha, hide!"

So Martha hid herself, and in came little Bob, the father, with at least three feet of comforter, exclusive of the fringe, hanging down before him; and his threadbare clothes darned up and brushed, to look seasonable; and Tiny Tim upon his shoulder. Alas for Tiny Tim, he bore a little crutch, and had his limbs supported by an iron frame!

"Why, where's our Martha?" cried Bob Cratchit, looking round.

"Not coming," said Mrs. Cratchit.

"Not coming?" said Bob, with a sudden declension in his high spirits; for he had been Tim's blood-horse all the way from church, and had come home rampant—"not coming upon Christmas day?"

Martha didn't like to see him disappointed, if it were only in joke; so she came out prematurely from behind the closet door, and ran into his arms, while the two young Cratchits hustled Tiny Tim, and bore him off into the wash-house that he might hear the pudding singing in the copper.

"And how did little Tim behave?" asked Mrs. Cratchit, when she had rallied Bob on his credulity, and Bob had hugged his daughter to his heart's content.

"As good as gold," said Bob, "and better. Somehow he gets thoughtful, sitting by himself so much, and thinks the strangest things you ever heard. He told me, coming home, that he hoped the people saw him in the church, because he was a cripple, and it might be pleasant to them to remember, upon Christmas day, who made lame beggars walk and blind men see."

Bob's voice was tremulous when he told them this, and trembled more when he said that Tiny Tim was growing strong and hearty.

His active little crutch was heard upon the floor, and back came Tiny Tim before another word was spoken, escorted by his brother and sister to his stool beside the fire; and while Bob, turning up his cuffs—as if, poor fellow, they were capable of being made more shabby — compounded some hot mixture in a jug with gin and lemons, and stirred it round and round and put it on the hob to simmer, Master Peter and the two ubiquitous young Cratchits went to fetch the goose, with which they soon returned in high procession.

Mrs. Cratchit made the gravy (ready beforehand in a little saucepan) hissing hot; Master Peter mashed the potatoes with incredible vigor; Miss Belinda sweetened up the apple-sauce; Martha dusted the hot plates; Bob took Tiny Tim beside him in a tiny corner at the table; the two young Cratchits set chairs for everybody, not forgetting themselves, and mounting guard upon their posts, crammed spoons into their mouths, lest they should shriek for goose before their turn came to be helped.

At last the dishes were set on, and grace was said. It was succeeded by a breathless pause, as Mrs. Cratchit, looking slowly all along the carving-knife, prepared to plunge it in the breast; but when she did, and when the long-expected gush of stuffing issued forth, one murmur of delight arose all round the board, and even Tiny Tim, excited by the two young Cratchits, beat on the table with the handle of his knife, and feebly cried, Hurrah!

There never was such a goose. Bob said he didn't believe there ever was such a goose cooked Its tenderness and flavor, size and cheapness, were the themes of universal admiration. Eked out by apple-sauce and mashed potatoes, it was a sufficient dinner for the whole family; indeed, as Mrs. Cratchit said with great delight (surveying one small atom of a bone upon the dish), they hadn't ate it all at last!

Yet every one had had enough, and the youngest Cratchits in particular were steeped in sage and onion to the eyebrows But now, the plates being changed by Miss Belinda, Mrs. Cratchit left the room alone—too nervous to bear witnesses—to take the pudding up, and bring it in.

Suppose it should not be done enough! Suppose it should break in turning out! Suppose somebody should have got over the wall of the back yard, and stolen it, while they were merry with the goose—a supposition at which the two young Cratchits became livid! All sorts of horrors wre supposed.

Hallo! A great deal of steam! The pudding was out of the copper. A smell like a washing-day! That was the cloth. A smell like an eating-house and a pastry-cook's next door to each other, wtih a laundress's next door to that! That was the pudding! In half a minute Mrs. Cratchit entered—flushed but smiling proudly—with the pudding, like a speckled cannon-ball, so hard and firm, blazing in half of half a quartern of ignited brandy, and bedight with Christmas holly stuck into the top.

Oh, a wonderful pudding! Bob Cratchit said, and calmly, too, that he regarded it as the greatest success achieved by Mrs. Cratchit since their marriage. Mrs. Cratchit said that now the weight was off her mind, she would confess she had had her doubts about the quantity of flour. Everybody had something to say about it, but nobody said or thought it was at all a small pudding for a large family. Any Cratchit would have blushed to hint at such a thing.

At last the dinner was all done, the cloth was cleared, the hearth swept, and the fire made up. The compound in the jug being tasted and considered perfect, apples and oranges were put upon the table, and a shovelful of chestnuts on the fire.

Then all the Cratchit family drew round the hearth, in what Bob Cratchit called a circle, and at Bob Cratchit's elbow stood the family display of glass—two tumblers, and a custard-cup without a handle.

These held the hot stuff from the jug, however, as well as golden goblets would have done; and Bob served it out with beaming looks, while the chestnuts on the fire sputtered and crackled noisily. Then Bob proposed:

"A merry Christmas to us all, my dears. God bless us!"

Which all the family reechoed.

"God bless us every one!" said Tiny Tim, the last of all.

He sat very close to his father's side, upon his little stool. Bob held his withered little hand in his, as if he loved the child, and wished to keep him by his side, and dreaded that he might be taken from him.

Scrooge raised his head speedily, on hearing his own name.

"Mr. Scrooge!" said Bob; "I'll give you Mr. Scrooge, the Founder of the Feast!"

"The Founder of the Feast, indeed!" cried Mrs. Cratchit, reddening. "I wish I had him here. I'd give him a piece of my mind to feast upon, and I hope he'd have a good appetite for it."

"My dear," said Bob, "the children! Christmas day."

"It should be Christmas day, I am sure," said she, "on which one drinks the health of such an odious, stingy, hard, unfeeling man as Mr. Scrooge. You know he is, Robert! Nobody knows it better than you do, poor fellow!"

"My dear," was Bob's mild answer, "Christmas day."

"I'll drink his health for your sake and the day's," said Mrs. Cratchit, "not for his. Long life to him! A merry Christmas and a happy New Year! He'll be very merry and very happy, I have no doubt!"

The children drank the toast after her. It was the first of their proceedings which had no heartiness in it. Tiny Tim drank it last of all, but he didn't care twopence for it. Scrooge was the Ogre of the family. The mention of his name cast a dark shadow on the party, which was not dispelled for full five minutes.

After it had passed away, they were ten times merrier than before, from the mere relief of Scrooge the Baleful being done with. Bob Cratchit told them how he had a situation in his eye for Master Peter, which would bring in, if obtained, full five and sixpence weekly. The two young Cratchits laughed tremendously at the idea of Peter's being a man of business; and Peter himself looked thoughtfully at the fire from between his collars, as if he were deliberating what particular investments he should favor when he came into the receipt of that bewildering income.

Martha, who was a poor apprentice at a milliner's, then told them what kind of work she had to do, and how many hours she worked at a stretch, and how she meant to lie abed to-morrow morning for a good long rest; to-morrow being a holiday she passed at home. Also how she had seen a countess and lord some days before, and how the lord "was much about as tall as Peter"; at which Peter pulled up his collars so high that you couldn't have seen his head if you had been there. All this time the chestnuts and the jug went round and round; and by and by they had a song, about a lost child traveling in the snow, from Tiny Tim, who had a plaintive little voice, and sang it very well indeed.

There was nothing of high mark in this. They were not a handsome family; they were not well dressed; their shoes were far from being water-proof; their clothes were scanty; and Peter might have known, and very likely did, the inside of a pawnbroker's. But they were happy, grateful, pleased with one another, and contented with the time, and when they faded, and looked happier yet in the bright sprinklings of the Spirit's torch at parting, Scrooge had his eye upon them, and especially on Tiny Tim, until the last.

It was a great surprise to Scrooge, as this scene vanished, to hear a hearty laugh. It was a much greater surprise to Scrooge to recognize it as his own nephew's, and to find himself in a bright, dry, gleaming room, with the Spirit standing smiling by his side, and looking at that same nephew.

It is a fair, even-handed, noble adjustment of things, that while there is infection in disease and sorrow, there is nothing in the world so irresistibly contagious as laughter and good-humor. When Scrooge's nephew laughed, Scrooge's niece by marriage laughed as heartily as he. And their assembled friends, being not a bit behindhand, laughed out lustily.

"He said that Christmas was a humbug, as I live!" cried Scrooge's nephew. "He believed it, too!"

"More shame for him, Fred!" said Scrooge's niece, indignantly. Bless those women! they never do anything by halves. They are always in earnest.

She was very pretty, exceedingly pretty. With a dimpled, surprised-looking, capital face; a ripe little mouth that seemed made to be kissed—as no doubt it was; all kinds of good little dots about her chin, that melted into one another when she laughed; and the sunniest pair of eyes you ever saw in any little creature's head. Altogether she was what you would have called provoking, but satisfactory, too. Oh, perfectly satisfactory!

"He's a comical old fellow," said Scrooge's nephew, "that's the truth; not so pleasant as he might be. However, his offenses carry their own punishment, and I have nothing to say against him.

Who suffers by his ill whims? Himself, always. Here he takes it into his head to dislike us, and he won't come and dine with us. What's the consequence? He doesn't lose much of a dinner."

"Indeed, I think he loses a very good dinner," interrupted Scrooge's niece. Everybody else said the same, and they must be allowed to have been competent judges, because they had just had dinner; and, with the dessert upon the table, were clustered round the fire, by lamplight.

"Well, I am very glad to hear it," said Scrooge's nephew, "because I haven't any great faith in these young housekeepers. What do *you* say, Topper?"

Topper clearly had his eye on one of Scrooge's niece's sisters, for he answered that a bachelor was a wretched outcast, who had no right to express an opinion on the subject. Whereat Scrooge's niece's sister—the plump one with the lace tucker, not the one with the roses—blushed.

After tea they had some music. For they were a musical family, and knew what they were about when they sang a Glee or Catch, I can assure you—especially Topper, who could growl away in the bass like a good one, and never swell the large veins in his forehead, or get red in the face over it.

But they didn't devote the whole evening to music. After a while they played at forfeits; for it is good to be children some-times, and never better than at Christmas, when its mighty Founder was a child himself. There was first a game at blind man's buff, though. And I no more believe Topper was really blinded than I believe he had eyes in his boots. Because the way in which he went after that plump sister in the lace tucker was an outrage on the credulity of human nature. Knocking down the fire-irons, tumbling over the chairs, bumping up against the piano, smothering himself among the curtains, wherever she went there went he!

He always knew where the plump sister was. He wouldn't catch anybody else. If you had fallen up against him, as some of them did, and stood there, he would have made a feint of endeavor-ing to seize you, which would have been an affront to your understanding, and would instantly have sidled off in the direction of the plump sister.

"Here is a new game," said Scrooge. "One half-hour, Spirit, only one!"

It was a Game called Yes and No, where Scrooge's nephew had to think of something, and the rest must find out what; he only answering to their questions yes or no, as the case was. The fire of questioning to which he was exposed elicited from him that he was thinking of an animal, a live animal, rather a disagreeable animal, a savage animal, an animal that growled and grunted sometimes, and talked sometimes, and lived in London, and walked about the streets, and wasn't made a show of, and wasn't led by anybody, and didn't live in a menagerie, and was never killed in a market, and was not a horse, or an ass, or a cow, or a bull, or a tiger, or a dog, or a pig, or a cat, or a bear.

At every new question put to him, this nephew burst into a fresh roar of laughter; and was so inexpressibly tickled, that he was obliged to get up off the sofa and stamp. At last the plump sister cried out:

"I have found it out! I know what it is, Fred! I know what it is!"

"What is it?" cried Fred.

"It's your uncle Scro-o-o-o-oge!"

Which it certainly was. Admiration was the universal sentiment, though some objected that the reply to "Is it a bear?" ought to have been "Yes."

Uncle Scrooge had imperceptibly become so gay and light of heart, that he would have drunk to the unconscious company in an inaudible speech. But the whole scene passed off in the breath of the last word spoken by his nephew; and he and the Spirit were again upon their travels.

Much they saw, and far they went, and many homes they visited, but always with a happy end. The Spirit stood beside sick-beds, and they were cheerful; on foreign lands, and they were close at home; by struggling men, and they were patient in their greater hope; by poverty, and it was rich. In almshouse, hospital, and jail, in misery's every refuge, where vain man in his little brief authority had not made fast the door, and barred the Spirit out, he left his blessing, and taught Scrooge his precepts. Suddenly, as they stood together in an open place, the bell struck twelve.

Scrooge looked about him for the Ghost, and saw it no more. As the last stroke ceased to vibrate, he remembered the prediction of old Jacob Marley, and, lifting up his eyes, beheld a solemn Fantom, draped and hooded, coming like a mist along the ground toward him.

Stave Four: The Last of the Spirits

The Fantom slowly, gravely, silently approached. When it came near him, Scrooge bent down upon his knee; for in the air through which this Spirit moved it seemed to scatter gloom and mystery.

It was shrouded in a deep black garment, which concealed its head, its face, its form, and left nothing of it visible save one out-stretched hand. He knew no more, for the Spirit neither spoke nor moved.

"I am in the presence of the Ghost of Christmas Yet to Come? Ghost of the Future! I fear you more than any specter I have seen. But as I know your purpose is to do me good, and as I hope to live to be another man from what I was, I am prepared to bear you company, and do it with a thankful heart. Will you not speak to me?"

It gave him no reply. The hand was pointed straight before them.

"Lead on! Lead on! The night is waning fast, and it is precious time to me, I know. Lead on, Spirit!"

They scarcely seemed to enter the city; for the city rather seemed to spring up about them. But there they were in the heart of it; on 'Change, among the merchants.

The Spirit stopped beside one little knot of business men. Observing that the hand was pointed to them, Scrooge advanced to listen to their talk.

"No," said a great fat man with a monstrous chin, "I don't know much about it either way. I only know he's dead."

"When did he die?" inquired another.

"Last night, I believe."

"Why, what was the matter with him? I thought he'd never die."

"God knows," said the first, with a yawn.

"What has he done with his money?" asked a red-faced gentleman.

"I haven't heard," said the man with the large chin. "Company, perhaps. He hasn't left it to me. That's all I know. By, by!"

Scrooge was at first inclined to be surprised that the Spirit should attach importance to conversation apparently so trivial; but feeling assured that it must have some hidden purpose, he set himself to consider what it was likely to be. It could scarcely be supposed to have any bearing on the death of Jacob, his old part-ner, for that was Past, and this Ghost's province was the Future.

He looked about in that very place for his own image; but

another man stood in his accustomed corner, and though the clock pointed to his usual time of day for being there, he saw no likeness of himself among the multitudes that poured in through the Porch. It gave him little surprise, however; for he had been revolving in his mind a change of life, and he thought and hoped he saw his new-born resolutions carried out in this.

They left this busy scene, and went into an obscure part of the town, to a low shop where iron, old rags, bottles, bones, and greasy offal were bought. A gray-haired rascal, of great age, sat smoking his pipe.

Scrooge and the Fantom came into the presence of this man, just as a woman with a heavy bundle slunk into the shop. But she had scarcely entered, when another woman, similarly laden, came in, too; and she was closely followed by a man in faded black. And after a short period of blank astonishment, in which the old man with the pipe had joined them, they all three burst into a laugh.

"Let the charwoman alone to be the first!" cried she who had entered first. "Let the laundress alone to be the second; and let the undertaker's man alone to be the third. Look here, old Joe, here's a chance! If we haven't all three met here without meaning it!"

"You couldn't have met in a better place. You were made free of it long ago, you know; and the other two ain't strangers. What have you got to sell? What have you got to sell?"

"Half a minute's patience, Joe, and you shall see."

"What odds, then! What odds, Mrs. Dilber?" said the woman. "Every person has a right to take care of themselves. *He* always did! Who's the worse for the loss of a few things like these? Not a dead man, I suppose."

Mrs. Dilber, whose manner was remarkable for general propitiation, said, "No, indeed, ma'am."

"If he wanted to keep 'em after he was dead, a wicked old screw, why wasn't he natural in his lifetime? If he had been, he'd have had somebody to look after him when he was struck with Death, instead of lying gasping out his last there, alone by himself."

"It's the truest word that ever was spoken; it's a judgment on him."

"I wish it was a little heavier judgment, and it should have been, you may depend upon it, if I could have laid my hands on anything else. Open that bundle, old Joe, and let me know the value of it. Speak out plain. I'm not afraid to be the first, nor afraid for them to see it."

Joe went down on his knees for the greater convenience of opening the bundle, and dragged out a large and heavy roll of some dark stuff.

"What do you call this? Bed-curtains!"

"Ah! Bed-curtains! Don't drop that oil upon the blankets, now."

"*His* blankets?"

"Whose else's, do you think? He isn't likely to take cold without 'em, I dare say. Ah! You may look through that shirt till your eyes ache; but you won't find a hole in it, nor a threadbare place. It's the best he had, and a fine one, too. They'd have wasted it by dressing him up in it, if it hadn't been for me."

Scrooge listened to this dialogue in horror.

"Spirit! I see, I see. The case of this unhappy man might be my own. My life tends that way now. Merciful Heaven, what is this?"

The scene had changed, and now he almost touched a bare, uncurtained bed. A pale light, rising in the outer air, fell straight upon this bed; and on it, unwatched, unwept, uncared for, was the body of this plundered unknown man.

"Spirit, let me see some tenderness connected with a death, or this dark chamber, Spirit, will be forever present to me."

The Ghost conducted him to poor Bob Cratchit's house—the dwelling he had visited before—and found the mother and the children seated round the fire.

Quiet. Very quiet. The noisy little Cratchits were as still as statues in one corner, and sat looking up at Peter, who had a book before him. The mother and her daughters were engaged in needlework. But surely they were very quiet!

"'And He took a child, and set him in the midst of them.'"

Where had Scrooge heard those words? He had not dreamed them. The boy must have read them out, as he and the Spirit crossed the threshold. Why did he not go on?

The mother laid her work upon the table, and put her hand up to her face.

"The color hurts my eyes," she said.

The color? Ah, poor Tiny Tim!

"They're better now again. It makes them weak by candle-light; and I wouldn't show weak eyes to your father when he comes home, for the world. It must be near his time."

"Past it, rather," Peter answered, shutting up his book. "But I think he has walked a little slower then he used, these few last evenings, mother."

"I have known him to walk with—I have known him to walk with Tiny Tim upon his shoulder, very fast indeed."

"And so have I," cried Peter. "Often."

"And so have I," exclaimed another. So had all.

"But he was very light to carry, and his father loved him so, that it was no trouble—no trouble. And there is your father at the door!"

She hurried out to meet him; and little Bob in his comforter— he had need of it, poor fellow—came in. His tea was ready for him on the hob, and they all tried who should help him to it most. Then the two young Cratchits got upon his knees and laid, each child, a little cheek against his face, as if they said, "Don't mind it, father. Don't be grieved!"

Bob was very cheerful with them, and spoke pleasantly to all the family. He looked at the work upon the table, and praised the industry and speed of Mrs. Cratchit and the girls. They would be done long before Sunday, he said.

"Sunday! You went to-day, then, Robert?"

"Yes, my dear," returned Bob. "I wish you could have gone. It would have done you good to see how green a place it is. But you'll see it often. I promised him that I would walk there on a Sunday. My little, little child! My little child!"

He broke down all at once. He couldn't help it. If he could have helped it, he and his child would have been farther apart, perhaps, than they were.

"Specter," said Scrooge, "something informs me that our parting moment is at hand. I know it, but I know not how. Tell me what man that was, with the covered face, whom we saw lying dead?"

The Ghost of Christmas Yet To Come conveyed him to a dismal, wretched ruinous churchyard.

The Spirit stood among the graves, and pointed down to One.

"Before I draw nearer to that stone to which you point, answer me one question. Are these the shadows of the things that Will be, or are they shadows of the things that May be only?"

Still the Ghost pointed downward to the grave by which it stood.

"Men's courses will foreshadow certain ends, to which, if persevered in, they must lead. But if the courses be departed from, the ends will change. Say it is thus with what you show me!"

The Spirit was immovable as ever.

Scrooge crept toward it, trembling as he went; and, following the finger, read upon the stone of the neglected grave his own name—Ebenezer Scrooge.

"Am *I* that man who lay upon the bed? No, Spirit! Oh, no, no! Spirit! hear me! I am not the man I was. I will not be the man I must have been but for this intercourse. Why show me this, if I am past all hope? Assure me that I yet may change these shadows you have shown me by an altered life."

For the first time the kind hand faltered.

"I will honor Christmas in my heart, and try to keep it all the year. I will live in the Past, the Present, and the Future. The Spirits of all three shall strive within me. I will not shut out the lessons that they teach. Oh, tell me I may sponge away the writing on this stone!"

Holding up his hands in one last prayer to have his fate reversed, he saw an alteration in the Fantom's hood and dress. It shrunk, collapsed, and dwindled down into a bedpost.

Yes, and the bedpost was his own. The bed was his own, the room was his own. Best and happiest of all, the Time before him was his own, to make amends in!

He was checked in his transports by the churches ringing out the lustiest peals he had ever heard.

Running to the window, he opened it, and put out his head. No fog, no mist, no night; clear, bright, stirring, golden day.

"What's to-day?" cried Scrooge, calling downward to a boy in Sunday clothes, who perhaps had loitered in to look about him.

"Eh?"

"What's to-day, my fine fellow?"

"Today! Why, Christmas Day."

"It's Christmas day! I haven't missed it. Hallo, my fine fellow!"

"Hallo!"

"Do you know the Poulterer's in the next street but one, at the corner?"

"I should hope I did."

"An intelligent boy! A remarkable boy! Do you know whether they've sold the prize Turkey that was hanging up there? Not the little prize Turkey—the big one?"

"What, the one as big as me?"

"What a delightful boy! It's a pleasure to talk to him. Yes, my buck!"

"It's hanging there now."

"It is? Go and buy it."

"Walk-er!" exclaimed the boy.

"No, no, I am in earnest. Go and buy it, and tell 'em to bring it here, that I may give them the direction where to take it. Come back with the man, and I'll give you a shilling. Come back with him in less than five minutes, and I'll give you half a crown!"

The boy was off like a shot.

"I'll send it to Bob Cratchit's! He sha'n't know who sends it. It's twice the size of Tiny Tim. Joe Miller never made such a joke as sending it to Bob's will be!"

The hand in which he wrote the address was not a steady one; but write it he did, somehow, and went down-stairs to open the street door, ready for the coming of the poulterer's man.

It *was* a Turkey! He never could have stood upon his legs, that bird. He would have snapped 'em short off in a minute, like sticks of sealing-wax.

Scrooge dressed himself "all in his best," and at last got out into the streets. The people were by this time pouring forth, as he had seen them with the Ghost of Christmas Present; and walking with his hands behind him, Scrooge regarded every one with a delighted smile. He looked so irresistibly pleasant, in a word, that three or four goodhumored fellows said, "Good morning, sir! A merry Christmas to you!" And Scrooge said often afterward, that, of all the blithe sounds he had ever heard, those were the blithest in his ears.

In the afternoon, he turned his steps toward his nephew's house.

He passed the door a dozen times, before he had the courage to go up and knock. But he made a dash, and did it.

"Is your master at home, my dear?" said Scrooge to the girl. "Nice girl! Very."

"Yes, sir."

"Where is he, my love?"

"He's in the dining-room, sir, along with mistress."

"He knows me," said Scrooge, with his hand already on the dining-room lock. "I'll go in here, my dear."

"Fred!"

"Why, bless my soul!" cried Fred, "who's that?"

"It's I. Your Uncle Scrooge. I have come to dinner. Will you let me in, Fred?"

Let him in! It is a mercy he didn't shake his arm off. He was at home in five minutes. Nothing could be heartier. His niece looked just the same. So did Topper when *he* came. So did the plump sister when *she* came. So did every one when *they* came. Wonderful party, wonderful games, wonderful unanimity, won-der-ful happiness!

But he was early at the office next morning. Oh, he was early there! If he could only be there first, and catch Bob Cratchit coming late! That was the thing he had set his heart upon.

And he did it. The clock struck nine. No Bob. A quarter past. No Bob. Bob was full eighteen minutes and a half behind his time. Scrooge sat with his door wide open, that he might see him come into the Tank.

Bob's hat was off before he opened the door; his comforter, too. He was on his stool in a jiffy; driving away with his pen, as if he were trying to overtake nine o'clock.

"Hallo!" growled Scrooge in his accustomed voice, as near as he could feign it. "What do you mean by coming here at this time of day?"

"I am very sorry, sir. I *am* behind my time."

"You are? Yes. I think you are. Step this way, if you please."

"It's only once a year, sir. It shall not be repeated. I was making rather merry yesterday, sir."

"Now, I'll tell you what, my friend. I am not going to stand this sort of thing any longer. And therefore," Scrooge continued, leaping from his stool, and giving Bob such a dig in the waistcoat that he staggered back into the Tank again—"and therefore I am about to raise your salary!"

Bob trembled, and got a little nearer to the ruler.

"A merry Christmas, Bob!" said Scrooge, with an earnestness that could not be mistaken, as he clapped him on the back. "A merrier Christmas, Bob, my good fellow, than I have given you for many a year! I'll raise your salary and endeavor to assist your struggling family, and we will discuss your affairs this very afternoon, over a Christmas bowl of smoking bishop, Bob! Make up the fires, and buy a second coal-scuttle before you dot another i, Bob Cratchit!"

Scrooge was better than his word. He did it all, and infinitely more; and to Tiny Tim, who did *not* die, he was a second father. He became as good a friend, as good a master, and as good a man as the good old city knew, or any other good old city, town, or borough in the good old world. Some people laughed to see the alteration in him; but his own heart laughed, and that was quite enough for him.

He had no further intercourse with spirits, but lived in that respect upon the total-abstinence principle ever afterward; and it was always said of him, that he knew how to keep Christmas well, if any man alive possessed the knowledge. May that be truly said of us, and all of us! And so, as Tiny Tim observed, God bless us, every one!"

Discussion of "A Christmas Carol"

Charles Dickens (1812-1870) is regarded by many as the greatest English novelist of all time, and perhaps he is. Others have written single novels as good as the best of Dickens's, maybe even better. But who else has written fifteen novels including eight as good as *The Pickwick Papers, Oliver Twist, Nicholas Nickleby, Martin Chuzzlewit, David Copperfield, Bleak House, A Tale of Two Cities,* and *Great Expectations?* Some might answer Scott, who wrote even more novels—but they are not as good. Others might say Hardy, and here the argument seems better, for Hardy wrote almost as many novels as Dickens, including almost as many of first quality. But beyond these there seems no serious rival for Dickens as the great giant of English fiction. Defoe, Richardson, Fielding, Smollett, Sterne, Jane Austen, Thackeray, Trollope, the Bronte sisters, George Eliot, Meredith, George Moore, Conrad, Bennett, Galsworthy, Lawrence, Forster, Joyce, Woolf, Maugham—all of these, and others, are major novelists, and some of them have written very great works; but as they are examined one by one, their novels as a whole are found to be either fewer or weaker than Dickens's, and he stands steady as the giant among them.

Two qualities shine above all others in Dickens's writing: One is the enormous abundance of his creative energy, especially in characterization. Literally hundreds of individualized characters so vividly described as to be unforgettable walk the pages of his books. Other novelists, such as Joyce and Conrad, have probed more deeply into a single complex personality; but no others, not even Scott, have created as many memorable characters.

The other quality is his sheer genius as a story-teller, with an exuberant style that sweeps his readers along in a wonderful journey of delight and yet retains an impressive rooting in realism and serious meaning. Dickens, the most popular of all great English novelists, is of the people, a folk writer, with an unparalleled capacity to win and hold a vast audience of readers.

One might expect such a writer to be fundamentally an optimist, and Dickens is. His eyes are not closed to evil; in fact, his novels and stories are filled with incidents and characters of evil. Even so, his faith in the ultimate triumph of good over evil is not only clear but is the central message of his work.

Within this framework we read "A Christmas Carol," which was written in 1843 as the first and best of a series of annual Christmas stories by Dickens. It is the most famous Christmas story in the world, and perhaps the best known short story in English. However, in spite of its great and deserved popularity, there are still many people who have not read it, and many others who have not read it for years. Hence its inclusion here.

The story communicates so masterfully, both in pleasure and in meaning, that no discussion seems needed. We therefore leave the story to speak for itself.

Three Short Christmas Poems

As a somber contrast to Dickens's "A Christmas Carol" we turn to three poems—"After Christmas" by W. H. Auden (1907-   ), great contemporary English poet; "White Christmas" by W. R. Rodgers (1909-   ), a gifted Irish poet; and "Karma" by E. A. Robinson (1869-1935), one of the great American poets of the past century.

Auden's "After Christmas," from *For the Time Being*, is an ironic and indignant poem reminding us that after almost twenty centuries Christ's message has not really penetrated the human soul nor very much modified human conduct. Once a year Christmas serves as a reminder of the lofty ideals of Christ's message and example, but after Christmas the ideals tend to be treated as warmed-up leftovers as people return to the routine of school and work and daily chores. Christ is forgotten and the realm of the world triumphs over the realm of the spirit.

"White Christmas" by Rodgers, although more figurative in its image-filled phrases, is also more angry. The emphasis here is on the commercialism and artificiality of Christmas. Sentiment is described as fluffy snow and the milk of human kindness is "tinned." The genuine spirit and vitality of Christmas are gone, replaced by a cheap surface pretense and a vulgar displaying of Christmas as merchandise to be bought and sold and haggled over for profit.

Robinson's "Karma" is a little story poem about a man who has financially destroyed a competitor in a business deal and now, briefly, has a twinge of conscience, brought on partly by seeing someone dressed as Santa Claus jingling a bell and collecting offerings on a street corner. He satisfies his conscience by giving "from the fullness of his heart . . . a dime for Jesus who had died for man." Again we feel the irony, the anger, and the indignation.

The message of all three poems is, of course, basically the same, which is the reason for our considering them together. "But all are exaggerations," readers may say. "Life is not like this, and people are not this bad." True, most people are not this bad. But if there is any truth in the poems, they are valuable as reminders of that truth. If Christmas is to any extent commercialized, if its sentiments are to any extent spoken but not lived, if its ideals are to any extent smothered in the rush of daily living—then the poems need to be faced squarely rather than avoided or dismissed.

After Christmas

(From "For the Time Being")

by W. H. Auden

Well, so that is that. Now we must dismantle the tree,
Putting the decorations back into their cardboard boxes—
Some have got broken—and carrying them up to the attic.
The holly and the mistletoe must be taken down and burnt,
And the children got ready for school. There are enough
Left-overs to do, warmed-up, for the rest of the week—
Not that we have much appetite, having drunk such a lot,
Stayed up so late, attempted—quite unsuccessfully—
To love all our relatives, and in general
Grossly overestimated our powers. Once again
As in previous years we have seen the actual Vision and failed
To do more than entertain it as an agreeable
Possibility, once again we have sent Him away,
Begging though to remain His disobedient servant,
The promising child who cannot keep His word for long.
The Christmas Feast is already a fading memory,
And already the mind begins to be vaguely aware
Of an unpleasant whiff of apprehension at the thought
Of Lent and Good Friday which cannot, after all, now
Be very far off. But, for the time being, here we all are,
Back in the moderate Aristotelian city
Of darning and the Eight-Fifteen, where Euclid's geometry
And Newton's mechanics would account for our experience,
And the kitchen table exists because I scrub it.
It seems to have shrunk during the holidays. The streets
Are much narrower than we remembered; we had forgotten
The office was as depressing as this. To those who have seen
The Child, however dimly, however incredulously,
The Time Being is, in a sense, the most trying time of all.
For the innocent children who whispered so excitedly
Outside the locked door where they knew the presents to be
Grew up when it opened. Now, recollecting that moment
We can repress the joy, but the guilt remains conscious;
Remembering the stable where for once in our lives
Everything became a You and nothing was an It.
And craving the sensation but ignoring the cause,
We look round for something, no matter what, to inhibit

Our self-reflection, and the obvious thing for that purpose
Would be some great suffering. So, once we have met the Son,
We are tempted ever after to pray to the Father:
"Lead us into temptation and evil for our sake."
They will come, all right, don't worry; probably in a form
That we do not expect, and certainly with a force
More dreadful than we can imagine. In the meantime
There are bills to be paid, machines to keep in repair,
Irregular verbs to learn, the Time Being to redeem
From insignificance. The happy morning is over,
The night of agony still to come; the time is noon:
When the Spirit must practise his scales of rejoicing
Without even a hostile audience, and the Soul endure
A silence that is neither for nor against her faith
That God's Will will be done, that, in spite of her prayers,
God will cheat no one, not even the world of its triumph.

White Christmas

by W. R. Rodgers

Punctually at Christmas the soft plush
Of sentiment snows down, enbosoms all
The sharp and pointed shapes of venom, shawls
The hills and hides the shocking holes of this
Uneven world of want and wealth, cushions
With cosy wish like cotton-wool the cool
Arm's-length interstices of caste and class,
And into obese folds subtracts from sight
All truculent acts, bleeding the world white.

Punctually that glib pair, Peace and Goodwill,
Emerges royally to take the air,
Collect the bows, assimilate the smiles,
Of waiting men. It is a genial time;
Angels, like stalactites, descend from heaven;
Bishops distribute their own weight in words,
Congratulate the poor on Christlike lack;
And the member for the constituency
Feeds the five thousand, and has plenty back.

Punctually, to-night, in old stone circles
Of set reunion, families stiffly sit
And listen: this is the night and this the happy time
When the tinned milk of human kindness is
Upheld and holed by radio-appeal:
Hushed are hurrying heels on hard roads,
And every parlour's a pink pond of light
To the cold and travelling man going by
In the dark, without a bark or a bite.

But punctually to-morrow you will see
All this silent and dissembling world
Of stilted sentiment suddenly melt
Into mush and watery welter of words
Beneath the warm and moving traffic of
Feet and actual fact. Over the stark plain
The silted mill-chimneys once again spread
Their sackcloth and ashes, a flowing mane
Of repentance for the false day that's fled.

Karma

by Edwin Arlington Robinson

Christmas was in the air and all was well
With him, but for a few confusing flaws
In divers of God's images. Because
A friend of his would neither buy nor sell,
Was he to answer for the axe that fell?
He pondered; and the reason for it was,
Partly, a slowly freezing Santa Claus
Upon the corner, with his beard and bell.

Acknowledging an improvident surprise,
He magnified a fancy that he wished
The friend whom he had wrecked were here again.
Not sure of that, he found a compromise;
And from the fullness of his heart he fished
A dime for Jesus who had died for man.

SECTION FOUR

Good Versus Evil

GOOD VERSUS EVIL

Introductory Comments

Probably literature has been concerned with no other subject so much as with the relationship between good and evil in the universe, and this is especially true of the great works of literature. Indeed, the most challenging questions that have faced thinking man through the ages in religion and philosophy as well as in literature have often had their roots in the nature of good and evil in relation to each other and in relation to God and man. As members of the Church we are fortunate in having special insight into these problems through the inspired writings of our modern prophets, but even for us there are some questions not fully answered. And related to the over-all problem of good and evil is the whole concern for the nature of sin and how to triumph over sin—that is, sin and redemption from sin.

We now present four poems and three short stories to explore the general subject of good versus evil in the universe and the related problem of sin and repentance.

If space permitted, we would include at least one of the truly profound works dealing with this subject—such a work, for example, as Dante's *Divine Comedy,* or Dostoyevsky's *Crime and Punishment,* or Shakespeare's *Macbeth* or another of his great tragedies, or Goethe's *Faust,* or Ibsen's *Hedda Gabler,* or Hawthorne's *The Scarlet Letter,* or Melville's *Moby Dick,* or Conrad's *Heart of Darkness.* But each is too long to be squeezed in. So we must content ourselves with shorter, simpler, and (in most instances) lesser works. But still very good ones.

The Tiger

by William Blake

Tiger! Tiger! burning bright
In the forests of the night,
What immortal hand or eye
Could frame thy fearful symmetry?

In what distant deeps or skies
Burnt the fire of thine eyes?
On what wings dare he aspire?
What the hand dare seize the fire?

And what shoulder, and what art,
Could twist the sinews of thy heart?
And when thy heart began to beat,
What dread hand? And what dread feet?

What the hammer? What the chain?
In what furnace was thy brain?
What the anvil? What dread grasp
Dare its deadly terrors clasp?

When the stars threw down their spears,
And water'd heaven with their tears,
Did he smile his work to see?
Did He who made the Lamb make thee?

Tiger! Tiger! burning bright
In the forests of the night,
What immortal hand or eye,
Dare frame thy fearful symmetry?

Discussion of "The Tiger"

"The Tiger" by William Blake (1757-1827)[1] intro-
duces us vividly to the whole question of the place of evil in
the universe. It should be read as a companion poem to
"The Lamb," which appears on p. 91 of this book. When
so read, the contrast between the two poems is obvious and

strong. "The Lamb" is a tender, lovely poem. "The Tiger" is fierce and grim. But the contrast goes far beyond just a difference in language and tone. The reader easily sees that the lamb is a symbol of all that is beautiful and good in the world, whereas the tiger is a symbol of all that is destructive and evil. The key line in the second poem, linking the two poems together and plunging to the heart of the problem posed by the second poem, occurs in the fifth stanza: "Did He who made the Lamb make thee?" Did God, the creator of all that is good in the world, also create evil? Blake does not answer the question, or even suggest an answer. At least not in this poem. He simply asks it, perhaps the most profound question that confronts thinking man: What is the source of evil in the universe?

---

[1]For a brief discussion of Blake's life and work, see pp. 91-92.

Dark in the Forest, Strange as Time

by Thomas Wolfe

Some years ago, among the people standing on one of the platforms of the Munich railway station, beside the Swiss express, which was almost ready to depart, there were a woman and a man —a woman so lovely that the memory of her would forever haunt the mind of him who saw her, and a man on whose dark face the legend of a strange and fatal meeting was already visible.

The woman was at the flawless summit of a mature and radiant beauty, packed to the last red ripeness of her lip with life and health, a miracle of loveliness in whom all the elements of beauty had combined with such exquisite proportion and so rhythmical a balance that even as one looked at her he could scarcely believe the evidence of his eyes. Thus, although not over tall, she seemed at times to command a superb and queenly height, then to be almost demurely small and cozy as she pressed close to her companion . . .

The woman was fashionably dressed; her little toque-like hat fitted snugly down over a crown of coppery reddish hair and shaded her eyes which had a smoke-blue and depthless quality that could darken almost into black, and change with every swiftest shade of feeling that passed across her face. She was talking to the man in low and tender tones, smiling a vague voluptuous smile as she looked at him. She spoke eagerly, earnestly, gleefully to him, and from time to time burst into a little laugh that came welling low, rich, sensual, and tender from her throat.

As they walked up and down the platform talking, the woman thrust her small gloved hand through the arm of his heavy overcoat and snuggled close to him, sometimes nestling her lovely head, which was as proud and graceful as a flower, against his arm. Again they would pause, and look steadfastly at each other for a moment. Now she spoke to him with playful reproof, chided him, shook him tenderly by the arms, pulled the heavy furred lapels of his overcoat together, and wagged a small gloved finger at him warningly.

And all the time the man looked at her, saying little, but devouring her with large dark eyes that were burning steadily with the fires of death, and that seemed to feed on her physically, with an insatiate and voracious tenderness of love. He was a Jew, his figure immensely tall, cadaverous, and so wasted by disease that it was lost, engulfed, forgotten in the heavy and expensive garments that he wore.

His thin white face, which was wasted almost to a fleshless integument of bone and skin, converged to an immense nose, so that his face was not so much a face as a great beak of death, lit by two blazing and voracious eyes and colored on the flanks with two burning flags of red. Yet, with all its ugliness of disease and emaciation it was a curiously memorable and moving face, a visage somehow nobly tragic with the badge of death.

But now the time had come for parting. The guards were shouting warnings to the passengers, all up and down the platform there were swift serried movements, hurried eddyings among the groups of friends. One saw people embracing, kissing, clasping hands, crying, laughing, shouting, going back for one hard swift kiss, and then mounting hastily into their compartments. And one heard in a strange tongue the vows, oaths, promises, the jests and swift allusions, that were secret and precious to each group and that sent them off at once in roars of laughter, the words of farewell that are the same the whole world over:

"Otto! Otto! . . . Have you got what I gave you? . . . Feel! Is it still there?" He felt, it was still there: fits of laughter.

"Will you see Else?"

"How's that? Can't hear"—shouting, cupping hand to ear, and turning head sideways with a puzzled look.

"I—say—will—you—see—Else?" fairly roared out between cupped palms above the tumult of the crowd.

"Yes. I think so. We expect to meet them at St. Moritz."

"Tell her she's got to write."

"Hey? I can't hear you." Same pantomine as before.

"I—say—tell—her—she's got—to write"—another roar.

"Oh, yes! Yes!" Nodding quickly, smiling, "I'll tell her."

"—or I'll be mad at her!"

"What? Can't hear you for all this noise"—same business as before.

"I—say—tell—her—I'll—be—mad—if she — doesn't — write" roared out again deliberately at the top of his lungs.

Here, a man who had been whispering slyly to a woman, who was trembling with smothered laughter, now turned with grinning face to shout something at the departing friend, but was checked by the woman who seized him by the arm and with a face reddened by laughter, gasped hysterically.

"No! No.!"

But the man, still grinning, cupped his hands around his mouth and roared:

"Tell Uncle Walter he has got to wear his—"

"How's that? Can't hear!"—cupping ear and turning head to one side as before.

"I—say," the man began to roar deliberately.

"No! No! No! Sh-h!" the woman gasped frantically, tugging at his arm.

"—to—tell—Uncle Walter—he—must—wear—his—woolen"

"No! No! No!—Heinrich! . . . Sh-h!" the woman shrieked.

"—The—heavy—ones—Aunt—Bertha embroidered with his—initials" " the man went on relentlessly.

Here the whole crowd roared, and the women screamed with laughter, shrieking protests, and saying:

"Sh-h! Sh-h!" loudly.

"Ja—I'll tell him!" the grinning passenger yelled back at him as soon as they had grown somewhat quieter. "Maybe—he hasn't —got—'em—any—more," he shouted as a happy afterthought. "Maybe—one—of—the Fräuleins—down—there—" he gasped and choked with laughter.

"Otto!" the women shrieked. "Sh-h!"

"Maybe—one—of—the—Fräuleins — got them—away—from" he began to gasp with laughter.

"O-o-o-to! . . . Shame on you—Sh-h!" the women screamed.

"Souvenir—from—old—München," roared back his fellow wit, and the whole group was convulsed again. When they had recovered somewhat, one of the men began in a wheezing and faltering tone, as he wiped at his streaming eyes:

"Tell—Else"—here his voice broke off in a feeble squeak, and he had to pause to wipe his eyes again.

"What?"—the grinning passenger yelled back at him.

"Tell—Else," he began again more strongly, "that Aunt—Bertha . . . " He groaned weakly again, faltered, wiped at his streaming eyes, and was reduced to palsied silence.

"What?—What?" shouted the grinning passenger sharply, clapping his hand to his attentive ear. "Tell Else what?"

"Tell—Else—Aunt—Bertha—is—sending—her—recipe—for—layer—cake," the man fairly screamed now as if he would get it out at any cost before his impending and total collapse. The total effect of that apparently meaningless reference to Aunt Bertha's layer cake was astonishing: nothing that had gone before could approach the spasmodic effect it had upon this little group of friends. They were instantly reduced to a shuddering paralysis of laughter, they staggered drunkenly about, clasped one another feebly for support, tears streamed in torrents from their swollen eyes, and from their wide-open mouths there came occasionally feeble wisps of sound, strangled gasps, faint screams from the women, a panting palsied fit of mirth from which they finally emerged into a kind of hiccoughing recovery.

What it was—the total implication of that apparently banal reference which had thrown them all into such a convulsive fit of merriment—no stranger could ever know, but its effect upon the other people was infectious; they looked toward the group of friends, and grinned, laughed, and shook their heads at one another. And so it went all up and down the line. Here were people grave, gay, sad, serious, young, old, calm, casual, and excited; here were people bent on business and people bent on pleasure; here people sharing by every act, word, and gesture the excitement, joy, and hope which the voyage wakened in them, and people who looked wearily and indifferently about them, settled themselves in their seats and took no further interest in the events of the departure—but everywhere it was the same.

People were speaking the universal language of departure, that varies not all the whole world over—that language which is often banal, trivial, and even useless, but on this account curiously moving, since it serves to hide a deeper emotion in the hearts of men, to fill the vacancy that is in their hearts at the thought of parting, to act as a shield, a concealing mask to their true feeling.

And because of this there was for the youth, the stranger, and the alien who saw and heard these things, a thrilling and poignant quality in the ceremony of the train's departure. As he saw and heard these familiar words and actions—words and actions that beneath the guise of an alien tongue were identical to those he had seen and known all his life, among his own people—he felt suddenly, as he had never felt before, the overwhelming loneliness of familiarity, the sense of the human identity that so strongly unites all the people in the world, and that is rooted in the structure of man's life, far below the tongue he speaks, the race of which he is a member.

But now that the time had come for parting, the woman and the dying man said nothing. Clasped arm to arm they looked at each other with a stare of burning and voracious tenderness. They embraced, her arms clasped him, her living and voluptuous body drew toward him, her red lips clung to his mouth as if she could never let him go. Finally, she fairly tore herself away from him, gave him a desperate little push with her hands, and said, "Go, go! It's time!"

Then the scarecrow turned and swiftly climbed into the train, a guard came by and brutally slammed the door behind him, the train began to move slowly out of the station. And all the time the man was leaning from a window in the corridor looking at her, and the woman was walking along beside the train, trying to keep him in sight as long as she could. Now the train gathered motion, the woman's pace slowed, she stopped, her eyes wet, her lips murmuring words no one could hear, and as he vanished from her sight she cried, "Auf Wiedersehn!" and put her hand up to her lips and kissed it to him.

For a moment longer the younger man, who was to be this specter's brief companion of the journey, stood looking out the corridor window down the platform toward the great arched station sheds, seeming to look after the people departing up the platform, but really seeing nothing but the tall, lovely figure of the woman as she walked slowly away, head bent, with a long, deliberate stride of incomparable grace, voluptuous undulance. Once she paused to look back again, then turned and walked on slowly as before.

Suddenly she stopped. Some one out of the throng of people on the platform had approached her. It was a young man. The woman paused in a startled manner, lifted one gloved hand in protest, started to go on, and the next moment they were locked in a savage embrace, devouring each other with kisses.

When the traveller returned to his seat, the dying man who had already come into the compartment from the corridor and had fallen back into the cushions of his seat, breathing hoarsely, was growing calmer, less exhausted. For a moment the younger man looked intently at the beak-like face, the closed weary eyes, wondering if this dying man had seen that meeting on the station platform, and what knowledge such as this could now mean to him. But that mask of death was enigmatic, unrevealing; the youth found nothing there that he could read. A faint and strangely luminous smile was playing at the edges of the man's thin mouth, and his burning eyes were now open, but far and sunken and seemed to be looking from an unspeakable depth at something that was far away. In a moment, in a profound and tender tone, he said:

"Zat vas my wife. Now in ze vinter I must go alone, for zat iss best. But in ze spring ven I am better she vill come to me."

All through the wintry afternoon the great train rushed down across Bavaria. Swiftly and powerfully it gathered motion, it left the last scattered outposts of the city behind it, and swift as dreams the train was rushing out across the level plain surrounding Munich.

The day was gray, the sky impenetrable and somewhat heavy,

and yet filled with a strong, clean Alpine vigor, with that odorless and yet exultant energy of cold mountain air. Within an hour the train had entered Alpine country, now there were hills, valleys, the immediate sense of soaring ranges, and the dark enchantment of the forests of Germany, those forests which are something more than trees—which are a spell, a magic, and a sorcery, filling the hearts of men, and particularly those strangers who have some racial kinship with that land, with a dark music, a haunting memory, never wholly to be captured.

It is an overwhelming feeling of immediate and impending discovery, such as men might have who come for the first time to their father's country. It is like coming to that unknown land for which our spirits long so passionately in youth, which is the dark side of our soul, the strange brother and the complement of the land we have known in our childhood. And it is revealed to us instantly the moment that we see it with a powerful emotion of perfect recognition and disbelief, with that dreamlike reality of strangeness and familiarity which dreams and all enchantment have.

What is it? What is this wild fierce joy and sorrow swelling in our hearts? What is this memory that we cannot phrase, this instant recognition for which we have no words? We cannot say. We have no way to give it utterance, no ordered evidence to give it proof, and scornful pride can mock us for a superstitious folly. Yet we will know the dark land at the very moment that we come to it, and though we have no tongue, no proof, no utterance for what we feel, we have what we have, we know what we know, we are what we are.

And what are we? We are the naked men, the lost Americans. Immense and lonely skies bend over us, ten thousand men are marching in our blood. Where does it come from—the sense of strangeness, instant recognition, the dream-haunted, almost captured, memory? Where does it come from, the constant hunger and the rending lust, and the music, dark and solemn, elfish, magic, sounding through the wood? How is it that this boy, who is American, has known this strange land from the first moment that he saw it?

How is it that from his first night in a German town he has understood the tongue he never heard before, has spoken instantly, saying all he wished to say, in a strange language which he could not speak, speaking a weird argot which was neither his nor theirs, of which he was not even conscious, so much did it seem to be the spirit of a language, not the words, he spoke, and instantly, in this fashion, understood by every one with whom he talked?

No. He could not prove it, yet he knew that it was there, buried deep in the brain and blood of man, the utter knowledge of this land and of his father's people. He had felt it all, the tragic and insoluble admixture of the race. He knew the terrible fusion of the brute and of the spirit. He knew the nameless fear of the old barbaric forest, the circle of barbaric figures gathered round him in their somber and unearthly ring, the sense of drowning in the blind forest horrors of barbaric time. He carried all within himself, the slow gluttony and lust of the unsated swine, as well as the strange and powerful music of the soul.

He knew the hatred and revulsion from the never-sated beast— the beast with the swine-face and the quenchless thirst, the never-ending hunger, the thick, slow, rending hand that fumbled with a smouldering and unsated lust. And he hated the great beast with the hate of hell and murder because he felt and knew it in himself and was himself the prey of its rending, quenchless, and obscene desires. Rivers of wine to drink, whole roast oxen turning on the spit, and through the forest murk, the roaring wall of huge beast-bodies and barbaric sound about him, the lavish flesh of the great blonde women, in brutal orgy of the all-devouring, never-sated maw of the huge belly, without end or surfeit—all was mixed into his blood, his spirit, and his life.

It had been given to him somehow from the dark time-horror of the ancient forest together with all that was magical, glorious, strange and beautiful: the husky horn-notes sounding faint and elfin through the forests, the infinite strange weavings, dense mutations of the old Germanic soul of man. How cruel, baffling, strange, and sorrowful was the enigma of the race: the power and strength of the incorruptible and soaring spirit rising from the huge corrupted beast with such a radiant purity, and the powerful enchantments of grand music, noble poetry, so sorrowfully and unalterably woven and in-wrought with all the blind brute hunger of the belly and the beast of man.

It was all his, and all contained in his one life. And it could, he knew, never be distilled out of him, no more than one can secrete from his flesh his father's blood, the ancient and immutable weavings of dark time. And for this reason, as he now looked out the window of the train at that lonely Alpine land of snow and dark enchanted forest he felt the sense of familiar recognition instantly, the feeling that he had always known this place, that it was home. And something dark, wild, jubilant, and strange was exulting, swelling in his spirit like a grand and haunting music heard in dreams.

And now, a friendly acquaintance having been established, the specter, with the insatiate, possessive curiosity of his race, began to ply his companion with innumerable questions concerning his life, his home, his profession, the journey he was making, the reason for that journey. The young man answered readily, and without annoyance. He knew that he was being pumped unmercifully, but the dying man's whispering voice was so persuasive, friendly, gentle, his manner so courteous, kind, and insinuating, his smile so luminous and winning, touched with a faint and yet agreeable expression of weariness, that the questions almost seemed to answer themselves.

The young man was an American, was he not? . . . Yes. And how long had he been abroad—two months? Three months? No? Almost a year So long as that! Then he liked Europe, yes? It was his first trip? No? His fourth?—The specter lifted his eyebrows in expressive astonishment, and yet his sensitive thin mouth was touched all the time by his faint, wearily cynical smile.

Finally, the boy was pumped dry: the specter knew all about him. Then for a moment he sat staring at the youth with his faint, luminous, subtly mocking, and yet kindly smile. At last, wearily, patiently, and with the calm finality of experience and death, he said:

"You are very young. Yes. Now you vant to see it all, to haf it all—but you haf nothing. Zat iss right—yes?" he said with his persuasive smile. "Zat vill all change. Some day you vill vant only a little—maybe, den, you *haf* a little—" and he flashed his luminous winning smile again. "Und zat iss better—Yes?" He smiled again, and then said wearily, "I know. I know. Myself I haf gone eferyvere like you. I haf tried to see eferyt'ing—und I haf had nothing. Now I go no more. Eferyvere it iss ze same," he said wearily, looking out the window, with a dismissing gesture of his thin white hand. "Fields, hills, mountains, riffers, cities, peoples—you vish to know about zem all. Vun field, vun hill, vun riffer," the man whispered, "zat iss enough!"

He closed his eyes for a moment: when he spoke again his whisper was almost inaudible—"Vun life, vun place, vun time."

Darkness came, and the lights in the compartment were turned on. Again that whisper of waning life made its insistent, gentle, and implacable demand upon the youth. This time it asked that the light in the compartment be extinguished, while the specter stretched himself out upon the seat to rest. The younger man consented willingly and even gladly: his own journey was near its end and outside the moon, which had risen early, was shining down upon the Alpine forests and snows with a strange, brilliant, and haunting magic which gave to the darkness in the compartment some of its own ghostly and mysterious light.

The specter lay quietly stretched out on the cushions of the seat, his eyes closed, his wasted face, on which the two bright flags of burning red now shone with vermilion hue, strange and ghastly in the magic light as the beak of some great bird. The man scarcely seemed to breathe: no sound or movement of life was perceptible in the compartment except the pounding of the wheels, the leathery stretching and creaking sound of the car, and all that strange-familiar and evocative symphony of sounds a train makes—that huge symphonic monotone which is itself the sound of silence and forever.

For some time held in that spell of magic light and time, the youth sat staring out the window at the enchanted world of white and black that swept grandly and strangely past in the phantasmal radiance of the moon. Finally he got up, went out into the corridor, closing the door carefully behind him, and walked back down the narrow passageway through car after car of the rocketing train until he came to the dining car.

Here all was brilliance, movement, luxury, sensual warmth and gaiety. All the life of the train now seemed to be concentrated in this place. The waiters, surefooted and deft, were moving swiftly down the aisle of the rocketing car, pausing at each table to serve people from the great platters of well-cooked food which they carried on trays. Behind them the *sommelier* was pulling corks from tall frosty bottles of Rhine wine: he would hold the bottle between his knees as he pulled, the cork would come out with an exhilarating pop, and he would drop the cork then into a little basket.

At one table a seductive and beautiful woman was eating with a jaded-looking old man. At another a huge and powerful-looking German, with a wing collar, a shaven skull, a great swine face and a forehead of noble and lonely thought, was staring with a concentrated look of bestial gluttony at the tray of meat from which the waiter served him. He was speaking in a guttural and lustful tone, saying, "Ja! . . . Gut! . . . und etwas von diesem hier auch. . . ."

The scene was one of richness, power and luxury, evoking as it did the feeling of travel in a crack European express, which is different from the feeling one has when he rides on an American train. In America, the train gives one a feeling of wild and lonely joy, a sense of the savage, unfenced, and illimitable wilderness of the country through which the train is rushing, a wordless and unutterable hope as one thinks of the enchanted city toward which he is speeding; the unknown and fabulous promise of the life he is to find there.

In Europe, the feeling of joy and pleasure is more actual, ever present. The luxurious trains, the rich furnishings, the deep maroons, dark blues, the flesh, well-groomed vivid colors of the cars, the good food and the sparkling, heady wine, and the worldly, wealthy, cosmopolitan look of the travellers—all of this fills one with a powerful sensual joy, a sense of expectancy about to be realized. In a few hours' time one goes from country to country, through centuries of history, a world of crowded culture, and whole nations swarming with people, from one famous pleasure-city to another.

And, instead of the wild joy and nameless hope one feels as he looks out the window of an American train, one feels here (in Europe) an incredible joy of realization, an immediate sensual gratification, a feeling that there is nothing on earth but wealth, power, luxury, and love, and that one can live and enjoy this life, in all the infinite varieties of pleasure, forever.

When the young man had finished eating, and paid his bill, he began to walk back again through corridor after corridor along the length of the rocketing train. When he got back to his compartment he saw the specter lying there as he had left him, stretched out upon the seat, with the brilliant moonlight still blazing on the great beak of his face.

The man had not changed his position by an inch, and yet at once the boy was conscious of some subtle, fatal change he could not define. What was it? He took his seat again and for some time stared fixedly at the silent ghostly figure opposite him. Did he not breathe? He thought, he was almost sure, he saw the motion of his breathing, the rise and fall of the emaciated breast, and yet he was not sure. But what he plainly saw now was that a line, vermilion in its moon-dark hue, had run out of the corner of the firm set mouth and that there was a large vermilion stain upon the floor.

What should he do? What could be done? The haunted light of the fatal moon seemed to have steeped his soul in its dark sorcery, in the enchantment of a measureless and inert calmness. Already, too, the train was slackening its speed, the first lights of the town appeared, it was his journey's end.

And now the train was slowing to a halt. There were the flare of rails, the switch-lights of the yard, small, bright, and hard, green, red, and yellow, poignant in the dark, and on other tracks he could see the little goods cars and the strings of darkened trains, all empty, dark, and waiting with their strange attentiveness of recent life. Then the long station quays began to slide slowly past the windows of the train, and the sturdy goat-like porters were coming on the run, eagerly saluting, speaking, calling to the people in the train who had already begun to pass their baggage through the window.

Softly the boy took his overcoat and suit-case from the rack above his head and stepped out into the narrow corridor. Quietly he slid the door of the compartment shut behind him. Then, for a moment, still unsure, he stood there looking back. In the semi-darkness of the compartment the spectral figure of the cadaver lay upon the cushions, did not move.

Was it not well to leave all things as he had found them, in silence, at the end? Might it not be that in this great dream of time in which we live and are the moving figures, there is no greater certitude than this: that, having met, spoken, known each other for a moment, as somewhere on this earth we were hurled onward through the darkness between two points of time, it is well to be content with this, to leave each other as we met, letting each one go alone to his appointed destination, sure of this only, needing only this—that there will be silence for us all and silence only, nothing but silence, at the end?

Already the train had come to a full stop. The boy went down the corridor to the end, and in a moment feeling the bracing shock of the cold air upon his flesh, breathing the vital and snow-laden air into his lungs, he was going down the quay with a hundred other people, all moving in the same direction, some toward certitude and home, some toward a new land, hope, and hunger, the swelling prescience of joy, the promise of a shining city. He knew that he was going home again.

Discussion of "Dark in the Forest, Strange as Time"

Thomas Wolfe (1900-1938) is an American novelist and short-story writer especially renowned for the richly poetic qualities of his prose style and for the intense, brooding subjectivity of his semi-autobiographical subject matter. Among his important works are *Of Time and the River, The Web and the Rock, You Can't Go Home Again, From Death to Morning,* and *Look Homeward, Angel.*

Sometimes Wolfe has a tendency to be too ornate, too luxurious in his prose style; and some readers may feel that

"Dark in the Forest, Strange as Time" is unnecessarily complex. But most readers sensitive to the aesthetic loveliness of a rich prose style will find this one of the most beautifully written stories they have ever read. Note, for example, the melodious style of the opening paragraphs describing the man and woman (husband and wife), or such a beautifully written paragraph (in prose style if not in idea) as the next to the last one in the story, or for that matter almost any section of the story.

The story begins with seven paragraphs of superb writing in the rich style we have been discussing. In these seven paragraphs all is loveliness, both the language and the scene described. Not even the obvious sickness of the husband can mar the beauty of the scene, made all the lovelier by the seeming deep love between this man and his younger but radiantly mature wife.

Abruptly with the words "Otto! Otto!" in paragraph eight the prose style totally changes, dropping to choppy slang phrases and an unattractive, unpoetic colloquialism. Partly this is done, of course, to portray realistically the conversation of the ordinary people who are introduced at this point. But why have the conversation between Otto and his friends in the story at all, one might ask, when it so clearly interrupts the main drama of the story? One explanation is that the loftiness of the main story is heightened by contrast with the drabness of this conversation, and another is that the parting of the two central lovers (the man and his wife) is made acceptable and universalized by being placed amid all the other partings of real life. There is also still another reason, even more fundamental, to be explained later.

After the interruption of the conversation between Otto and his friends, and after two or three paragraphs of commentary on the nature of partings the world over, the story returns to the central drama, with the paragraph beginning, "But now that the time had come for parting, the woman and the dying man said nothing. . . ." And for three paragraphs we again have the love between the sick man and his radiant young wife described—a love seemingly very intense, very deep, and very beautiful.

Nothing prepares us for the abrupt ugliness of the incident in the next paragraph as the radiant woman, having left her sick husband, walks down the train platform and yields in passionate embrace to a young lover. The betrayal, the unfaithfulness, the deceit is just as shocking as it is crude. We as readers rebel against it, just as the author intended we should.[1] The remainder of the story is principally descriptive commentary by Wolfe intended to develop the central ideas of the story, and to these we now turn for the rest of our discussion.

Two major themes are developed throughout this story. One is that there is a harmony, a unity, a similarity among human beings the world over. In spite of all the differences, there are fundamental needs and qualities that bind all human life, and especially bind a person to all those who share with him a common racial ancestry. As key passages exploring this theme, note the two following:

> People were speaking the universal language of departure, that varies not all the whole world over. . . . As he saw and heard these familiar words and actions—words and actions that beneath the guise of an alien tongue were identical to those he had seen and known all his life, among his own people—he felt suddenly, as he had never felt before, the overwhelming loneliness of familiarity, the sense of the human identity that so strongly unites all the people in the world, and that is rooted in the structure of man's life, far below the tongue he speaks, the race of which he is a member. . . .
>
> It is an overwhelming feeling of immediate and impending discovery, such as men might have who come for the first time to

---

[1]Does the sick husband know that his wife is unfaithful to him? Evidence within the story suggests that he does. Note, for example, his comment to the young man: "You are very young. Yes. Now you vant to see it all, to haf it all—but you haf nothing. . . . Zat vill all change. Some day you vill vant only a little—maybe, den, you *haf* a little. . . ."

their father's country. It is like coming to that unknown land
for which our spirits long so passionately in youth, which is the
dark side of our soul, the strange brother and the complement
of the land we have known in our childhood. And it is revealed
to us instantly the moment that we see it with a powerful emotion
of perfect recognition and disbelief, with that dream-like reality
of strangeness and familiarity which dreams and all enchantment have.

The second central theme, and the one that caused this
story to be included in the present book, is that in every
human being there are capacities for good and for evil. In
fact, human nature is characterized within itself by contrast,
by paradox. In every earthly personality, and in mortal life
as a whole, there are beautiful tendencies and ugly tendencies, tender qualities and harsh qualities, holy aspirations
and animal desires. The difference between the good person and the bad person is not that one has noble desires
and the other evil desires but that the one by an exercise
of will power cultivates his noble desires and subdues his
evil desires, and the other through failure to exert his will
power wastes his noble potentialities and submits to his
animal desires. Man's greatest battles are never conflicts
with external forces but always struggles with himself. If
one can win the battle to control the evil tendencies within
himself, all other battles are secondary.

No writer has described more eloquently this good-
evil duality of man's nature than has Thomas Wolfe in this
story. Note, for example, the two following passages:

He had felt it all, the tragic and insoluble admixture of the
race. He knew the terrible fusion of the brute and of the spirit.
He knew the nameless fear of the old barbaric forest, the circle
of barbaric figures gathered round him in their somber and unearthly ring, the sense of drowning in the blind forest horrors of
barbaric time. He carried all within himself, the slow gluttony
and lust of the unsated swine, as well as the strange and powerful music of the soul. . . .

How cruel, baffling, strange, and sorrowful was the enigma of
the race: the power and strength of the incorruptible and

soaring spirit rising from the huge corrupted beast with such a radiant purity, and the powerful enchantments of grand music, noble poetry, so sorrowfully and unalterably woven and in-wrought with all the blind brute hunger of the belly and the beast of man.

Much of the excellence of the story comes from the fact that this sense of contrast is felt in every aspect of the work—the beautiful love contrasted with the ugly love, youth contrasted with age, health contrasted with sickness, the fleshliness of the woman contrasted with the spirituality of the man, ornate language contrasted with blunt language, etc. Many other works have been written on the relationship between good and evil in the universe—and in the human heart—but few have explored the subject as memorably as Wolfe has here done. (Perhaps the very greatest short story on the subject is Joseph Conrad's "Heart of Darkness." Those interested are urged to read Conrad's masterpiece—one of the profoundest works of literature in any language.)

Sonnet #94

by William Shakespeare

They that have power to hurt and will do none,
That do not do the thing they most do show,
Who, moving others, are themselves as stone,
Unmoved, cold, and to temptation slow;
They rightly do inherit heaven's graces,
And husband nature's riches from expense;
They are the lords and owners of their faces,
Others but stewards of their excellence.
The summer's flower is to the summer sweet,
Though to itself it only live and die,
But if that flower with base infection meet,
The basest weed outbraves his dignity:
    For sweetest things turn sourest by their deeds;
    Lilies that fester smell far worse than weeds.

Discussion of Shakespeare's Sonnet #94

One of the strongest brief statements on one aspect of good versus evil in man's character appears in Sonnet #94 by William Shakespeare (1564-1616)[1] First Shakespeare describes that kind of man who, by force of personality, stands high above ordinary people — a great tower of strength influencing others but himself not swayed by petty whims and fancies. A pillar of granite, he stands mighty and strong, sustained by his convictions. In his might he has power to hurt others but will not. He soars above the common weaknesses and is as stone to the temptations that destroy lesser men. Such a man rightly is to be looked on as having heavenly powers and displaying humanity's best qualities. Such a man is also rightly to be honored and followed.

[1]For a brief comment on Shakespeare's life and works, see pp. 453-54.

But what if this great leader falls? No one, not even the mightiest, is absolutely beyond temptation. Little people are capable of accomplishing a little good or committing a little evil. Great people are capable of accomplishing a great good or committing a great evil. And the fall of a great man is awful to behold. If a little person deceives or embezzles or is immoral, this is bad enough; but if a great leader deceives or embezzles or is immoral, calamity engulfs the whole community.

> For sweetest things turn sourest by their deeds;
> Lilies that fester smell far worse than weeds.[1]

This is the essence of tragedy—a basically good and great man crumbling to ruin, with his world crumbling around him, in consequence of some flaw in his own character to which he succumbs.

(Note on line 6: "Husband" means "hoard," and "expense" means "expenditure"—that is, "waste.")

---

[1] In form, this is what we call an English or Elizabethan or Shakespearean Sonnet, rhyming abab cdcd efef gg. Such a sonnet traditionally develops its central thought steadily through three quatrains and then rises to an epigrammatic, summarizing climax in the closing couplet. Note how successfully Shakespeare climaxes and lifts this sonnet in its final line. "Lilies that fester smell far worse than weeds."

The Rime of the Ancient Mariner

by Samuel Taylor Coleridge

Part I

It is an ancient Mariner,
And he stoppeth one of three.
"By thy long gray beard and glittering eye,
Now wherefore stopp'st thou me?

The Bridegroom's doors are opened wide.   5
And I am next of kin;
The guests are met, the feast is set:
May'st hear the merry din."

He holds him with his skinny hand,
"There was a ship," quoth he.   10
"Hold off! unhand me, gray-beard loon!"
Eftsoons his hand dropt he.

He holds him with his glittering eye—
The Wedding-Guest stood still,
And listens like a three years' child: 15
The Mariner hath his will.

The Wedding-Guest sat on a stone:
He cannot choose but hear;
And thus spake on that ancient man,
The bright-eyed Mariner.   20

"The ship was cheered, the harbor cleared,
Merrily did we drop
Below the kirk, below the hill,
Below the lighthouse top.

The Sun came up upon the left,   25
Out of the sea came he!
And he shone bright, and on the right
Went down into the sea.

Higher and higher every day,
Till over the mast at noon—"   30
The Wedding-Guest here beat his breast,
For he heard the loud bassoon.

The bride hath paced into the hall,
Red as a rose is she;
Nodding their heads before her goes   35
The merry minstrelsy.

The Wedding-Guest he beat his breast,
Yet he cannot choose but hear;
And thus spake on that ancient man,
The bright-eyed Mariner.   40

"And now the Storm-blast came, and he
Was tyrannous and strong:
He struck with his o'ertaking wings,
And chased us south along.

With sloping masts and dipping prow,   45
As who pursued with yell and blow
Still treads the shadow of his foe,
And forward bends his head,
The ship drove fast, load roared the blast,
And southward aye we fled.   50

And now there came both mist and snow,
And it grew wondrous cold:
And ice, mast-high, came floating by,
As green as emerald.

And through the drifts the snowy clifts   55
Did send a dismal sheen:
Nor shapes of men nor beasts we ken—
The ice was all between.

The ice was here, the ice was there,
The ice was all around: 60
It cracked and growled, and roared and howled,
Like noises in a swound![1]

At length did cross an Albatross,
Thorough the fog it came;
As if it had been a Christian soul,   65
We hailed it in God's name.

---

[1]*Swound* is swoon or dream.

It ate the food it ne'er had eat,
And round and round it flew.
The ice did split with a thunder-fit;
The helmsman steered us through!   70

And a good south wind sprung up behind;
The Albatross did follow,
And every day, for food or play,
Came to the mariners' hollo!

In mist or cloud, on mast or shroud,   75
It perched for vespers nine;
While all the night, through fog-smoke white,
Glimmered the white moon-shine."

"God save thee, ancient Mariner!
From the fiends, that plague thee thus!—   80
Why look'st thou so?"—"With my crossbow
I shot the Albatross!"

Part II

"The Sun now rose upon the right:
Out of the sea came he,
Still hid in mist, and on the left   85
Went down into the sea.

And the good south wind still blew behind,
But no sweet bird did follow,
Nor any day for food or play
Came to the mariners' hollo!   90

And I had done a hellish thing,
And it would work 'em woe:
For all averred, I had killed the bird
That made the breeze to blow.
'Ah wretch!' said they, the bird to slay,   95
That made the breeze to blow!'

Nor dim nor red, like God's own head,
The glorious Sun uprist:
Then all averred, I had killed the bird
That brought the fog and mist.   100
"Twas right,' said they, 'such birds to slay,
That bring the fog and mist.'

The fair breeze blew, the white foam flew,
The furrow followed free;
We were the first that ever burst   105
Into that silent sea.

Down dropt the breeze, the sails dropt down,
'Twas sad as sad could be;
And we did speak only to break
The silence of the sea!   110

All in a hot and copper sky,
The bloody Sun, at noon,
Right up above the mast did stand,
No bigger than the Moon.

Day after day, day after day,   115
We stuck, nor breath nor motion;
As idle as a painted ship
Upon a painted ocean.

Water, water, everywhere,
And all the boards did shrink;   120
Water, water, everywhere,
Nor any drop to drink.

The very deep did rot: O Christ!
That ever this should be!
Yea, slimy things did crawl with legs   125
Upon the slimy sea.

About, about, in reel and rout
The death-fires danced at night;[1]
The water, like a witch's oils,
Burnt green, and blue, and white.   130

And some in dreams assuréd were
Of the Spirit that plagued us so;
Nine fathom deep he had followed us
From the land of mist and snow.

And every tongue through utter drought,   135
Was withered at the root;
We could not speak, no more than if
We had been choked with soot.

---

[1]*Death-fires* are phosphorescent lights that are supposed to forebode death.

Ah! well-a-day! what evil looks
Had I from old and young!   140
Instead of the cross, the Albatross
About my neck was hung.

Part III

"There passed a weary time. Each throat
Was parched, and glazed each eye.
A weary time! a weary time!   145
How glazed each weary eye,
When looking westward, I beheld
A something in the sky.

At first it seemed a little speck,
And then it seemed a mist;   150
It moved and moved, and took at last
A certain shape, I wist.[1]

A speck, a mist, a shape, I wist!
And still it neared and neared:
As if it dodged a water-sprite,   155
It plunged and tacked and veered.

With throats unslaked, with black lips baked,
We could nor laugh nor wail;
Through utter drought all dumb we stood!
I bit my arm, I sucked the blood,   160
And cried, A sail! A sail!

With throats unslaked, with black lips baked,
Agape they heard me call:
Gramercy! they for joy did grin,[2]
And all at once their breath drew in,   165
As they were drinking all.

See! see! (I cried) she tacks no more!
Hither to work us weal;
Without a breeze, without a tide,
She steadies with upright keel!   170

---

[1] *Wist* means thought or knew.
[2] *Gramercy* means great thanks.

The western wave was all a-flame.
The day was well nigh done!
Almost upon the western wave
Rested the broad bright Sun;
When that strange shape drove suddenly   175
Betwixt us and the Sun.

And straight the Sun was flecked with bars,
(Heaven's Mother send us grace!)
As if through a dungeon-grate he peered
With broad and burning face.   180

Alas! (thought I, and my heart beat loud)
How fast she nears and nears!
Are those her sails that glance in the Sun,
Like restless gossameres?[1]

Are those her ribs through which the Sun   185
Did peer, as through a grate?
And is that Woman all her crew?
Is that a Death? and are there two?
Is Death that woman's mate?

Her lips were red, her looks were free,   190
Her locks were yellow as gold:
Her skin was as white as leprosy,
The Nightmare Life-in-Death was she,
Who thicks man's blood with cold.

The naked hulk alongside came,   195
And the twain were casting dice;
'The game is done! I've won! I've won!'
Quoth she, and whistles thrice.

The Sun's rim dips; the stars rush out:
At one stride comes the dark;   200
With far-heard whisper, o'er the sea,
Off shot the spectre-bark.

We listened and looked sideways up!
Fear at my heart, as at a cup,
My life-blood seemed to sip!   205
The stars were dim, and thick the night,
The steersman's face by his lamp gleamed white;

---

[1]*Gossameres* are fine spider-webs.

From the sails the dew did drip—
Till clomb above the eastern bar
The hornéd Moon, with one bright star   210
Within the nether tip.

One after one, by the star-dogged Moon,
Too quick for groan or sigh,
Each turned his face with a ghastly pang,
And cursed me with his eye.   215

Four times fifty living men,
(And I heard nor sigh nor groan)
With heavy thump, a lifeless lump,
They dropped down one by one.

The souls did from their bodies fly,—   220
They fled to bliss or woe!
And every soul, it passed me by,
Like the whizz of my cross-bow!"

Part IV

"I fear thee, ancient Mariner!   225
I fear thy skinny hand!
And thou art long, and lank, and brown,
As is the ribbed sea-sand.

I fear thee and thy glittering eye,
And thy skinny hand, so brown."—
"Fear not, fear not, thou Wedding-Guest!   230
This body dropt not down.

Alone, alone, all, all alone,
Alone on a wide, wide sea!
And never a saint took pity on
My soul in agony.   235

The many men, so beautiful!
And they all dead did lie:
And a thousand slimy things
Lived on; and so did I.

I looked upon the rotting sea,   240
And drew my eyes away;
I looked upon the rotting deck,
And there the dead men lay.

I looked to heaven, and tried to pray;
But or ever a prayer had gusht,   245
A wicked whisper came, and made
My heart as dry as dust.

I closed my lids, and kept them close,
And the balls like pulses beat;
For the sky and the sea, and the sea and the sky   250
Lay like a load on my weary eye,
And the dead were at my feet.

The cold sweat melted from their limbs,
Nor rot nor reek did they:
The look with which they looked on me   255
Had never passed away.

An orphan's curse would drag to hell
A spirit from on high;
But oh! more horrible than that
Is the curse in a dead man's eye!   260
Seven days, seven nights, I saw that curse,
And yet I could not die.

The moving moon went up the sky,
And nowhere did abide:
Softly she was going up,   265
And a star or two beside—

Her beams bemocked the sultry main,
Like April hoar-frost spread;
But where the ship's huge shadow lay,
The charmèd water burnt alway   270
A still and awful red.

Beyond the shadow of the ship,
I watched the water-snakes:
They moved in tracks of shining white,
And when they reared, the elfish light   275
Fell off in hoary flakes.

Within the shadow of the ship
I watched their rich attire:
Blue, glossy green, and velvet black
They coiled and swam; and every track   280
Was a flash of golden fire.

O happy living things! no tongue
Their beauty might declare:
A spring of love gushed from my heart,
And I blessed them unaware: 285
Sure my kind saint took pity on me,
And I blessed them unaware.

The self-same moment I could pray;
And from my neck so free
The Albatross fell off, and sank   290
Like lead into the sea.

Part V

"Oh sleep! it is a gentle thing,
Beloved from pole to pole!
To Mary Queen the praise be given!
She sent the gentle sleep from Heaven,   295
That slid into my soul.

The silly buckets on the deck,[1]
That had so long remained,
I dreamt that they were filled with dew;
And when I awoke, it rained.   300

My lips were wet, my throat was cold,
My garments all were dank;
Sure I had drunken in my dreams,
And still my body drank.

I moved, and could not feel my limbs: 305
I was so light—almost
I thought that I had died in sleep,
And was a blesséd ghost.

And soon I heard a roaring wind:
It did not come anear;   310
But with its sound it shook the sails,
That were so thin and sere.

The upper air burst into life
And a hundred fire-flags sheen,[2]
To and fro they were hurried about!   315
And to and fro, and in and out,
The wan stars danced between.

---

[1]*Silly* in this case means useless, because they are empty.
[2]*Sheen* means bright.

And the coming wind did roar more loud,
And the sails did sigh like sedge;
And the rain poured down from one black cloud;   320
The Moon was at its edge.

The thick black cloud was cleft, and still
The Moon was at its side:
Like water shot from some high crag,
The lightning fell with never a jag,   325
A river steep and wide.

The loud wind never reached the ship,
Yet now the ship moved on!
Beneath the lightning and the Moon
The dead men gave a groan.   330

They groaned, they stirred, they all uprose,
Nor spake, nor moved their eyes;
It had been strange, even in a dream,
To have seen those dead men rise.

The helmsman steered, the ship moved on;   335
Yet never a breeze up-blew;
The mariners all 'gan work the ropes,
Where they were wont to do;
They raised their limbs like lifeless tools—
We were a ghastly crew.   340

The body of my brother's son
Stood by me, knee to knee:
The body and I pulled at one rope,
But he said nought to me."—

"I fear thee, ancient Mariner!"   345
"Be calm, thou Wedding-Guest!
'Twas not those souls that fled in pain,
Which to their corses came again,
But a troop of spirits blest:

For when it dawned—they dropped their arms,   350
And clustered round the mast;
Sweet sounds rose slowly through their mouths,
And from their bodies passed.

Around, around, flew each sweet sound,
Then darted to the Sun;   355
Slowly the sounds came back again,
Now mixed, now one by one.

Sometimes a-dropping from the sky
I heard the sky-lark sing;
Sometimes all little birds that are,   360
How they seemed to fill the sea and air
With their sweet jargoning!

And now 'twas like all instruments,
Now like a lonely flute;
And now it is an angel's song,   365
That makes the heavens be mute.

It ceased; yet still the sails made on
A pleasant noise till noon,
A noise like of a hidden brook
In the leafy month of June,   370
That to the sleeping woods all night
Singeth a quiet tune.

Till noon we quietly sailed on,
Yet never a breeze did breathe:
Slowly and smoothly went the ship,   375
Moved onward from beneath.

Under the keel nine fathom deep,
From the land of mist and snow,
The spirit slid: and it was he
That made the ship to go.   380
The sails at noon left off their tune,
And the ship stood still also.

The Sun, right up above the mast,
Had fixed her to the ocean:
But in a minute she 'gan stir,   385
With a short uneasy motion—
Backwards and forwards half her length
With a short uneasy motion.

Then like a pawing horse let go,
She made a sudden bound: 390
It flung the blood into my head,
And I fell down in a swound.

How long in that same fit I lay,
I have not to declare,[1]
But ere my living life returned,
I heard and in my soul discerned
Two voices in the air.

'Is it he?' quoth one, 'Is this the man?
By him who died on cross,
With his cruel bow he laid full low
The harmless Albatross.

The spirit who bideth by himself
In the land of mist and snow,
He loved the bird that loved the man
Who shot him with his bow.'

The other was a softer voice,
As soft as honey-dew:
Quoth he, 'The man hath penance done,
And penance more will do.'

Part VI

First Voice

" 'But tell me, tell me! speak again,
Thy soft response renewing—
What makes that ship drive on so fast?
What is the ocean doing?'

Second Voice

'Still as a slave before his lord,
The ocean hath no blast;
His great bright eye most silently
Up to the Moon is cast—

If he may know which way to go;
For she guides him smooth or grim.
See, brother, see! how graciously
She looketh down on him.'

First Voice

'But why drives on that ship so fast,
Without or wave or wind?'

[1] *I have not* means I have not the power.

395

400

405

410

415

420

Second Voice

'The air is cut away before,
And closes from behind.   425

Fly, brother, fly! more high, more high!
Or we shall be belated:
For slow and slow that ship will go,
When the Mariner's trance is abated.'

I woke, and we were sailing on   430
As in a gentle weather:
'Twas night, calm night, the moon was high;
The dead men stood together.

All stood together on the deck,
For a charnel-dungeon fitter: 435
All fixed on me their stony eyes,
That in the Moon did glitter.

The pang, the curse, with which they died,
Had never passed away:
I could not draw my eyes from theirs,   440
Nor turn them up to pray.

And now this spell was snapt: once more
I viewed the ocean green,
And looked far forth, yet little saw
Of what had else been seen—   445

Like one, that on a lonesome road
Doth walk in fear and dread,
And having once turned round walks on,
And turns no more his head;
Because he knows, a frightful fiend   450
Doth close behind him tread.

But soon there breathed a wind on me,
Nor sound nor motion made:
Its path was not upon the sea,
In ripple or in shade.   455

It raised my hair, it fanned my cheek
Like a meadow-gale of spring—
It mingled strangely with my fears,
Yet it felt like a welcoming.

Swiftly, swiftly flew the ship,   460
Yet she sailed softly too:
Sweetly, sweetly blew the breeze—
On me alone it blew.

Oh! dream of joy! is this indeed
The light-house top I see?   465
Is this the hill? is this the kirk?
Is this mine own countree?

We drifted o'er the harbor-bar,
And I with sobs did pray—
O let me be awake, my God!   470
Or let me sleep alway.

The harbor-bay was clear as glass,
So smoothly it was strewn!
And on the bay the moonlight lay,
And the shadow of the Moon.   475

The rock shone bright, the kirk no less,
That stands above the rock:
The moonlight steeped in silentness
The steady weathercock.

And the bay was white with silent light,   480
Till rising from the same,
Full many shapes, that shadows were,
In crimson colors came.

A little distance from the prow
Those crimson shadows were: 485
I turned my eyes upon the deck—
Oh, Christ! what saw I there!

Each corse lay flat, lifeless and flat,
And, by the holy rood![1]
A man all light, a seraph-man,   490
On every corse there stood.

This seraph-band, each waved his hand;
It was a heavenly sight!
They stood as signals to the land,
Each one a lovely light;   495

---

[1] *Rood* means cross.

This seraph-band, each waved his hand,
No voice did they impart—
No voice; but oh! the silence sank
Like music on my heart.

But soon I heard the dash of oars,   500
I heard the Pilot's cheer;
My head was turned perforce away
And I saw a boat appear.

The Pilot and the Pilot's boy,
I heard them coming fast: 505
Dear Lord in Heaven! it was a joy
The dead men could not blast.

I saw a third—I heard his voice:
It is the Hermit good!
He singeth loud his godly hymns   510
That he makes in the wood.
He'll shrieve my soul, he'll wash away
The Albatross's blood.

Part VII

"This Hermit good lives in that wood
Which slopes down to the sea.   515
How loudly his sweet voice he rears!
He loves to talk with marineres
That come from a far countree.

He kneels at morn, and noon, and eve—
He hath a cushion plump: 520
It is the moss that wholly hides
The rotted old oak-stump.

The skiff-boat neared: I heard them talk,
'Why this is strange I trow!
Where are those lights so many and fair,   525
That signal made but now?'

'Strange, by my faith!' the Hermit said—
'And they answered not our cheer!
The planks look warped! and see those sails,
How thin they are and sere!   530
I never saw aught like to them,
Unless perchance it were

Brown skeletons of leaves that lag
My forest-brook along;
When the ivy-tod is heavy with snow,[1]   535
And the owlet whoops to the wolf below,
That eats the she-wolf's young.'

'Dear Lord! it hath a fiendish look'—
(The Pilot made reply)
'I am a-feared'—'Push on, push on!'   540
Said the Hermit cheerily.

The boat came closer to the ship,
But I nor spake nor stirred;
The boat came close beneath the ship,
And straight a sound was heard.   545

Under the water it rumbled on,
Still louder and more dread:
It reached the ship, it split the bay;
The ship went down like lead.

Stunned by that loud and dreadful sound,   550
Which sky and ocean smote,
Like one that hath been seven days drowned
My body lay afloat;
But swift as dreams, myself I found
Within the Pilot's boat.   555

Upon the whirl, where sank the ship,
The boat spun round and round;
And all was still, save that the hill
Was telling of the sound.

I moved my lips—the Pilot shrieked   560
And fell down in a fit;
The holy Hermit raised his eyes,
And prayed where he did sit.

I took the oars: the Pilot's boy,
Who now doth crazy go,   565
Laughed loud and long, and all the while
His eyes went to and fro.
'Ha! ha!' quoth he, 'full plain I see,
The Devil knows how to row.'

---

[1]*Ivy-tod* is ivy-bush.

And now, all in my own countree,   570
I stood on the firm land!
The Hermit stepped forth from the boat,
And scarcely he could stand.

'Oh shrieve me, shrieve me, holy man!'
The Hermit crossed his brow,[1]   575
'Say quick,' quoth he, 'I bid thee say—
What manner of man art thou?'

Forthwith this frame of mine was wrenched
With a woeful agony,
Which forced me to begin my tale;   580
And then it left me free.

Since then, at an uncertain hour,
That agony returns:
And till my ghastly tale is told,
This heart within me burns.   585

I pass, like night, from land to land;
I have strange power of speech;
That moment that his face I see,
I know the man that must hear me:
To him my tale I teach.   590

What loud uproar bursts from that door!
The wedding-guests are there:
But in the garden-bower the bride
And brides-maids singing are:
And hark the little vesper bell,   595
Which biddeth me to prayer!

O Wedding-Guest! this soul hath been
Alone on a wide, wide sea:
So lonely 'twas, that God himself
Scarce seeméd there to be.   600

O sweeter than the marriage-feast,
'Tis sweeter far to me,
To walk together to the kirk
With a goodly company!—

---

[1]*Crossed his brow* means to make the sign of the cross on his forehead.

To walk together to the kirk,   605
And all together pray,
While each to his great Father bends,
Old men, and babes, and loving friends
And youths and maidens gay!

Farewell, farewell! but this I tell   610
To thee, thou Wedding-Guest!
He prayeth well, who loveth well
Both man and bird and beast.

He prayeth best, who loveth best
All things both great and small;   615
For the dear God who loveth us,
He made and loveth all."

The Mariner, whose eye is bright,
Whose beard with age is hoar,
Is gone: and now the Wedding-Guest   620
Turned from the bridegroom's door.

He went like one that hath been stunned,
And is of sense forlorn:[1]
A sadder and a wiser man,
He rose the morrow morn.   625

Discussion of "The Rime of the Ancient Mariner"

Samuel Taylor Coleridge (1772-1834) is not only one
of England's great poets but possibly her most profound
literary critic. As a poet his powers of the creative imagination are vast, but are tragically coupled with smothering
tendencies towards despondency and lack of self-discipline,
with the consequence that his poetic output is small. Among
the whole of England's lyric poets perhaps none had greater
artistic power than Coleridge, yet he functioned as a poet
for only about five years—from 1796, when he formed his
deep friendship with William Wordsworth, to 1801, when

---

[1]*Forlorn* means deprived.

despondency through sickness and marriage problems almost destroyed him. Thereafter he recovered sufficiently to become a brilliant lecturer, essayist, critic, and philosopher —but only occasionally to write poetry. And even in the five years of his triumph as a poet, several of his finest poems were left unfinished, including "Kubla Khan" and "Christabel"—two of the most wonderful fragments in English poetry.

"The Rime of the Ancient Mariner" is Coleridge's masterpiece, and one of the great poems of world literature. Like many great works, it can be read in different ways and admired by different levels of readers. It can be read— and is read by many junior high school students—as an exciting adventure story about an old sailor and his sort of hoodooed voyage from his home country in Europe southward through the Atlantic Ocean, around the tip of South America, northward through the Pacific Ocean, and finally back to his home, with a variety of startling and suspense-filled incidents along the way. Or it can be read primarily as an aesthetic experience, with the reader responding to the rich and varied artistry of the work. Or it can be read as a vision of good and evil, the two forces locked in endless conflict, with special attention to the inescapable consequences of an immoral act. And these are only three ways of reading the poem.

Considered as a work of art, "The Rime of the Ancient Mariner" is unquestionably one of the great and finished poems of the world, a masterpiece of imagery and atmosphere, a masterful combination of simplicity and subtlety in both content and structure. The basic stanza form is very simple—the old ballad stanza, in fact, consisting of four lines, the first and third being unrhymed four-foot lines, and the second and fourth rhymed three-foot lines. But Coleridge employs such a wonderful combination of varied stanzas, internal rhymes, exciting alliteration, skillful onomatopoeia (the sound of the words suggesting their meaning), shimmering rythms, and vivid metaphors and similes that the whole poem is a brilliant triumph of variety in unity. Several hours could be spent talking about the artistic technique and achievement of the work.

Our primary concern in this book, however, is with meaning rather than aesthetics. Therefore, we turn attention principally to the theme and substance of the poem. Like most of the very greatest works of art, this poem is concerned with the relationship between good and evil in the universe. But Coleridge does not present evil in a sentimental or melodramatic fashion, as a thing so obvious that people can recognize and shun it without difficulty. Rather, in the words of Ernest Bernbaum, evil in such a poem as this is

> . . . a veiled yet dreadful power, half-repellant, half-fascinating, seizing upon us when least expected, and visiting consequences upon us that are unforeseen. It is a vision of Evil perfectly true to life. But a vision of Evil—not an analysis of it, nor a sermon upon it. In this poem Coleridge sought the golden mean between the kind of romance which is invented to point a moral, and the kind which is invented merely to entertain and which sheds no illumination upon life. . . . Coleridge's aim in *The Ancient Mariner* . . . was neither to produce maxims for the practical guidance of life nor to entertain us with strange fancies. He removed the incidents . . . out of the commonplace conditions of ordinary life, into realms where the forces of good and evil seemed invested with supernatural qualities. The . . . supernatural in these worlds of his, however, was not arbitrary but seemed in harmony with universal laws, and thus bore the marks of authenticity. It suggested the eternal mystery of the interpenetration throughout universal life of spirit and matter, of good and evil. And even more clearly, the human in this poem was true to permanent laws; what the Ancient Mariner felt in his circumstances . . . was unerringly in accord with our common human nature.[1]

To read and fully appreciate a poem such as this, to recognize fully its power and greatness and *truth*, we need

---

[1]Ernest Bernbaum, *Guide Through the Romantic Movement* (New York: The Ronald Press, 1949), pp. 61-62.

to approach it as Coleridge, in words now world-famous, recommended we should approach any high-quality work of imaginative literature, with that "willing suspension of disbelief . . . which constitutes poetic faith,"[1] letting the poem speak for itself, and letting ourselves be caught up in its magic and its wonder.

Part I of the poem tells how the Ancient Mariner, he of the "skinny hand" and "glittering eye," intercepts a man on his way to a wedding and, impatient though the man is to get to the celebration, *compels* him to listen to a story of a strange sea voyage—how a ship sailed southward, across the equator, and into unfamiliar waters, there to be beaten by storm-blasts and driven into a bitter-cold area where "ice, mast-high, came floating by, as green as emerald." Lost in this desolate region, surrounded by cracking, growling, roaring, howling ice, the sailors take heart when an albatross joins their ship, for according to an ancient myth, an albatross is a good omen, a sign that the ship will have safe voyage. And sure enough, the ice-pack splits sufficiently for the helmsman to steer the ship into more open water where a wind pushes them forward for nine joyous days, with the blessed albatross accompanying them. And then, abruptly, as Part I ends, the Mariner tells how "with my cross-bow I shot the Albatross." Why? Coleridge deliberately gives no reason. The Mariner apparently kills without reason. He commits sin wantonly, whimsically, irresponsibly, thoughtlessly, with total lack of regard for the value of life.

Part II begins with the comment that "the sun now rose upon the right," indicating that the ship has rounded Cape Horn at the southern tip of South America and is facing northward into the Pacific Ocean. At first the other sailors accuse the old Mariner of having "done a hellish thing" in killing the blessed albatross; but when a good wind continues for several days and all seems well, they

---

[1]From *Biographia Literaria*, Chapter XIV.

compliment him for destroying "the bird that brought the fog and mist." Thus, by approving of the crime, they become accomplices to the crime, "accessories after the fact" as a lawyer would say. They too are now guilty, and so they must pay the penalty of sin; but they are not as guilty as the Mariner, and so their penalty will not be as heavy. For a brief time the fair breeze continues. Then it stops, as they again reach the equator, with the "bloody Sun" burning out of a "hot and copper sky" directly from above. There, day after day, they sit in a motionless sea, "as idle as a painted ship upon a painted ocean." Salt water is all around them, but there is none to drink, and "slimy things did crawl with legs upon the slimy sea." Driven mad by the agonizing thirst, with parched throats the sailors curse the Mariner for their misery. And the Mariner comments to the Wedding Guest, "Instead of the cross, the Albatross about my neck was hung." There is an old superstition dating back to medieval times that terrible betrayers are mysteriously branded with a cross, even as the Mariner apparently is mysteriously marked with an albatross, the sign of his sin; or perhaps it is simply that the shipmates hang the dead bird around his neck in an effort to throw the whole guilt on him.

Part III opens with the Mariner and all of the sailors in utterly desolate condition, "With throats unslaked and black lips baked." So parched are their throats that the Mariner has to bite his arm and suck blood to moisten his tongue sufficiently to cry "A sail! a sail!" when a small ship appears on the horizon. At first the Mariner hails it as a ship of mercy, but then is haunted by its skeleton-like appearance and its ghastly crew of two. The "captain" has skin "as white as leprosy" for "the Night-mare Life-in-Death was she, who thicks man's blood with cold." And her mate is Death. The two are casting dice to see who shall win the old Mariner, with the loser to get the other seamen. Life-in-Death, the most grisly of the two, wins, and so, going by default to Death the loser, the sailors one by one curse the Mariner with their eyes and die.

The first six lines of Part IV are spoken by the Wedding Guest, reminding us as Coleridge does from time to time that the poem is narrated by the Ancient Mariner to the man intercepted on his way to the wedding-feast. "I fear thee," says the Wedding Guest, and, ironically, the Mariner says, "Fear not," for I did not die. Full well he knows that his fate is far worse than death.

> The many men, so beautiful!
> And they all dead did lie:
> And a thousand thousand slimy things
> Lived on; and so did I.

All around him lie the dead men cursing him with their glazed eyes. In agony he tries to pray, "but or ever a prayer had gusht, a wicked whisper came, and made my heart as dry as dust." Thus, amidst the rottenness of dead men on a dead ship in a dead ocean, the Mariner lives on, suffering the anguish of his crime.

But then, in spite of all his misery, he miraculously becomes conscious of beauty as he watches some water snakes:

> Beyond the shadow of the ship,
> I watched the water-snakes:
> They moved in tracks of shining white,
> And when they reared, the elfish light
> Fell off in hoary flakes.
>
> Within the shadow of the ship
> I watched their rich attire:
> Blue, glossy green, and velvet black,
> They coiled and swam; and every track
> Was a flash of golden fire.

And miraculously, at the climactic moment and dramatic center of the poem, he is so moved by the beauty of the snakes that he exclaims "O happy living things!" as "a spring of love gushed from my heart, and I blessed them unaware." Earlier he had violated the law of love by shooting the albatross; now he fulfills the law of love by blessing the snakes, the lowliest of God's creations. He has come to recognize the sacredness of life, and the unity of all living things.

> The self-same moment I could pray;
> And from my neck so free
> The Albatross fell off, and sank
> Like lead into the sea.

The Mariner has now sinned, suffered the inevitable consequences of sin, and enjoyed the first glorious fruits of redemption from sin through repentance. The poem, as a parable of good versus evil, could end here; but it does not, for Coleridge is aware of the complex nature of punishment and redemption, and he goes on to explore these complexities.

Part V opens with the most delicate, soft lines in the whole poem, suggesting the soothing peace of mind that is the reward of genuine repentance. Up to this point, demons had controlled the ship; from here on it is guided by angelic spirits, who bring healing rain from the sky, and who inhabit the bodies of the dead men to do the work on the ship. Note, incidentally, the effectiveness in wording of such a stanza as the following:

> The body of my brother's son
> Stood by me, knee to knee:
> The body and I pulled at one rope,
> But he said nought to me.

Lovely birds now make beautiful music as the ship moves steadily onward, impelled by the power of supernatural forces. All seems well for the Mariner, but Part V ends with the ominous words, spoken by one of the demon spirits: "The man hath penance done, and penance more will do."

That one can never totally recover from the consequences of sin is Coleridge's point emphasized in Parts VI and VII. Coleridge had unusual insight into the nature of good and evil; but, as L.D.S. readers with their greater insight through the restored Gospel will see, apparently he did not understand the full power of the redeeming mission of Christ. The Mariner genuinely repents, and yet he still feels the consequence of the sin once committd. The accusation of the dead men, who suffered because of his sin, never fully fades from their eyes, even as the anguish of remembrance never fully fades from his conscience. He is still tormented by memory as the voyage ends and he returns to his home country. Briefly he hopes to escape this torment and be fully free as, at the very end of Part VI, he turns to a hermit (a holy man) with the thought, "He'll shrieve my soul, he'll wash away the Albatross's blood."

But Coleridge knew, as any wise man knows, that one mortal being has not the authority to save another mortal being from his sins, and so the plea to the hermit is in vain. The Gospel teaches that every person will be held responsible for the sins he knowingly commits. The Atonement of the Saviour, however, makes it possible for him to be saved if he repents and gives obedience to the laws and ordinances of the Gospel. Coleridge partly understood this truth, but not understanding it fully, in Part VII of the poem he leaves the Mariner largely redeemed through repentance from his sin but still remembering it, still suffering from it:

> Since then, at an uncertain hour,
> That agony returns:
> And till my ghastly tale is told,
> This heart within me burns.

In this discussion, only the moral aspects of the poem have been emphasized. Although these are important to the poem—and they are very important—to emphasize them alone somewhat distorts the poem. Therefore, the reader is invited to consider also those other aspects that make the poem great: its artistic richness, the magic of its haunting descriptions, the structural unity of its myriad details, and the compelling power of its fascinating narrative. All of these combine to make "The Rime of the Ancient Mariner" one of the truly great poems of the world's literature.

The Invisible Collection

by Stefan Zweig

Translated by M. L. Nielsen

At the first station past Dresden, an elderly gentleman entered our compartment and, after giving a friendly greeting, looked up and nodded in my direction with special emphasis as if to an old friend. I was at a loss to know who he might be. But then he smiled and mentioned his name. Of course I knew him! He was one of the most respected art-dealers in Berlin, in whose shop I had often examined and bought rare books and autographs before the war. After we had chatted for a time about trivialities, he suddenly said:

"I must tell you the object of the journey I'm returning from, because I've had an experience which is about the most unusual thing that has ever happened to me in the thirty-seven years of my activity as an art peddler. No doubt you know what things are like in the art trade these days, since money values have become as insubstantial as vapor: the newly-rich have suddenly discovered a passion for Gothic madonnas and incunabula and old prints and pictures. You just can't conjure up enough to satisfy them; in fact you have to be on your guard to prevent them from stripping your very house and room. They'd like to buy the cuff-links off your shirts and the lamp from your writing-table. And it's getting more and more difficult to obtain new merchandise. I see that you're shocked to hear me refer to these things which we've always looked upon with reverence as merchandise. But this wretched tribe has accustomed even me to looking upon a wonderful Venetian incunabulum as nothing more than security for so and so many dollars, and a drawing of Guercino as the incarnation of a few hundred-franc notes.

"There's no defense against the intrusive insistence of these people with their sudden mania for buying, and so the other day I found that once more I had been completely cleaned out over night and was of a mind to close up the shop altogether. But then I began to feel ashamed to see the store which my father took over from my grandfather cluttered up with trashy merchandise which not so long ago no second-hand dealer in the north-end would have bothered to pile onto his cart. In this dilemma I hit upon the idea of looking through our old account books to ferret out some former customers from whom I might pilfer back a few decent items.

"Such an old list of customers is always a kind of morgue, especially in times like these, and it didn't tell me much. Most of those who had bought from us in earlier days had long since been forced to dispose of their holdings at auction, or had died, and from the few who were still about there was little to hope for. But then I happened to stumble onto a whole bundle of letters from a man who was probably our oldest customer and who had slipped from my memory for the simple reason that, since the start of the World War, since 1914, he had never once sent us any kind of inquiry nor any order. The correspondence went back—and this is truly no exaggeration—almost sixty years; he had bought from my father and even my grandfather, though I couldn't recall that he had ever entered our shop in the thirty-seven years of my own activity.

"Everything pointed to the conclusion that this man must have been a peculiar, old-fashioned, abusive type of person, one of those vanished Menzel or Spitzweg Germans who have survived as unique specimens here and there in provincial towns right up to our own day. His letters were neatly-written calligraphics, with amounts underlined with a ruler or in red ink, and figures invariably written twice in order to allow no chance for error. This, plus the fact that he always wrote on cheap block paper and sent his letters in a motley assortment of cheap envelopes, indicated the pettiness and fanatical miserliness of a hopeless provincial. In addition to his name, these unusual documents invariably bore the ceremonious title: Forestry-and-Agricultural-Commissioner, Retired; Lieutenant, Retired; Holder of the Iron Cross, First Class. As a veteran of 'seventy he must be carrying, if still alive, at least a good eighty years on his back. But this crabbed, ridiculous old miser showed extraordinary shrewdness, excellent knowledge and the finest kind of taste as a collector of old prints. As I gradually put together his orders over a period of nearly sixty years, the first of which ran to no more than a few cents, it became clear that, in the days when one could still buy a whole heap of the most beautiful German woodcuts for a few marks, this little provincial must have quietly brought together a collection of copperplate prints which could certainly stand honorable comparison with any of the noisily-publicized collections of the newly-rich. Because even what he had bought from us in the course of a half-century for a few marks or a few cents represented today an astonishing value, and it was reasonable to expect that he had struck as good a bargain at auctions and with other dealers. Although no further order had come from him since 1914, I was so familiar with every happening in the art trade

that the auction or closed sale of such a stock could not have escaped me. And so this unusual man must still be alive, or the collection must be in the hands of his heirs.

"I became interested in the matter, and the very next day,
last evening, I started out on a trip to one of the most outlandish
provincial cities of Saxony; and as I sauntered from the railway
station through the main street, I could scarcely conceive of the
possibility that here, amidst all these banal and shoddy houses
with their middle-class rubbish, in one of these rooms, there should
live a person possessing the most beautiful pictures of Rembrandt
along with prints of Durer and Mantegnas in perfect condition.
When I inquired at the post office whether a forestry or agricul-
tural commissioner of a certain name lived in the city, I was astonished to learn that the old gentleman was still living, and before it
was yet noon I set out on the way to his house—not, I must confess,
without a certain feeling of excitement.

"I had no trouble finding where he lived. It was in the second
story of one of those scanty-small-town houses which was probably hastily thrown together by some speculating building con-
tractor back in the 'sixties. A worthy master-tailor lived on the first
floor; upstairs on the left gleamed the doorplate of a postmaster,
and on the right finally a porcelain plate bearing the name of the
forestry-and-agricultural-commissioner. In answer to my hesitant
ringing the door was opened at once by a very old, white-haired lady
wearing a neat little black hood. I handed her my card and asked
whether I might speak with the forestry commissioner. Surprised
and with a certain air of mistrust, she looked first at me and then
at the card. Apparently a visit from the outside world was something of an event in this isolated little town, in this old-fashioned
house. I heard her whispering softly, and then suddenly a loud,
booming male voice: 'Ah, Herr R . . . from Berlin, from the big
art shop . . . show him in. . . . It's a pleasure!' And now the little
old grandmother came tripping back and invited me into the friendly
room.

"I took off my coat and hat and entered. In the middle of the
modest room, standing very erect, was an old but still vigorous-
looking man with bushy mustache who wore a belted lounging-robe
of semi-military cut. He was holding both hands heartily out toward
me, and yet the unmistakably happy and spontaneous welcome indicated by this gesture was contradicted by a strange stiffness in the
way the man stood there. He didn't advance a single step toward me,
and I was compelled—somewhat taken aback—to go right up to him
in order to grasp his hand. As I was about to do so, however,

it became clear from the fixed and immoveable way in which these hands were held that they were waiting for mine rather than seeking them. And in the next instant I understood everything: this man was blind.

"From the time of my childhood I have always been uncomfortable in the presence of a blind person. I have never been able to escape a certain feeling of shame and embarrassment stemming from the knowledge that the person before me is so completely alive and yet is incapable of having the same feeling with regard to me. Now too I had to fight to overcome an incipient fright as I looked into the dead eyes, directed fixedly into empty space, under the bristling, bushy white eyebrows. But the blind man didn't leave me much time for such discomfort, for as soon as my hand touched his he began to shake it vigorously and to renew his greeting with hearty and noisy joviality.

"'A strange visit,' he said, laughing fully in my direction, really a miracle that one of the fine gentlemen from Berlin should ever wander into our little hamlet. . . But that's the time to be on your guard, when one of the gentlemen dealers gets on a train. . . We have a saying in these parts: Lock your doors and your pocketbooks when the gypsies come around. . . Yes, I have an idea why you've hunted me out. . . Business is bad now in our poor, downtrodden Germany; there are no longer any buyers, and so the fine gentlemen turn their thoughts to their old customers once more and are out looking after their old flocks. . . But I'm afraid you won't have much luck with me; we poor old pensioners are happy to have a piece of bread on the table. We can't compete with the insane prices you're setting these days. . . My type is out of the running forever.'

"I assured him at once that he had misunderstood me, that I hadn't come to sell him something. I told him I just happened to be in the vicinity and hadn't wanted to miss the opportunity of paying my compliments to a person who was a customer of our house of long years' standing and one of the greatest collectors in Germany. Scarcely had I spoken the words 'one of the greatest collectors in Germany' when a striking transformation took place in the old gentleman's face. He still stood straight and stiff in the middle of the room, but now there came into his bearing a sudden expression of brightness and inner pride. He turned in the direction where he judged his wife to be, as if to say 'Do you hear?' and without a trace of that gruff military tone which he had been affecting, but with a happy voice that was actually soft and tender, he said: 'That is really very, very nice of you. . . And you won't have come in vain. . . You'll see something you don't get to see every day, not even in your snobbish Berlin . . . a few items that are as fine as anything you will find in the *Albertina* or in that accursed Paris. . . Yes, when one collects for sixty years, he manages to get together a lot of things that you won't find just lying about in the streets. Luise, hand me the key to the cabinet.'

"But now an unexpected thing happened. The little old grandmother, who had been standing at his side and silently following our conversation with a polite, smiling friendliness, suddenly raised both hands toward me in a gesture of entreaty, and at the same time shook her head vigorously, a sign which at first I didn't understand. Then she went up to her husband and gently placed both hands on his shoulder: 'But Hermann," she admonished, 'you didn't ask the gentleman whether he had time now to examine the collection. It's nearly noon, and after lunch you must rest for an hour as the doctor has ordered. Wouldn't it be better to show the gentleman all the things after lunch, and then we can drink coffee together. Then Annemarie will be here too; she understands everything so much better and can help you.'

"And once again, as soon as she had finished speaking, she repeated the same insistent gesture of entreaty, looking past the unsuspecting man. Now I understood. I knew that she wished me to decline an immediate inspection, and I quickly made up the excuse that I had an invitation to lunch. It would be a pleasure and an honor to examine his collection, I said, but it would scarcely be possible before three o'clock. At that time I would be happy to return.

"As vexed as a child from whom one has taken its favorite toy, the old man turned around. 'Of course,' he growled. 'the gentlemen from Berlin never have time for anything. But this is once when you'll have to take time, because this is not just three or four pieces. There art twenty-seven portfolios, each one for a different artist, and not one that isn't more than half full. At three o'clock then. But be punctual, otherwise we won't get through.'

"Again he stretched out his hand to me into empty space. 'But mind me now, it may delight you—or it may annoy you. And the more it annoys you, the happier I'll be. After all, that's the way we collectors are: everything for ourselves and nothing for the other fellow!' Once more he heartily shook my hand.

"The little old lady accompanied me to the door. Through it all I had noticed in her an expression of embarrassed, nervous anxiety. And now, right in the doorway, she began to stutter in

a suppressed voice: 'Could . . . could . . . my daughter Annemarie
call for you, before you come back? . . . It would be better for . . .
several reasons . . . No doubt you will eat at the hotel?'

" 'Certainly, I would be happy, it will be a pleasure,' I said.

"And so it turned out. An hour later, just as I had finished my
lunch in the small dining room of the hotel on the *Marktplatz*, a
rather spinsterish-looking girl, simply dressed, entered the room
and looked about searchingly. I went up to her, introduced myself,
and said that I was ready to leave at once to look over the collection. But she reddened suddenly, and with the same nervous embarrassment that her mother had displayed she begged to be per-
mitted to speak a few words with me first. And I could see at a
glance that it was very difficult for her. Each time she took hold
of herself and tried to speak, this fleeting, agitated redness spread
itself all the way up to her forehead, and her hand twined itself
in her dress. Finally she began, her speech sticking in her throat
and faltering time and again.

" 'My mother sent me to you . . . She told me everything, and
. . . we have a great favor to ask of you. . . You see, we want to
inform you before you go to father . . . Naturally father will want
to show you his collection, and the collection . . . the collection . . .
is no longer quite complete. . . A number of items are missing . . .
quite a lot, unfortunately. . .' She had to get her breath again,
then she suddenly looked full at me and said in a hurried voice:

" 'I must speak frankly to you. . . You know what the times
are like, you'll understand everything. . . Father became totally
blind after the war broke out. His vision was often impaired even
before that, but at that time the excitement robbed him of the light
completely. You see, he wanted to join up and march against
France in spite of his seventy-six years, and when the army failed
to move right along as it had done in 1870, he was terribly disturbed by it all, and his vision began to fail with alarming speed.
Otherwise he is still perfectly robust; until a short time ago he
was still able to walk for hours and even go hunting, of which he
was very fond. But now it's all over with his walks, and the only
pleasure that was left to him was his collection. He looks at it
every day . . . that is, he doesn't look at it, of course, he can't
see anything any more, but every afternoon he takes all the portfolios out, so that he can at least touch the pieces, one after the
other, always in the same order, which he has known by memory
for decades. . . That's all he's interested in now, and I always
have to read to him from the newspaper about the auctions, and the
higher the prices he hears about, the happier it makes him . . . be-

cause . . . and this is what is so terrible . . . father doesn't understand anything about the prices and about the conditions today. . .
He doesn't know that we have lost everything and that we couldn't
live two days out of the month on his pension . . . and on top
of that my sister's husband was killed in the war and left her with
four small cihldren. . . But father knows nothing of our material
difficulties.

" 'In the beginning we cut expenses, cut them even more than
before, but that didn't help. Then we began to sell. Of course
we did not touch the beloved collection. We sold the little bit of
finery we had, but, Lord in heaven, what did that amount to? For
sixty years, after all, father had spent every extra cent for his
prints. And one day there wasn't anything left . . . we didn't know
which way to turn . . . and then . . . then . . . mother and I sold one
of the prints. Father would never have allowed it. He just doesn't
know how bad things are, he has no idea how hard it is to scare
up a little bit of food and undercover somewhere. He doesn't even
know that we have lost the war and that Alsace and Lorraine have
been lost. We no longer read him all these things from the papers,
so that he won't excite himself.

" 'It was a very valuable item that we sold, a Rembrandt etching. The dealer offered us many, many thousands of marks for it,
and we hoped it would take care of us for years. But you know
how the mony melts away. . . We had put all the balance in the
bank, and in two months it was all gone. And so we had to sell
another piece, and another, and the dealer was always so slow
in sending the money that it had already lost its value. Then we
tried the auctions, but there too they swindled us in spite of prices
that ran into the millions. By the time the millions reached us,
they were always worthless paper. In this way the best part
of his collection down to a few remaining good items has gradually
slipped away, and only to eke out the barest, scantiest kind of
existence. And father suspects nothing.

" 'And that's why mother was so worried when you came
today . . . because if he opens the portfolios for you everything
will be lost. You see, we put cheap copies or sheets of the same
size in his old mats, each of which he recognizes when he feels it,
so that he doesn't notice anything when he runs his fingers over
them. And if only he can touch them and go through them item
by item (he knows the exact order by heart), he gets the same
pleasure from them that he used to when he could see them. And
there is no one else in this small town whom father would consider
worthy of seeing his treasures . . . and he loves every single sheet

with such a fanatical love that I think his heart would break if
he suspected that the whole lot of it has long since slipped away
from under his very hands. You are the first one in all these years,
since the former director of the Dresden gallery of etchings died,
to whom he was wanted to show his collection. And so I beg
of you. . .

"And suddenly the aging girl raised her hands toward me,
and there was a sparkle of tears in her eyes. '. . . We beg of
you . . . don't make him unhappy . . . all of us unhappy . . . don't
destroy this last illusion for him. Help us make him believe that
all these prints which he is going to describe to you are still there.
He wouldn't live through it if he had the faintest suspicion. Maybe
we did wrong him, but there was nothing else we could do. We
had to live . . . and human lives, the lives of four fatherless children like my sister's, are surely more important than printed sheets.
After all we haven't yet robbed him of a single bit of pleasure; he
is happy to be able to leaf through his portfolios every afternoon
for three hours, talking with each sheet as if it were a living thing.
And today . . . perhaps today would have been his happiest day,
for he has been waiting for years for the opportunity to show his
favorites to a connoisseur. Please . . . I beg of you with outstretched hand, don't rob him of this happiness!'

"All this was said in a manner more moving than my narrative
can possibly convey. Good Lord, as a dealer I had seen many
of these people who had been basely swindled by the inflation,
people who had been cheated of costly, centuries-old family possessions for a mere piece of buttered bread. But fate had here
played an odd trick which I found strangely moving. Of course I
promised to keep silent and to do my best.

"So we started out together. On the way I learned with bitterness with what trifling sums these poor, unknowing women had
been cheated. But that only strengthend my determination to help
them to the limit. We climbed the stairs, and the moment we
opened the door we heard from within the room the happy, bluster-
ing voice of the old man: 'Come in! Come in!' With the sensitive
ears of the blind he must have heard our footsteps while we were
still on the stairway.

" 'Hermann has been so impatient to show you his treasures
that he couldn't even sleep today," said the little old lady with a
smile. A single glance from her daughter had reassured her that
I had agreed to their request. The piles of portfolios were spread
out on the table awaiting us, and as soon as the blind man felt

my hand he grasped my arm, and without further greeting pushed me into a chair.

" 'So, and now we can begin—there is a lot to see, and the gentlemen from Berlin never have any time. This first portfolio here is master Dürer, and, as you will soon discover, fairly complete, though of course some of the prints are finer than others. Well, you can judge for yourself. Just look at that!'—he opened to the first page of the portfolio—'the *Great Horse.*'

"And now, with the tender care which one usually employs when handling something fragile, he took from the portfolio with gentle, cautious fingertips a mat which framed a blank, yellow piece of paper, and enraptured he held the worthless scrap before him. Without really seeing it, he looked at it for minutes on end, holding the empty sheet ecstatically at eye-level, with arm extended. His whole countenance magically expressed the intent look of the beholder, and in his staring eyes with their dead pupils there suddenly appeared—was it a reflection from the paper or a brilliance that came from within?—a mirror-like brightness, a knowing light.

" 'Well,' he said proudly, 'have you ever seen a finer impression? How sharply, how clearly every detail stands out. I've compared the Dresden print with this one and it seems completely dull and lifeless. And on top of that the pedigree! There'—and turning the sheet over he pointed with such exactitude to particular spots that involuntarily I looked to see whether there were not some marks on the back after all—'there you have the stamp of the Nagler collection, and here those of Remy and Esdaile; they didn't dream, these illustrious owners of an earlier day, that their sheet would someday find its way into this little room.'

"I felt a cold chill in my spine as I heard this unsuspecting man praise an empty sheet with such enthusiasm. It was uncanny to see how he pointed with his fingernail and with millimeter accuracy to all the invisible collectors' marks which still existed only in his phantasy. My throat was constricted with something very like horror; I could think of nothing to say; but as I looked up in confusion at the two women, I saw again the hand of the trembling and excited old lady raised in supplication. And so I took hold of myself and began to speak my part.

" 'Amazing,' I finally managed to stammer. 'A wonderful specimen.' At once his whole face lit up with pride. 'But that's nothing yet,' he said triumphantly, 'wait until you see the *Melancholia,* or the *Passion* here, an illuminated copy such as you will scarcely find in like quality anywhere. Just look'—and again his fingers brushed gently across an imaginary picture— 'just look at

338

Out of the Best Books

this fresh, warm, pithy tone. With all its fine dealers and museum doctors, Berlin would stand on its head at sight of that.'

"And so it went on, this tumultuous, triumphant commentary, for two whole hours. No, I can't possibly describe to you how ghostly it was to look with him at those hundred or two-hundred empty scraps of paper or shabby reproductions, and to see that in the memory of this tragically deceived man they were so incredibly real that he was able to praise and describe every single one in faultless order and minute detail. The invisible collection which must long since have been scattered to the four winds was still there for this blind man. For him it was unimpaired, and his vision of it was so intense and overpowering that even I almost found myself beginning to believe in it.

"Only once did the awful danger of an awakening break into the dream-like certainty of his visionary rapture. As he came to Rembrandt's *Antiope* (a test impression which must really have had an incalculable value) he had again praised the sharpness of the print, and, as he did so, had run his nervously clairvoyant finger affectionately over the lines of the imprint. But his refined sense of touch was unable to distinguish the expected depressions in the strange sheet, and something like a shadow abruptly passed across his forehead. His voice faltered. 'But that is . . . surely that is the *Antiope*?' he murmured, somewhat embarrassed, where-upon I immediately primed myself, hastily took the framed sheet from his hands and gave a glowing description of the etching in all possible detail, for I knew it very well too. The face of the blind man, which had taken on a confused look, now relaxed once more, and the more I praised, the greater grew the jovial hearti-ness and ingenuous gaiety of the gnarled, weather-beaten old man.

" 'Here at last is a man who knows what is good,' he cried out in triumph, turning to his family. 'Finally, finally someone from whom you too can hear how much my pictures are worth. You've always been suspicious and scolded me because I put all my money into my collection. It's true. For sixty years no beer, no wine, no tobacco, no trips, no visits to the theater, no books. All that time I have just saved and saved for these pictures. But you'll see someday, when I am gone—then you will be rich, richer than any-one in town, and as rich as the richest in Dresden. Then at last you will be glad that I was so foolish. But as long as I live not a single picture leaves this house—first they've got to carry me out, and then my collection can go.'

"And with these words he ran his hand tenderly, as if over some living thing, across the long-since empty portfolios. It was frightening and at the same time touching, because in all the years of war I had not seen so complete and pure an expression of happiness in a German countenance. At his side stood the women, uncannily like those female figures in the German master's etching who, having come to visit the grave of their Saviour, stand before the broken, empty tomb in an attitude expressive at once of fearful alarm and devout, joyful wonderment. Just as in that picture the disciples are illumined by a divine presentiment of the Saviour, so were these two aging, worn and simple women illumined by the child-like bliss of this old man. They stood there half-laughing, half-weeping, a sight more moving than any I have ever experienced. But the old man couldn't get his fill of my praise; again and again he piled up the sheets and turned through them, thirstily drinking in every word. And so it was a relief for me when at last the deceitful portfolios were put aside and he was reluctantly forced to clear the table for the coffee.

"But what was my feeling of guilt compared with the soaring spirits of this man who seemed to have grown thirty years younger! He related a thousand anecdotes about his purchases and his prize catches, and again and again, refusing all offers of aid, he got up and felt his way to the portfolios to fetch another picture. He was filled with a gay intoxication as if from wine. And when I finally said that I must take my leave, he acted as surly as a self-willed child and sulkily stamped his foot, saying that it was out of the question, since I had seen scarcely half of the collection. The women had all they could do to make him understand, in his stubborn ill humor, that he mustn't detain me longer or I would miss my train.

"When, after long and desperate resistance, he finally gave in, and it came time to say farewell, his voice grew very gentle. He took both my hands, and his fingers felt their way caressingly along them up to my wrists with that expressiveness peculiar to blind people, as if they wanted to know more of me and to convey more love than words can possibly do.

" 'Your visit has made me so very, very happy,' he began, with an outpouring of emotion which I can never forget. 'It has been a real blessing to be able at last, at long last, to look through my beloved pictures with a connoisseur. But you shall see that you didn't come to visit this old blind man in vain. I promise you here in front of my wife as a witness that I shall put a clause in my will giving your old and tried firm the right to conduct the auction of my collection. You shall have the honor of administering this unknown treasure'—and he placed his hand lovingly on the plundered

portfolios—'until the day when it is scattered into the world. Just
promise me that you will prepare a fine catalogue. That shall be
my tombstone; I need none better.'

"I looked at the wife and daughter. They held close to one
another, and from time to time a tremor ran from one to the other,
as if they were a single body quivering there in a unity of feeling.
As for me, I was filled with a feeling of solemnity on hearing this
pathetically unsuspecting man hand over into my keeping like a
treasure his invisible collection which had long since been scattered abroad like so much dust. Deeply moved, I promised him
what I could never fulfill. Again a gleam of light came into the
dead pupils of his eyes, and I sensed in him an inner longing which
was trying to grasp me bodily. I sensed it from the tender, loving
pressure of the fingers which were holding mine and sealing a
solemn compact.

"The women accompanied me to the door. They did not
dare to speak, because his sentitive ears would have caught every
word, but how warm with tears, how filled with gratitude, were
the glances which shone upon me. I felt my way down the steps
in a veritable stupor. Actually I felt ashamed. I had come like an
angel in a fairy-tale into a poor man's humble dwelling, I had
caused a blind man to see for an hour by abetting a pious fraud and
lying without shame, I who had come in truth as a shabby tradesman to practice my cunning and relieve someone of a few valuable
items. Yet what I took away with me was worth much more: once
more I had been privileged to experience, in a period of insensibility
and joylessness, pure rapture incarnate, a sort of spiritually-illu-
mined ecstasy directed solely at art. And that is something which
our people appear long since to have forgotten. I was filled with—
I do not know how else to say it—with reverence, yet at the same
time I was ashamed without knowing exactly why.

"As I reached the street, I heard the rattling of a window
from above and heard a voice calling my name. Yes, it was he.
The old man had insisted on looking out with unseeing eyes in the
direction where he judged me to be. He was leaning out so far
that the two women had to take the precaution of holding him. He
waved his handkerchief, and with the carefree, blithe voice of
a boy he called out: 'A good journey to you!' It was a sight I shall
not forget: the happy face of the gray-headed old man up there
in the window, hovering far above all the morose, harassed, officious
people of the streets, held gently aloft out of our unpleasant world

of reality by the white cloud of kindly illusion. And I couldn't help thinking again of those wise, old words—I believe they are Goethe's—: 'Collectors are happy people.' "

Discussion of "The Invisible Collection"

Stefan Zweig (1881-1942), German-Austrian playwright, biographer, and short-story writer, of Jewish parentage, is best known for his psychological portraits of literary and historical figures, including Verlaine, Stendhal, Tolstoi, Balzac, Dickens, Dostoyevsky, Freud, Mary Antoinette, and Mary Queen of Scotland. During his closing years Zweig fled to Brazil, where he died in 1942.

"The Invisible Collection" is probably Zweig's best-known short story. Most readers will find it a very appealing, moving story and will be drawn into it emotionally as it dramatizes the ruinous power of inflation upon sensitive people who are its tragic victims. Its effectiveness is heightened by a skillful use of dramatic irony, as speech after speech is spoken by the blind old man without his being aware of the pathetic irony of his words.

The principal reason the story is included in this section on Good and Evil is that it involves a fundamental ethical problem, which readers are invited to consider: Did the wife and daughter do right in deceiving the old man about his art collection? Does the narrator of the story do right in furthering the deception? Obviously it involves, for both the women and the narrator, deliberate telling of lies; and obviously all of them sense the wrong of telling lies. Yet they choose to tell them. Are they to be commended or censured for their actions?

Before answering, the reader should reflect that the

ethical problem posed by the story is not an isolated one.
As children we like to assume that the world is simply and
clearly divided into right and wrong realms, and that all
we need do is choose the right and shun the wrong. But,
unfortunately—or fortunately?—life isn't this simple. One
of the most painful things we must learn in the process of
growing up is that rarely do we have the opportunity to
choose between alternatives one of which is fully right and
the other fully wrong. The world, its people, and its decisions do not consist primarily of black and white but rather
of shades of gray in between. Sometimes we can choose
between all-right and all-wrong, but more often we must
weigh the good and the bad in one choice against the good
and the bad in the other, making the choice that has the
most of good and the least of bad in it. For example, when
we vote for a mayor or a governor or a president, we do not
have one candidate who is all-good and another who is
all-bad. Both are mixtures of good and bad. Thus in vot-
ing for the one with the most good in him, we also vote for
the one with some bad in him. And we are confronted with
similar complexities in most of the other choices of our lives
—in selecting a husband or a wife, in deciding on a job,
in choosing a school, or teachers within a school, even in
buying a house or an automobile. Moreover, is it sometimes even necessary to commit one wrong in order to avoid
committing a greater wrong? Was carrying on the deception about the art collection a lesser evil than hurting the
old man? And finally, lest we think that we moderns are
the only ones faced with such complex and difficult decisions, we should remember that centuries ago Adam had
the same problem—and chose to break one law in order to
fulfill another law.

    As a last thought before we leave this discussion, lest
there should seem to be any suggestion that dishonesty is
all right, we should remember that the Lord has declared,
"Thou shalt not lie; he that lieth and will not repent shall
be cast out."

The Hound of Heaven

by Francis Thompson

I fled Him, down the nights and down the days;
  I fled Him, down the arches of the years;
I fled Him, down the labyrinthine ways
    Of my own mind; and in the mist of tears
I hid from Him, and under running laughter.   5
       Up vistaed hopes I sped;
       And shot, precipitated,
Adown Titantic glooms of chasméd fears,
    From those strong Feet that followed, followed after.
      But with unhurrying chase,   10
      And unperturbéd pace,
    Deliberate speed, majestic instancy,
      They beat—and a Voice beat
      More instant than the Feet—
    "All things betray thee, who betrayest Me."   15

      I pleaded, outlaw-wise,
By many a hearted casement, curtained red,
   Trellised with interwining charities
(For, though I knew His love Who followéd,
      Yet was I sore adread   20
Lest, having Him, I must have naught beside);
But, if one little casement parted wide,
   The gust of His approach would clash it to.
Fear wist not to evade, as Love wist to pursue.[1]
Across the margent of the world I fled,[2]   25
   And troubled the gold gateways of the stars,
   Smiting for shelter on their clangéd bars;
      Fretted to dulcet jars
And silvern chatter the pale ports o' the moon.[3]
I said to dawn, Be sudden; to eve, Be soon;   30
   With thy young skyey blossoms heap me over
    From this tremendous Lover!
Float thy vague veil about me, lest He see!

---

[1]*Wist* means knew.
[2]*Margent* means edge, boundary.
[3]*Fretted . . . moon* means troubled the doors of the moon until they vibrated
with sweet sounds.

I tempted all His servitors, but to find
My own betrayal in their constancy,   35
In faith to Him their fickleness to me,
  Their traitorous trueness, and their loyal deceit.
To all swift things for swiftness did I sue;
  Clung to the whistling mane of every wind.
    But whether they swept, smoothly fleet,   40
    The long savannahs of the blue;[1]
      Or whether, Thunder-driven,
      They clanged his chariot 'thwart a heaven
Plashy with flying lightnings round the spurn o' their feet—
  Fear wist not to evade as Love wist to pursue.   45
      Still with unhurrying chase,
      And unperturbéd pace,
    Deliberate speed, majestic instancy,
      Came on the following Feet,
      And a Voice above their beat—   50
  "Naught shelters thee, who wilt not shelter Me."

I sought no more that after which I strayed
    In face of man or maid;
But still within the little children's eyes
    Seems something, something that replies;   55
They at least are for me, surely for me!
I turned me to them very wistfully;
But, just as their young eyes grew sudden fair
    With dawning answers there,
Their angel plucked them from me by the hair.   60
"Come then, ye other children, Nature's—share
With me" (said I) "your delicate fellowship;
      Let me greet you lip to lip,
      Let me twine with you caresses,
        Wantoning   65
      With our Lady-Mother's vagrant tresses,
        Banqueting
      With her in her wind-walled palace,
      Underneath her azured dais,
      Quaffing, as your taintless way is,   70
        From a chalice
Lucent-weeping out of the dayspring."[2]

---

[1]*Savannahs* are open, level regions.
[2]*Lucent-weeping* is dripping with luminous drops.

So it was done;
I in their delicate fellowship was one—
Drew the bolt of Nature's secrecies.   75
I knew all the swift importings
      On the willful face of skies;
      I knew how the clouds arise
      Spuméd of the wild sea-snortings;
        All that's born or dies   80
      Rose and drooped with—made them shapers
Of mine own moods, or wailful or divine—
      With them joyed and was bereaven.
      I was heavy with the even,
      When she lit her glimmering tapers   85
      Round the day's dead sanctities.
      I laughed in the morning's eyes.
I triumphed and I saddened with all weather,
      Heaven and I wept together,
And its sweet tears were salt with mortal mine;   90
Against the red throb of its sunset heart
      I laid my own to beat,
      And share commingling heat;
But not by that, by that, was eased my human smart.
In vain my tears were wet on Heaven's gray cheek.   95
For ah! we know not what each other says,
      These things and I; in sound *I* speak—
Their sound is but their stir, they speak by silences.
Nature, poor stepdame, cannot slake my drouth;
      Let her, if she would owe me,   100
Drop yon blue bosom-veil of sky, and show me
      The breasts o' her tenderness;
Never did any milk of hers once bless
      My thirsting mouth.
      Nigh and nigh draws the chase,   105
      With unperturbéd pace,
      Deliberate speed, majestic instancy;
      And past those noiséd Feet
      A voice comes yet more fleet—
"Lo! naught contents thee, who content'st not Me."   110

Naked I wait Thy love's uplifted stroke!
My harness piece by piece Thou hast hewn from me,

And smitten me to my knee;
I am defenseless utterly.
I slept, me thinks, and woke,   115
And, slowly gazing, find me stripped in sleep.
In the rash lustihead of my young powers,
I shook the pillaring hours
And pulled my life upon me; grimed with smears,[1]
I stand amid the dust o' the mounted years—   120
My mangled youth lies dead beneath the heap.
My days have crackled and gone up in smoke,
Have puffed and burst as sun-starts on a stream.
Yea, faileth now even dream
The dreamer, and the lute the lutanist;   125
Even the linked fantasies, in whose blossomy twist
I swung the earth a trinket at my wrist,
Are yielding; cords of all too weak account
For earth with heavy griefs so overplussed.
Ah! is Thy love indeed   130
A weed, albeit an amaranthine weed,[2]
Suffering no flowers except its own to mount?
Ah! must—
Designer infinite!—
Ah! must Thou char the wood ere Thou canst limn with it?[3]   135
My freshness spent its wavering shower i' the dust;
And now my heart is as a broken fount,
Wherein tear-drippings stagnate, spilt down ever
From the dank thoughts that shiver
Upon the sighful branches of my mind.   140
Such is; what is to be?
The pulp so bitter, how shall taste the rind?
I dimly guess what Time in mists confounds;
Yet ever and anon a trumpet sounds
From the hid battlements of Eternity;   145
Those shaken mists a space unsettle, then
Round the half-glimpséd turrets slowly wash again.
But not ere him who summoneth
I first have seen, enwound

---

[1]*Shook . . . me* is as Samson shook the pillars of the temple at Gaza and pulled down the roof on his head; see *Judges*, 16:29-30.
[2]*Amaranthine* means immortal like the amaranth, which grows in the fields of Heaven.
[3]*Limn* means draw—as with charcoal.

With glooming robes purpureal, cypresscrowned;[1]   150
His name I know, and what his trumpet saith.
Whether man's heart or life it be which yields
     Thee harvest, must Thy harvest fields
     Be dunged with rotten death?

     Now of that long pursuit   155
     Comes on at hand the bruit;[2]
That Voice is round me like a bursting sea:
     "And is thy earth so marred,
     Shattered in shard on shard?[3]
Lo, all things fly thee, for thou fliest Me!   160

     Strange, piteous, futile thing,
Wherefore should any set thee love apart?
Seeing none but I makes much of naught" (He said),
     "And human love needs human meriting,
     How hast thou merited—   165
Of all man's clotted clay the dingiest clot?
     Alack, thou knowest not
How little worthy of any love thou art!
Whom wilt thou find to love ignoble thee
     Save Me, save only Me?   170
All which I took from thee I did but take,
     Not for thy harms,
But just that thou might'st seek it in My arms.
     All which thy child's mistake
Fancies as lost, I have stored for thee at home;   175
     Rise, clasp My hand, and come!"

     Halts by me that footfall;
     Is my gloom, after all,
Shade of His hand, outstretched caressingly?
     "Ah, fondest, blindest, weakest,   180
     I am He Whom thou seekest!
Thou dravest love from thee, who dravest Me."

---

[1]*Purpureal* is purple, as of royalty. *Cypresscrowned* is used as a symbol of
sorrow and death.
[2]*Bruit* means noise, clamor.
[3]*Shard* is fragment.

Discussion of "The Hound of Heaven"

In the full history of English poetry there have been few other poets as pathetically ill-suited for the day-to-day responsibilities of life as Francis Thompson (1859-1907). Timid in personality, delicate in health, and day-dreaming in attitude, he floundered from one apprenticeship to another, pushed by his parents in their desire to find something that he could do well. But he could do nothing well—except write poetry, which he did in secret. For several years he shined shoes, cleaned shops, and performed other odd jobs in the slum streets of London, often sleeping on park benches or in the streets themselves, and more often than not eating scraps shared with him by the poor of the district who felt sorry for him. Meanwhile, he continued writing poetry—on paper sacks, in the blank pages of old magazines, on whatever scraps of paper he could find.

One might expect that his poems would be bitter, grim, harshly realistic. But they are exquisitely otherwise. Instead of making him brutal and embittered, the miseries of his life made him increasingly tender in religious devotion and increasingly delicate in poetic imagery.

"The Hound of Heaven" is one of the great short religious poems of the English language. It is not only vivid in imagery and lavish in music but also rich in thought. It is not an easy poem, but it is an extraordinarily beautiful poem, in both aesthetics and meaning.

In reading the poem one should first of all understand that Thompson intends no blasphemy or heresy with the term "Hound of Heaven," referring to Christ. The phrase comes from Shelley's *Prometheus Unbound,* in which Shelley refers admiringly to Christ as "heaven's wingéd hound." Thompson uses the phrase in the sense of an analogy. As the hound pursues the rabbit, ever drawing closer in the chase, so does Christ in His love pursue the sinning mortal who in his rebellion would escape the influence of Christ.

But let us turn to the body of the poem. The best way to read a poem such as this, or any good poem for that matter, is out loud, letting the eye savor the rich figurativeness of the images and the ear the rich music of the lines. And perhaps the best way for us to give help to the reader is to look at the poem section by section, commenting on those spots that may give difficulty.

The "I" of the poem is the sinner who would escape Christ. "I fled him" day and night, through the years, rationalizing, justifying, determined to find adjustment in an anti-religious life, says the speaker in lines 1-15; but Christ's voice and presence ever drew nearer, whispering "All things betray thee, who betrayest Me"—that is, nothing in the universe created by Christ will shelter the defiant sinner from the embracing love of Christ. This same idea, variously worded, becomes a refrain in the poem. See, for example, line 51 ("Naught shelters thee, who wilt not shelter Me"), line 110 ("Lo! naught contents thee, who content'st not Me"), and line 160 ("Lo, all things fly thee, for thou fliest Me!").

In lines 20-21 the speaker confesses a fear shared by many who refuse to turn to religion: "Yet was I sore adread lest, having Him, I must have naught beside." By this he means, of course, that he feared turning to Christ would compel him to give up all the things that he enjoyed in life, all its pleasures and its beauties. This fear is repeated later in the poem, in lines 130-132, when the speaker says, "Ah! is Thy love indeed a weed, albeit an amaranthine weed, Suffering no flowers except its own to mount?"

Another key statement, perhaps the one very most central to understanding the poem, appears in line 24 (and is repeated in line 45): "Fear wist not to evade, as Love wist to pursue." If one observes that the fear is the speaker's and the love is Christ's, the line becomes immediately clear: The sinner's fear does not know how to evade Christ so well as Christ's love knows how to pursue the sinner.

With these difficult key lines clarified, the poem now moves along with rich understanding. The speaker endeavors to escape from Christ among people, especially among children, and also in all the wonders of nature. But no matter where he turns, he finds unhappiness, frustration, lack of fulfillment. Denying Christ, he finds only misery, the anguish of a guilt-filled conscience. Neither human companionship nor work nor pleasure nor dreaming can bring happiness to the Christian who defies Christ.

The climax of the poem comes in line 111 when the speaker finally, with a broken and a contrite spirit, humbled and repentant, acknowledges his need for religion and for Christ. "Naked I wait Thy love's uplifted stroke!" he says. He even acknowledges that he has been his own destroyer, comparing himself (lines 117-121) to Samson, who shook the pillars of the temple that brought the building crumbling upon him. And now he stands with his "mangled youth" lying "dead beneath the heap." Even my creative work as a poet now fails to bring happiness, he says:

> Yea, faileth now even dream
> The dreamer, and the lute the lutanist;
> Even the linked fantasies, in whose blossomy twist
> I swung the earth a trinket at my wrist,
> Are yielding.   (lines 124-128)

"My heart is as a broken fount," he adds in line 137, as I turn my life to Thee, ready for Thy judgment, Thy mercy, and Thy love.

The most pathetic line of the entire poem is number 166, in which Thompson has Christ describe the speaker of the poem (Thompson himself) as "of all man's clotted clay the dingiest clot," so lowly that he is totally unworthy of any person's love, and therefore must turn to Christ to find love. Most readers will probably sense self-pity in these lines, but will forgive Thompson because of the sad circumstances of his years of poverty and loneliness.

The poem ends with the assurance by Christ that in the embrace of His love even the lowliest of men can find happiness and peace of mind. "Rise, clasp My hand, and come!" Christ invites, and adds:

"Ah, fondest, blindest, weakest,
I am He whom thou seekest!
Thou dravest love from thee, who dravest Me."

Some readers may find the poem over-involved in figurative phrases, and perhaps even a little repetitious. But the power of its message is universal: That there really is no happiness for the person who denies religion and defies Christ. Happiness comes only through embracing Christ and His love and His way of life.

The Happy Prince

by Oscar Wilde

High above the city, on a tall column, stood the statue of the Happy Prince. He was gilded all over with thin leaves of fine gold, for eyes he had two bright sapphires, and a large red ruby glowed on his sword-hilt.

He was very much admired, indeed. "He is as beautiful as a weathercock," remarked one of the Town Councillors who wished to gain a reputation for having artistic tastes; "only not quite so useful," he added, fearing lest people should think him unpractical, which he really was not.

"Why can't you be like the Happy Prince?" asked a sensible mother of her little boy who was crying for the moon. "The Happy Prince never dreams of crying for anything."

"I am glad there is someone in the world who is quite happy," muttered a disappointed man as he gazed at the wonderful statue.

"He looks just like an angel," said the Charity Children as they came out of the cathedral in their bright scarlet cloaks, and their clean white pinafores.

"How do you know?" said the Mathematical Master, "you have never seen one."

"Ah! but we have, in our dreams," answered the children; and the Mathematical Master frowned and looked very severe, for he did not approve of children dreaming.

One night there flew over the city a little Swallow. His friends had gone away to Egypt six weeks before, but he had stayed behind, for he was in love with the most beautiful Reed. He had met her early in the spring as he was flying down the river after a big yellow moth, and had been so attracted by her slender waist that he had stopped to talk to her.

"Shall I love you?" said the Swallow, who liked to come to the point at once, and the Reed made him a low bow. So he flew round and round her, touching the water with his wings, and making silver ripples. This was his courtship, and it lasted all through the summer.

"It is a ridiculous attachment," twittered the other Swallows, "she has no money, and far too many relations;" and, indeed, the river was quite full of Reeds. Then, when the autumn came, they all flew away.

After they had gone he felt lonely, and began to tire of his lady-love. She has no conversation," he said, "and I am afraid that she is a coquette, for she is always flirting with the wind." And

certainly, whenever the wind blew, the Reed made the most graceful curtsies. "I admit that she is domestic," he continued, "but I love
travelling, and my wife, consequently, should love travelling also."

"Will you come away with me?" he said finally to her; but the
Reed shook her head, she was so attached to her home.

"You have been trifling with me," he cried. "I am off to the
Pyramids. Good-bye!" and he flew away.

All day long he flew, and at night-time he arrived at the city.
"Where shall I put up?" he said; "I hope the town has made preparations."

Then he saw the statue on the tall column. "I will put up there,"
he cried; "it is a fine position with plenty of fresh air." So he
alighted just between the feet of the Happy Prince.

"I have a golden bedroom," he said softly to himself as he
looked round, and he prepared to go to sleep; but just as he was
putting his head under his wing a large drop of water fell on him.
"What a curious thing!" he cried, "there is not a single cloud in
the sky, the stars are quite clear and bright, and yet it is raining.
The climate in the north of Europe is really dreadful. The Reed used
to like the rain, but that was merely her selfishness."

Then another drop fell.

"What is the use of a statue if it cannot keep the rain off?" he
said; "I must look for a good chimney-pot," and he determined to
fly away.

But before he had opened his wings, a third drop fell, and he
looked up, and saw—Ah! what did he see?

The eyes of the Happy Prince were filled with tears, and tears
were running down his golden cheeks. His face was so beautiful in
the moonlight that the little Swallow was filled with pity.

"Who are you?" he said.

"I am the Happy Prince."

"Why are you weeping then?" asked the Swallow; "you have
quite drenched me."

"When I was alive and had a human heart," answered the
statue, "I did not know what tears were, for I lived in the Palace
of Sans Souci, where sorrow is not allowed to enter. In the daytime
I played with my companions in the garden, and in the evening I
led the dance in the Great Hall. Round the garden ran a very lofty
wall, but I never cared to ask what lay beyond it, everything about
me was so beautiful. My courtiers called me the Happy Prince, and
happy indeed I was, if pleasure be happiness. So I lived, and so I
died. And now that I am dead they have set me up here so high

that I can see all the ugliness and all the misery of my city, and though my heart is made of lead yet I cannot choose but weep."

"What, is he not solid gold?" said the Swallow to himself. He was too polite to make any personal remarks out loud.

"Far away," continued the statue in a low, musical voice, "far away in a little street there is a poor house. One of the windows is open, and through it I can see a woman seated at a table. Her face is thin and worn, and she has coarse red hands, all pricked by the needle, for she is a seamstress. She is embroidering passion-flowers on a satin gown for the loveliest of the Queen's maids-of-honor to wear at the next Court-ball. In a bed in the corner of the room her little boy is lying ill. He has a fever, and is asking for oranges. His mother has nothing to give him but river water, so he is crying. Swallow, Swallow, little Swallow, will you not bring her the ruby out of my sword-hilt? My feet are fastened to this pedestal and I cannot move."

"I am waited for in Egypt," said the Swallow. "My friends are flying up and down the Nile, and talking to the large lotus-flowers. Soon they will be going to sleep in the tomb of the great King. The King is there himself in his painted coffin. He is wrapped in yellow linen, and embalmed with spices. Round his neck is a chain of pale green jade, and his hands are like withered leaves."

"Swallow, Swallow, little Swallow," said the Prince, "will you not stay with me for one night, and be my messenger? The boy is so thirsty, and the mother so sad."

"I don't think I like boys," answered the Swallow. "Last summer, when I was staying on the river, there were two rude boys, the miller's sons, who were always throwing stones at me. They never hit me, of course; we swallows fly far too well for that, and besides, I come of a family famous for its agility; but still, it was a mark of disrespect."

But the Happy Prince looked so sad that the little Swallow was sorry. "It is very cold here," he said; "but I will stay with you for one night, and be your messenger."

"Thank you, little Swallow," said the Prince.

So the Swallow picked out the great ruby from the Prince's sword, and flew away with it in his beak over the roofs of the town.

He passed by the cathedral tower, where the white marble angels were sculptured. He passed by the palace and heard the sound of dancing. A beautiful girl came out on the balcony with her lover. "How wonderful the stars are," he said to her, "and how wonderful is the power of love!" "I hope my dress will be ready in time fo the State-ball," she answered; "I have ordered passion-flowers to be embroidered on it; but the seamstresses are so lazy."

He passed over the river, and saw the lanterns hanging to the masts of the ships. He passed over the Ghetto, and saw the old Jews bargaining with each other, and weighing out money in copper scales. At last he came to the poor house and looked in. The boy was tossing feverishly on his bed, and the mother had fallen asleep, she was so tired. In he hopped, and laid the great ruby on the table beside the woman's thimble. Then he flew gently round the bed, fanning the boy's forehead with his wings. "How cool I feel," said the boy, "I must be getting better;" and he sank into a delicious slumber.

Then the Swallow flew back to the Happy Prince and told him what he had done. "It is curious," he remarked, "but I feel quite warm now, although it is so cold."

"That is because you have done a good action," said the Prince. And the little Swallow began to think, and then he fell asleep. Thinking always made him sleepy.

When day broke he flew down to the river and had a bath. "What a remarkable phenomenon," said the Professor of Ornithology as he was passing over the bridge. "A swallow in winter!" And he wrote a long letter about it to the local newspaper. Every one quoted it, it was full of so many words that they could not understand.

"To-night I go to Egypt," said the Swallow, and he was in high spirits at the prospect. He visited all the public monuments, and sat a long time on top of the church steeple. Wherever he went the sparrows chirruped, and said to each other, "What a distinguished stranger!" so he enjoyed himself very much.

When the moon rose he flew back to the Happy Prince. "Have you any commissions for Egypt?" he cried. "I am just starting."

"Swallow, Swallow, little Swallow," said the Prince, "will you not stay with me one night longer?"

"I am waited for in Egypt," answered the Swallow. "To-morrow my friends will fly up to the Second Cataract. The river-horse couches there among the bulrushes, and on a great granite throne sits the God Memmon. All night long he watches the stars, and when the morning star shines he utters one cry of joy, and then he is silent. At noon the yellow lions come down to the water's edge to drink. They have eyes like green beryls, and their roar is louder than the roar of the cataract."

"Swallow, Swallow, little Swallow," said the Prince, "far across the city I see a young man in a garret. He is leaning over a desk covered with papers, and in a tumbler by his side there is a bunch of withered violets. His hair is brown and crisp, and his lips are red as a pomegranate, and he has large and dreamy eyes. He is trying to finish a play for the Director of the Theatre, but he is too cold to write any more. There is no fire in the grate, and hunger has made him faint."

"I will wait with you one night longer," said the Swallow, who really had a good heart. "Shall I take him another ruby?"

"Alas! I have no ruby now," said the Prince; "my eyes are all that I have left. They are made of rare sapphires, which were brought out of India a thousand years ago. Pluck out one of them and take it to him. He will sell it to the jeweller, and buy food and firewood, and finish his play."

"Dear Prince," said the Swallow, "I cannot do that;" and he began to weep.

"Swallow, Swallow, little Swallow," said the Prince, "do as I command you."

So the Swallow plucked out the Prince's eye, and flew away to the student's garret. It was easy enough to get in, as there was a hole in the roof. Through this he darted, and came into the room. The young man had his head buried in his hands, so he did not hear the flutter of the bird's wings, and when he looked up he found the beautiful sapphire lying on the withered violets.

"I am beginning to be appreciated," he cried; "this is from some great admirer. Now I can finish my play," and he looked quite happy.

The next day the Swallow flew down to the harbour. He sat on the mast of a large vessel and watched the sailors hauling big chests out of the hold with ropes. "Heave a-hoy!" they shouted as each chest came up. "I am going to Egypt!" cried the Swallow, but nobody minded, and when the moon rose he flew back to the Happy Prince.

"I am come to bid you good-bye," he cried.

"Swallow, Swallow, little Swallow," said the Prince, "will you not stay with me one night longer?"

"It is winter," answered the Swallow, "and the chill snow will soon be here. In Egypt the sun is warm on the green palm-trees, and the crocodiles lie in the mud and look lazily about them. My companions are building a nest in the Temple of Baalbec, and the pink and white doves are watching them, and cooing to each other. Dear Prince, I must leave you, but I will never forget you, and next spring I will bring you back two beautiful jewels in place of those you have given away. The ruby shall be redder than a red rose, and the sapphire shall be as blue as the great sea."

"In the square below," said the Happy Prince, "there stands a little match girl. She has let her matches fall in the gutter, and they are all spoiled. Her father will beat her if she does not bring home some money, and she is crying. She has no shoes or stockings, and her little head is bare. Pluck out my other eye, and give it to her, and her father will not beat her."

"I will stay with you one night longer," said the Swallow, "but I cannot pluck out your eye. You would be quite blind then."

"Swallow, Swallow, little Swallow," said the Prince, "do as I command you."

So he plucked out the Prince's other eye, and darted down with it. He swooped past the match-girl, and slipped the jewel into the palm of her hand. "What a lovely bit of glass," cried the little girl; and she ran home, laughing.

Then the Swallow came back to the Prince. "You are blind now," he said, "so I will stay with you always."

"No, little Swallow," said the poor Prince, "you must go away to Egypt."

"I will stay with you always," said the Swallow, and he slept at the Prince's feet.

All the next day he sat on the Prince's shoulder, and told him stories of what he had seen in strange lands. He told him of the red ibises, who stand in long rows on the banks of the Nile, and catch gold fish in their beaks; of the Sphinx, who is as old as the world itself, and lives in the desert, and knows everything of the merchants, who walk slowly by the side of their camels, and carry amber beads in their hands; of the King of the Mountains of the Moon, who is as black as ebony, and worships a large crystal; of the great green snake that sleeps in a palm-tree, and has twenty priests to feed it with honey-cakes; and of the pygmies who sail over a big lake on large flat leaves, and are always at war with the butterflies.

"Dear little Swallow," said the Prince, "you tell me of marvelous things, but more marvellous than anything is the suffering of men and of women. There is no Mystery so great as Misery. Fly over my city, little Swallow, and tell me what you see there."

So the Swallow flew over the great city, and saw the rich making merry in their beautiful houses, while the beggars were sitting at the gates. He flew into dark lanes, and saw the white faces of starving children looking out listlessly at the black streets. Under the archway of a bridge two little boys were lying in one another's arms to try and keep themselves warm. "How hungry we are!" they said.

"You must not lie here," shouted the Watchman, and they wandered out into the rain.

Then he flew back and told the Prince what he had seen.

"I am covered with fine gold," said the Prince, "you must take it off, leaf by leaf, and give it to my poor; the living always think that gold can make them happy."

Leaf after leaf of the fine gold the Swallow picked off, till the Happy Prince looked quite dull and grey. Leaf after leaf of the fine gold he brought to the poor, and the children's faces grew rosier, and they laughed and played games in the street. "We have bread now!" they cried.

Then the snow came, and after the snow came the frost. The streets looked as if they were made of silver, they were so bright and glistening; long icicles like crystal daggers hung down from the eaves of the houses, everybody went about in furs, and the little boys wore scarlet caps and skated on the ice.

The poor little Swallow grew colder and colder, but he would not leave the Prince, he loved him too well. He picked up crumbs outside the baker's door when the baker was not looking, and tried to keep himself warm by flapping his wings.

But at last he knew that he was going to die. He had just strength to fly up to the Prince's shoulder once more. "Good-bye dear Prince!" he murmured, "will you let me kiss your hand?"

"I am glad that you are going to Egypt at last, little Swallow," said the Prince, "you have stayed too long here; but you must kiss me on the lips, for I love you."

"It is not to Egypt that I am going," said the Swallow. "I am going to the House of Death. Death is the brother of Sleep, is he not?"

And he kissed the Happy Prince on the lips, and fell down dead at his feet.

At that moment a curious crack sounded inside the statue, as if something had broken. The fact is that the leaden heart had snapped right in two. It certainly was a dreadfully hard frost.

Early the next morning the Mayor was walking in the square below in company with the Town Councillors. As they passed the column he looked up at the statue! "Dear me! how shabby the Happy Prince looks!" he said.

"How shabby indeed!" cried the Town Councillors, who always agreed with the Mayor, and they went up to look at it.

"The ruby has fallen out of his sword, his eyes are gone, and he is golden no longer," said the Mayor; "in fact, he is little better than a beggar!"

"Little better than a beggar," said the Town Councillors.

"And here is actually a dead bird at his feet!" continued the Mayor. "We must really issue a proclamation that birds are not to be allowed to die here." And the Town Clerk made a note of the suggestion.

So they pulled down the statue of the Happy Prince. "As he is no longer beautiful he is no longer useful," said the Art Professor at the University.

Then they melted the statue in a furnace, and the Mayor held a meeting of the Corporation to decide what was to be done with the metal. "We must have another statue of course," he said, "and it shall be a statue of myself."

"Of myself," said each of the Town Councillors, and they quarrelled. When I last heard of them they were quarrelling still.

"What a strange thing," said the overseer of the workmen at the foundry. "This broken lead heart will not melt in the furnace. We must throw it away." So they threw it on a dust heap where the dead Swallow was also lying.

"Bring me the two most precious things in the city," said God to one of His Angels; and the Angel brought Him the leaden heart and the dead bird.

"You have rightly chosen," said God, "for in my garden of Paradise this little bird shall sing for evermore, and in my city of gold the Happy Prince shall praise me."

Discussion of "The Happy Prince"

Few men have been gifted with the native brilliance and versatile talents of the Irish author Oscar Wilde (1856-1900), and few have had personal lives as shockingly and destructively tragic as his. As a writer he displayed his extraordinary skill in a novel (*The Picture of Dorian Gray*), in poetry (including *The Ballad of Reading Gaol*), in some of the wittiest plays of his generation (including *The Importance of Being Earnest*), in some excellent essays of literary criticism, in a volume of short stories, and in hundreds of eloquently written letters.

Wilde's short stories are different from everything else that he wrote. In his other works he is generally either witty or grim or classically learned; in his short stories (he called them fairy tales) he is tender, romantic, and idealistic. Such a "fairy tale" as "The Happy Prince" purports to be written for children, but the occasional sentences that are satiric plus the general substance of the story make clear that it was really intended for grown-up children. In spite of what some readers may react against as a too pretty, too easy story with a too sentimental and too didactic "moral," most readers will respond to "The Happy Prince" as a delicate and lovely little story, written with a charm that will appeal to child and adult alike.

SECTION FIVE

The Place of Suffering in Life

THE PLACE OF SUFFERING IN LIFE

Introductory Comments

Related to the general subject of good versus evil in the universe, and also to the more specific subject of the nature of sin, is the problem of suffering in human experience. Is suffering a punishment for sins committed and laws broken? Do the innocent suffer with the guilty? And if so, why? Is suffering sometimes a blessing in disguise? Can man grow through suffering? Is suffering indeed necessary for greatness? (Most great men *have* suffered.) And is suffering the cradle of great art? (Shelley said, "We learn in suffering what we teach in song."[1])

As with the whole problem of good versus evil, so with the subject of the place of suffering in life, many great works of literature pertain. Note, for example, the profound concern for the nature of suffering in *The Book of Job* in the Bible, or the suggestion of growth through suffering in the life of Hester Prynne in Hawthorne's *The Scarlet Letter*. If space allowed, we would explore the nature of suffering in some of these long and complex works. Because of limited space, however, we shall consider the subject in some shorter selections—two poems, five short stories, and an essay.

---

[1]See Shelley's "Julian and Maddalo."

The Lament

by Anton Chekhov

It is twilight. A thick wet snow is slowly twirling around the newly lighted street lamps, and lying in soft thin layers on roofs, on horses' backs, on people's shoulders and hats. The cab driver Iona Potapov is quite white, and looks like a phantom; he is bent double as far as a human body can bend double; he is seated on his box; he never makes a move. If a whole snowdrift fell on him, it seems as if he would not find it necessary to shake it off. His little horse is also quite white, and remains motionless; its immobility, its angularity, and its straight wooden-looking legs, even close by, give it the appearance of a gingerbread horse worth a *kopek*. It is, no doubt, plunged in deep thought. If you were snatched from the plow, from your usual gray surroundings, and were thrown into this slough full of monstrous lights, unceasing noise, and hurrying people, you too would find it difficult not to think.

Iona and his little horse have not moved from their place for a long while. They left their yard before dinner, and up to now, not a fare. The evening mist is descending over the town, the white lights of the lamps replacing brighter rays, and the hubbub of the street getting louder. "Cabby for Viborg way!" suddenly hears Iona. "Cabby!"

Iona jumps, and through his snow-covered eyelashes sees an officer in a greatcoat, with his hood over his head.

"Viborg way!" the officer repeats. "Are you asleep, eh? Viborg way!"

With a nod of assent Iona picks up the reins, in consequence of which layers of snow slip off the horse's back and neck. The officer seats himself in the sleigh, the cabdriver smacks his lips to encourage his horse, stretches out his neck like a swan, sits up, and, more from habit than necessity, brandishes his whip. The little horse also stretches its neck, bends its wooden-looking legs, and makes a move undecidedly.

"What are you doing, werewolf!" is the exclamation Iona hears from the dark mass moving to and fro, as soon as they have started.

"Where the devil are you going? To the r-r-right!"

"You do not know how to drive. Keep to the right!" calls the officer angrily.

A coachman from a private carriage swears at him; a passerby, who has run across the road and rubbed his shoulder against the horse's nose, looks at him furiously as he sweeps the snow from his sleeve. Iona shifts about on his seat as if he were on needles, moves his elbows as if he were trying to keep his equilibrium, and gapes about like someone suffocating, who does not understand why and wherefore he is there.

"What scoundrels they all are!" jokes the officer; "one would think they had all entered into an agreement to jostle you or fall under your horse."

Iona looks round at the officer, and moves his lips. He evidently wants to say something, but the only sound that issues is a snuffle.

"What?" asks the officer.

Iona twists his mouth into a smile, and with an effort says hoarsely:

"My son, *barin*, died this week."

"Hm! What did he die of?"

Iona turns with his whole body toward his fare, and says:

"And who knows! They say high fever. He was three days in the hospital, and then died. . . . God's will be done."

"Turn round! The devil!" sounds from the darkness. "Have you popped off, old doggie, eh? Use your eyes!"

"Go on, go on," says the officer, "otherwise we shall not get there by tomorrow, Hurry up a bit"

The cabdriver again stretches his neck, sits up, and, with a bad grace, brandishes his whip. Several times again he turns to look at his fare, but the latter has closed his eyes, and apparently is not disposed to listen. Having deposited the officer in the Viborg, he stops by the tavern, doubles himself up on his seat, and again remains motionless, while the snow once more begins to cover him and his horse. An hour, and another. . . . Then, along the footpath, with a squeak of galoshes, and quarreling, come three young men, two of them tall and lanky, the third one short and humpbacked.

"Cabby, to the Police Bridge!" in a cracked voice calls the humpback. "The three of us for two *griveniks*!"

Iona picks up his reins, and smacks his lips. Two *griveniks* is not a fair price, but he does not mind whether it is a *rouble* or five *kopeks*—to him it is all the same now, so long as they are fares. The young men, jostling each other and using bad language, approach the sleigh, and all three at once try to get onto the seat; then begins a discussion as to which two shall sit and who shall be the one to stand. After wrangling, abusing each other, and much petulance, it is at last decided that the humpback shall stand, as he is the smallest.

"Now then, hurry up!" says the humpback in a twanging voice as he takes his place and breathes in Iona's neck. "Old furry! Here, mate, what a cap you have! There is not a worse one to be found in all Petersburg! . . ."

"He-he! --he-he!" giggles Iona. "Such a . . ."

"Now you, 'such a,' hurry up, are you going the whole way at this pace?" Are you? . . . Do you want it in the neck?"

"My head feels like bursting," says one of the lanky ones. "Last night at the Donkmasovs, Vaska and I drank the whole of four bottles of cognac."

"I don't understand what you lie for," says the other lanky one angrily; "you lie like a brute."

"God strike me, it's the truth!"

"It's as much the truth as that a louse coughs!"

"He, he," grins Iona, "what gay young gentlemen!"

"Pshaw, go to the devil!" says the humpback indignantly.

"Are you going to get on or not, you old pest? Is that the way to drive! Use the whip a bit! Go on, devil, go on, give it to him well!"

Iona feels at his back the little man wriggling, and the tremble in his voice. He listens to the insults hurled at him, sees the people, and little by little the feeling of loneliness leaves him. The humpback goes on swearing until he gets mixed up in some elaborate six-foot oath, or chokes with coughing. The lankies begin to talk about a certain Nadejda Petrovna. Iona looks round at them several times; he waits for a temporary silence, then, turning round again, he murmurs:

"My son . . . died this week."

"We must all die," sighs the humpback, wiping his lips after an attack of coughing. "Now, hurry up, hurry up! Gentlemen, I really cannot go any farther like this! When will he get us there?"

"Well, just you stimulate him a little in the neck!"

"You old pest, do you hear, I'll bone your neck for you! If one treated the like of you with ceremony one would have to go on foot! Do you hear, old serpent Gorinytch! Or do you not care a spit?"

Iona hears rather than feels the blows they deal him.

"He, he," he laughs. "They are gay young gentlemen, God bless 'em!"

"Cabby, are you married?" asks a lanky one.

"I? He, he, gay young gentlemen! Now I have only a wife and the moist ground. . . . he, ho, ho . . . that is to say, the grave. My son has died, and I am alive. . . . A wonderful thing, death mistook the door . . . instead of coming to me, it went to my son. . . ."

Iona turns round to tell them how his son died, but at this moment, the humpback, giving a little sigh, announces, "Thank God, we have at last reached our destination," and Iona watches them disappear through the dark entrance. Once more he is alone, and again surrounded by silence. . . . His grief, which has abated for a short while, returns and rends his heart with greater force. With an anxious and hurried look, he searches among the crowds passing on either side of the street to find whether there may be just one person who will listen to him. But the crowds hurry by without noticing him or his trouble. Yet it is such an immense, illimitable grief. Should his heart break and the grief pour out, it would flow over the whole earth, so it seems, and yet no one sees it. It has managed to conceal itself in such an insignificant shell that no one can see it even by day and with a light.

Iona sees a hall porter with some sacking, and decides to talk to him.

"Friend, what sort of time is it?" he asks.

"Past nine. What are you standing here for? Move on."

Iona moves on a few steps, doubles himself up, and abandons himself to his grief. He sees it is useless to turn to people for help. In less than five minutes he straightens himself, holds up his head as if he felt some sharp pain, and gives a tug at the reins; he can bear it no longer. The stables," he thinks, and the little horse, as if it understands, starts off at a trot.

About an hour and a half later Iona is seated by a large dirty stove. Around the stove, on the floor, on the benches, people are snoring; the air is thick and suffocatingly hot. Iona looks at the sleepers, scratches himself, and regrets having returned so early.

"I have not even earned my fodder," he thinks. "That's what's my trouble. A man who knows his job, who has had enough to eat, and his horse too, can always sleep peacefully."

A young cabdriver in one of the corners half gets up, grunts sleepily, and stretches towards a bucket of water.

"Do you want a drink?" Iona asks him.

"Don't I want a drink?"

"That's so? Your good health! But listen, mate—you know, my son is dead. . . . Did you hear? This week, in the hospital. . . . It's a long story."

Iona looks to see what effect his words have, but sees none—the young man has hidden his face and is fast asleep again. The old man sighs, and scratches his head. Just as much as the young one wants to drink, the old man wants to talk. It will soon be a week since his son died, and he has not been able to speak about it properly to anyone. One must tell it slowly and carefully; how his son fell ill, how he suffered, what he said before he died, how he died. One must describe every detail of the funeral, and the journey to the hospital to fetch the dead son's clothes. His daughter Anissia has remained in the village—one must talk about her too. Is it nothing he has to tell? Surely the listener would gasp and sigh, and sympathize with him? It is better, too, to talk to women; although they are stupid, two words are enough to make them sob.

"I'll go and look after my horse," thinks Iona; there's always time to sleep. No fear of that!"

He puts on his coat, and goes to the stables to his horse; he thinks of the corn, the hay, the weather. When he is alone, he dares not think of his son; he can speak about him to anyone, but to think of him, and picture him to himself, is unbearably painful.

"Are you tucking in?" Iona asks his horse, looking at its bright eyes; "Go on, tuck in, though we've not earned our corn, we can eat hay. Yes! I am too old to drive—my son could have, not I. He was a first-rate cabdriver. If only he had lived!

Iona is silent for a moment, then continues:

"That's how it is, my old horse. There's no more Kuzma Ionitch. He has left us to live, and he went off pop. Now let's say, you had a foal, you were the foal's mother, and suddenly, let's say, that foal went and left you to live after him. It would be sad, wouldn't it?"

The little horse munches, listens, and breathes over its master's hand. . . .

Iona's feelings are too much for him, and he tells the little horse the whole story.

Discussion of "The Lament"

Anton Chekhov (1860-1904) is one of the greatest of Russia's authors and one of the greatest and most prolific of the world's short-story writers. His most internationally famous work is *The Cherry Orchard*, one of quite a few plays that he wrote. But he is even more important as a short-story writer. Indeed, he is perhaps more responsible than any other in shaping the realistic, plot-thin, "slice-of-life" story that has been so brilliant and so popular for the past half century in Europe and America. In such a story the goal is to capture an ordinary but meaningful moment in a person's life to reveal the essence of a personality or explore the heart of a truth. The range of Chekhov's stories is limited to the substance of commonplace life, but he recorded his observations with such sharpness, humor, compassion, and fidelity to truth that he is universally regarded as one of the truly great masters of the short story.

"The Lament" is one of the earliest of the 800 or so stories written by Chekhov, and it is a very simple story. At one time he classified it as among his "unimportant trifles," but it is now recognized as a classic. Like many of Chekhov's other stories, "The Lament" is movingly pathetic. Also like many others by him, it avoids sentimentality through a careful objectivity and neutrality in attitude. If Chekhov had treated the incident sentimentally—that is, if he had told it more emotionally than its material justified —then we would find it distasteful. But he tells it matter-of-factly, without preaching or other commentary, and the result is a simple but very touching description of a lonely old man and his grief over the death of his son.

The story is included here because it so clearly presents two universal human qualities: one, the need to share sorrow; and two, the difficulty of finding anyone genuinely sympathetic to share it with.

Sometimes, until we learn otherwise, we may imagine that people who grieve want to hold the grief within themselves. But it is not so. At least it generally is not so. Psychologically there is a necessity in most people to talk about their sorrows, and psychologically they are relieved by so talking. All people who hesitate to "intrude" upon the sorrow of another should remember this. (But should also remember that occasionally there is a person who, unlike most, does not want to share his sorrow—and should not be obliged to, even though he may suffer all the more for choosing to suffer alone.)

If it is true that most people need and want to share their grief, it is also true that most people do not want to be burdened (or even bothered) with such grief. Generally if a person starts to talk about his sorrow he can predict exactly what will happen. The person to whom he is talking will start to tell of a sorrow even greater. Everyone wants to talk about his troubles, and no one wants to listen. This is one of the ironies of human society. The lesson to be drawn is, of course, obvious. If a person wants to be truly useful and truly liked, all he need do is be genuinely sympathetic, genuinely a concerned listener. But the sympathy and concern have to be genuine; anything less than honesty is inadequate. . . . And so Iona Potapov turned in loneliness to his horse.

The Fly

by Katherine Mansfield

"Y' are very snug in here," piped old Mr. Woodifield, and he peered out of the great, green leather arm-chair by his friend, the boss's desk, as a baby peers out of its pram. His talk was over; it was time for him to be off. But he did not want to go. Since he had retired, since his . . . stroke, the wife and the girls kept him boxed up in the house every day of the week except Tuesday. On Tuesday he was dressed up and brushed and allowed to cut back to the City for the day. Though what he did there the wife and girls couldn't imagine. Made a nuisance of himself to his friends, they supposed. . . . Well, perhaps so. All the same, we cling to our last pleasures as the tree clings to its last leaves. So there sat old Woodifield, smoking a cigar and staring almost greedily at the boss, who rolled in his office chair, stout, rosy, five years older than he, and still going strong, still at the helm. It did one good to see him.

Wistfully, admiringly, the old voice added, "It's snug in here, upon my word!"

"Yes, it's comfortable enough, agreed the boss, and he flipped the *Financial Times* with a paper-knife. As a matter of fact he was proud of his room; he liked to have it admired, especially by old Woodifield. It gave him a feeling of deep, solid satisfaction to be planted there in the midst of it in full view of that frail old figure in the muffler.

"I've had it done up lately," he explained, as he had explained for the past—how many?—weeks. "New carpet," and he pointed to the bright red carpet with a pattern of large white rings. "New furniture," and he nodded towards the massive bookcase and the table with legs like twisted treacle. "Electric heating!" He waved almost exultantly towards the five transparent, pearly sausages glowing so softly in the tilted copper pan.

But he did not draw old Woodifield's attention to the photograph over the table of a grave-looking boy in uniform standing in one of those spectral photographers' parks with photographers' storm-clouds behind him. It was not new. It had been there for over six years.

"There was something I wanted to tell you," said old Woodifield, and his eyes grew dim remembering. "Now what was it? I had it in my mind when I started out this morning." His hands began to tremble, and patches of red showed above his beard.

Poor old chap, he's on his last pins, thought the boss. And, feeling kindly, he winked at the old man, and said jokingly, "I tell you what. I've got a little drop of something here that'll do you good before you go out into the cold again. It's beautiful stuff. It wouldn't hurt a child." He took a key off his watch-chain, unlocked a cupboard below his desk, and drew forth a dark, squat bottle. "That's the medicine," said he. "And the man from whom I got it told me on the strict Q. T. it came from the cellars at Windsor Castle."

Old Woodifield's mouth fell open at the sight. He couldn't have looked more surprised if the boss had produced a rabbit.

"It's whisky, ain't it?" he piped, feebly.

The boss turned the bottle and lovingly showed him the label. Whisky it was.

"D'you know," said he, peering up at the boss wonderingly, "they won't let me touch it at home." And he looked as though he was going to cry. . . .

But it warmed him; it crept into his chill old brain—he remembered.

"That was it," he said, heaving himself out of his chair. "I thought you'd like to know. The girls were in Belgium last week having a look at poor Reggie's grave, and they happened to come across your boy's. They are quite near each other, it seems."

Old Woodifield paused, but the boss made no reply. Only a quiver of his eyelids showed that he heard.

"The girls were delighted with the way the place is kept," piped the old voice. "Beautifully looked after. Couldn't be better if they were at home. You've not been across, have yer?"

"No, no!" For various reasons the boss had not been across.

"There's miles of it," quavered old Woodifield, "and it's all as neat as a garden. Flowers growing on all the graves. Nice broad paths." It was plain from his voice how much he liked a nice broad path.

The pause came again. Then the old man brightened wonderfully.

"D'you know what the hotel made the girls pay for a pot of jam?" he piped. "Ten francs! Robbery, I call it. It was a little pot, so Gertrude says, no bigger than a half-crown. And she hadn't taken more than a spoonful when they charged her ten francs. Gertrude brought the pot away with her to teach 'em a lesson. Quite right, too; it's trading on our feelings. They think because we're over there having a look around we're ready to pay anything. That's what it is." And he turned towards the door.

"Quite right, quite right!" cried the boss, though what was quite right he hadn't the least idea. He came around by his desk, followed the shuffling footsteps to the door, and saw the old fellow out. Woodifield was gone.

For a long moment the boss stayed, staring at nothing, while the grey-haired office messenger, watching him, dodged in and out of his cubby-hole like a dog that expects to be taken for a run. Then: "I'll see nobody for half an hour, Macey," said the boss. "Understand? Nobody at all."

"Very good, sir."

The door shut, the firm, heavy steps recrossed the bright carpet, the fat body plumped down in the spring chair, and leaning forward, the boss covered his face with his hands. He wanted, he intended, he had arranged to weep. . . .

It had been a terrible shock to him when old Woodifield sprang that remark upon him about the boy's grave. It was exactly as though the earth had opened and he had seen the boy lying there with Woodifield's girls staring down at him. For it was strange. Although over six years had passed away, the boss never thought of the boy except as lying unchanged, unblemished in his uniform, asleep forever. "My son!" groaned the boss. But no tears came yet. In the past, in the first months and even years after the boy's death, he had only to say those words to be overcome by such grief that nothing short of a violent fit of weeping could relieve him. Time, he had declared then, he had told everybody, could make no difference. Other men perhaps might recover, might live their loss down, but not he. How was it possible? His boy was an only son. Ever since his birth the boss had worked at building up this business for him; it had no other meaning if it was not for the boy. Life itself had come to have no other meaning. How on earth could he have slaved, denied himself, kept going all those years without the promise for ever before him of the boy's stepping into his shoes and carrying on where he left off?

And that promise had been so near being fulfilled. The boy had been in the office learning the ropes for a year before the war. Every morning they had started off together; they had come back by the same train. And what congratulations he had received as the boy's father! No wonder; he had taken to it marvellously. As to his popularity with the staff, every man jack of them down to old Macey couldn't make enough of the boy. And he wasn't in the least spoiled. No, he was just his bright natural self, with the right word for everybody, with that boyish look and his habit of saying, "Simply splendid!"

But all that was over and done with as though it never had been. The day had come when Macey had handed him the telegram that brought the whole place crashing about his head. "Deeply regret to inform you. . . ." And he had left the office a broken man, with his life in ruins.

Six years ago, six years. . . . How quickly time passed! It might have happened yesterday. The boss took his hands from his face; he was puzzled. Something seemed to be wrong with him. He wasn't feeling as he wanted to feel. He decided to get up and have a look at the boy's photograph. But it wasn't a favorite photograph of his; the expression was unnatural. It was cold, even stern-looking. The boy had never looked like that.

At that moment the boss noticed that a fly had fallen into his broad inkpot, and was trying feebly but desperately to clamber out again. Help! Help! said those struggling legs. But the sides of the inkpot were wet and slippery; it fell back again and began to swim. The boss took up a pen, picked the fly out of the ink, and shook it on to a piece of blotting-paper. For a fraction of a second it lay still on the dark patch that oozed round it. Then the front legs waved, took hold, and, pulling its small sodden body up, it began the immense task of cleaning the ink from its wings. Over and under, over and under, went a leg along a wing, as the stone goes over and under the scythe. Then there was a pause, while the fly, seeming to stand on the tips of its toes, tried to expand first one wing and then the other. It succeeded at last, and sitting down, it began, like a minute cat, to clean its face. Now one could imagine that the little front legs rubbed against each other lightly, joyfully. The horrible danger was over; it had escaped; it was ready for life again.

But just then the boss had an idea. He plunged his pen back into the ink, leaned his thick wrist on the blotting-paper, and as the fly tried its wings, down came a great, heavy blot. What would it make of that? What indeed! The little beggar seemed absolutely cowed, stunned, and afraid to move because of what would happen next. But then, as if painfully, it dragged itself forward. The front legs waved, caught hold, and, more slowly the task began again.

He's a plucky little devil, thought the boss, and he felt a real admiration for the fly's courage. That was the way to tackle things; that was the right spirit. Never say die; it was only a question of. . . . But the fly had again finished its laborious task, and the boss had just time to refill his pen, to shake fair and square on the new-cleaned body yet another dark drop. What about it this time. A painful moment of suspense followed. But behold, the front legs were again waving; the boss felt a rush of relief. He leaned over the fly and said to it tenderly, "You artful little beast." And he actually had the brilliant notion of breathing on it to help the drying process. All the same, there was something timid and weak about its efforts now, and the boss decided that this time should be the last, as he dipped the pen into the inkpot.

It was. The last blot fell on the soaked blotting-paper, and the draggled fly lay in it and did not stir. The back legs were stuck to the body; the front legs were not to be seen.

"Come on," said the boss. "Look sharp!" And he stirred it with his pen—in vain. Nothing happened or was likely to happen. The fly was dead.

The boss lifted the corpse on the end of the paper-knife and flung it into the waste-paper basket, but such a grinding feeling of wretchedness seized him that he felt positively frightened. He started forward and pressed the bell for Macey.

"Bring me some fresh blotting-paper," he said, sternly, "and look sharp about it." And while the old servant padded away he fell to wondering what it was he had been thinking about before. What was it? It was. . . He took out his handkerchief and passed it inside his collar. For the life of him he could not remember.

Discussion of "The Fly"

Katherine Mansfield (1888-1923) was born and spent her growing-up years in New Zealand, then traveled to England for university study, and later lived much of the time in various countries of continental Europe. Immensely talented, she was both a musician and a writer, but achieved her greatest recognition in the short story. And in this genre she is universally recognized as one of the most gifted of writers. Her stories are plot-thin but character-rich. Atmosphere, mood, impressions, the revelation of a person-ality—these are the most important ingredients of her writing; and everything is defined with a sharp precision of detail that is matched by few other writers. Although much of her personal life was filled with unhappiness and illness, Katherine Mansfield nevertheless so disciplined her very considerable talents that she unquestionably established herself as one of the most subtly penetrating short-story writers of all time.

The best of her stories are contained in three volumes: *In a German Pension, Bliss,* and *The Garden Party.* And the "best" is very good indeed, including such stories as "Miss Brill," "Marriage a la Mode," "A Cup of Tea," "The Daughters of the Late Colonel," "A Dill Pickle," "Bliss," "Life of Ma Parker," "The Garden Party," "The Doll's House," "The Man Without a Temperament," and dozens of others.

In one way "The Fly" is untypical of Katherine Mansfield's stories because it is a portrait of a man, and most of her stories are about women. But in the fact that it is primarily a character study, with little action, it is very typical.

Two persons appear in the story, but only one is important, and this the one whose name isn't given. Old Mr. Woodifield serves only as a means to provide conversation and contrast with "the boss," who is the central character. And all that happens and is said when the two are together serves only as background leading to the moment when the boss is alone.

The boss is old but prides himself that he is still vigorous, still "at the helm." He also prides himself in his prosperity, his material possessions. He is an opulently successful man and wants everyone to know it.

Just one thing mars the plushness of the boss's world, and this is remembrance of his son—his beloved only son, who was killed in war some six years before. With the death of his handsome son, around whom the boss had built all his dreams of the future, the boss's whole world crumbled. He was plunged into a grief so total that the passing of the years served only to intensify it.

In our analysis of the story, two questions need to be answered above all others: First, why does the boss kill the fly? Second, just how deep, how genuine, how healthy is the boss's grief for his son?

The incident involving the fly is central to the story. Indeed, note that the story is called "The Fly." If, as already suggested, the work is primarily a character study, just how does the incident with the fly illuminate the personality and character of the boss? The boss refers to the fly as a "plucky little devil," and we are told that he "felt a real admiration for the fly's courage." "That was the way to tackle things; that was the right spirit. Never say die." Is it that the boss sees in the fly the right way of responding to life—with courage, with persistence, with determination to triumph? Is it that the boss takes heart from the fly and decides to live his own life with vigor, gaining the courage to triumph over the death of his son— learning from the example of the fly much as, according to the old legend, King Bruce of Scotland anciently learned from the persistence of the spider? Perhaps.

Or is it that the boss, unable to weep as he desires, is angry with himself, and in his annoyance transfers his attention to the fly, taking out his anger and frustration by murdering the helpless insect—and then can't even remember the grief that so engulfed him before the little fly fell into the inkpot and distracted his attention? (Note that he is a bully to the fly just as he is a bully to his employees.)

How deep and genuine really is the boss's grief? We are told that "he wanted, he intended, he had arranged to weep." The boy has been dead for over six years, but to the father the death seems only yesterday. Does he want to overcome his sorrow, or does he want to keep it alive, to nurse it through the years? Does he, in fact, actually enjoy his grief? We, of course, admire a person who loves so deeply that the memory of a beloved one remains strong long after death has taken the one beloved. But does this accurately describe the boss's feeling? Is his grief really strong? Or is it rather that he wants his grief to be strong and is angry because he can't weep as he wants to? Are there people who enjoy sorrow, who enjoy feeling sorry for themselves so much that they unhealthily wallow in self-pity and weeping? Is the boss unselfish or selfish in his grief? Does he grieve for the son or for his own sense of loss? Should a person sorrow endlessly for one who is taken in death, or does the time come when one should triumph over the sorrow?[1] Sorrow can be a source of genuine growth. But does the old boss grow through sorrow, or does he simply wade unwholesomely in a muddy swamp of self-induced tears? Some people imagine that those who suffer openly, as the boss does, also suffer deeply. But is this always true? May it not be that sometimes the widow who sits in dry-eyed silence at her husband's funeral is suffering more deeply than the widow whose tears flow freely? Finally, how deep is the boss's grief if a fly falling into an inkpot could so divert his attention that after the fly's death he cannot even remember that he had set aside half an hour for weeping over the death of a son?

This story, as now must seem obvious, has been included in the section on "Suffering" as a contrast to Chekhov's "The Lament." In each story there is a father sorrowing for a dead son. But in "The Lament" we see simple, genuine grief, immediate and deep. In "The Fly" we see grief that, whatever it might once have been, is now stale and unhealthily selfish, confused with self-pity.

---

[1]Ecclesiastes 3:1 & 4 reads: "To every thing there is a season, and a time to every purpose under the heaven: . . . A time to weep, and a time to laugh; a time to mourn, and a time to dance."

War

by Luigi Pirandello

The passengers who had left Rome by the night express had had to stop until dawn at the small station of Fabriano in order to continue their journey by the small old-fashioned local joining the main line with Sulmona.

At dawn, in a stuffy and smoky second-class carriage in which five people had already spent the night, a bulky woman in deep mourning was hoisted in—almost like a shapeless bundle. Behind her, puffing and moaning, followed her husband—a tiny man, thin and weakly, his face death-white, his eyes small and bright and looking shy and uneasy.

Having at last taken a seat he politely thanked the passengers who had helped his wife and who had made room for her; then he turned round to the woman trying to pull down the collar of her coat, and politely inquired:

"Are you all right, dear?"

The wife, instead of answering, pulled up her collar again to her eyes, so as to hide her face.

"Nasty world," muttered the husband with a sad smile.

And he felt it his duty to explain to his traveling companions that the poor woman was to be pitied, for the war was taking away from her her only son, a boy of twenty to whom both had devoted their entire life, even breaking up their home at Sulmona to follow him to Rome, where he had to go as a student, then allowing him to volunteer for war with an assurance, however, that at least for six months he would not be sent to the front and now, all of a sudden, receiving a wire saying that he was due to leave in three days' time and asking them to go and see him off.

The woman under the big coat was twisting and wriggling, at times growling like a wild animal, feeling certain that all those explanations would not have aroused even a shadow of sympathy from those people who—most likely—were in the same plight as herself. One of them, who had been listening with particular attention, said:

"You should thank God that your son is only leaving now for the front. Mine has been sent there the first day of the war. He has already come back twice wounded and been sent back again to the front."

"What about me? I have two sons and three nephews at the front," said another passenger.

"Maybe, but in our case it is our *only* son," ventured the husband.

"What difference can it make? You may spoil your only son with excessive attentions, but you cannot love him more than you would all your other children if you had any. Paternal love is not like bread that can be broken into pieces and split amongst the children in equal shares. A father gives *all* his love to each one of his children without discrimination, whether it be one or ten, and if I am suffering now for two sons, I am not suffering half for each of them but double. . . ."

"True . . . true . . ." sighed the embarrassed husband, "but suppose (of course we all hope it will never be your case) a father has two sons at the front and he loses one of them, there is still one left to console him . . . while . . ."

"Yes," answered the other, getting cross, "a son left to console him but also a son left for whom he must survive, while in the case of the father of an only son if the son dies the father can die too and put an end to his distress. Which of the two positions is the worse? Don't you see how my case would be worse than yours?"

"Nonsense," interrupted another traveler, a fat, red-faced man with bloodshot eyes of the palest gray.

He was panting. From his bulging eyes seemed to spurt inner violence of an uncontrolled vitality which his weakened body could hardly contain.

"Nonsense," he repeated, trying to cover his mouth with his hand so as to hide the two missing front teeth. "Nonsense. Do we give life to our children for our own benefit?"

The other travelers stared at him in distress. The one who had had his son at the front since the first day of the war sighed: "You are right. Our children do not belong to us, they belong to the Country. . . ."

"Bosh," retorted the fat traveler. "Do we think of the Country when we give life to our children? Our sons are born because . . . well, because they must be born and when they come to life they take our own life with them. This is the truth. We belong to them but they never belong to us. And when they reach twenty they are exactly what we were at their age. We too had a father and a mother, but there were so many other things as well . . . girls, cigarettes, illusions, new ties . . . and the Country, of course, whose call we would have answered—when we were twenty—even if father and mother had said no. Now at our age, the love of our Country is still great, of course, but stronger than it is the love for our children. Is there any one of us here who wouldn't gladly take his son's place at the front if he could?"

There was a silence all round, everybody nodding as to approve.

"Why then," continued the fat man, "shouldn't we consider the feelings of our children when they are twenty? Isn't it natural that at their age they should consider the love for their Country (I am speaking of decent boys, of course) even greater than the love for us? Isn't it natural that it should be so, as after all they must look upon us as upon old boys who cannot move any more and must stay at home? If Country exists, if Country is a natural necessity, like bread, of which each of us must eat in order not to die of hunger, somebody must go to defend it. And our sons go, when they are twenty, and they don't want tears, because if they die, they die inflamed and happy (I am speaking, of course, of decent boys). Now, if one dies young and happy, without having the ugly sides of life, the boredom of it, the pettiness, the bitterness of disillusion . . . what more can we ask for him? Everyone should stop crying; everyone should laugh, as I do . . . or at least thank God—as I do— because my son, before dying, sent me a message saying that he was dying satisfied at having ended his life in the best way he could have wished. That is why, as you see, I do not even wear mourning. . . ."

He shook his light fawn coat as to show it; his livid lip over his missing teeth was trembling, his eyes were watery and motionless, and soon after he ended with a shrill laugh which might well have been a sob.

"Quite so . . . quite so . . ." agreed the others.

The woman who, bundled in a corner under her coat, had been sitting and listening had—for the last three months—tried to find in the words of her husband and her friends something to console here in her deep sorrow, something that might show her how a mother should resign herself to send her son not even to death but to a probably dangerous life. Yet not a word had she found amongst the many which had been said . . . and her grief had been greater in seeing that nobody—as she thought—could share her feelings.

But now the words of the traveler amazed and almost stunned her. She suddenly realized that it wasn't the others who were wrong and could not understand her but herself who could not rise up to the same height of those fathers and mothers willing to resign themselves, without crying, not only to the departure of their sons but even to their death.

She lifted her head, she bent over from her corner trying to listen with great attention to the details which the fat man was giving to his companions about the way his son had fallen as a hero, for his King and his Country, happy and without regrets. It seemed to her that she had stumbled into a world she had never dreamt of, a world so far unknown to her and she was so pleased to hear everyone joining in congratulating that brave father who could so stoically speak of his child's death.

Then suddenly, just as if she had heard nothing of what had been said and almost as if waking up from a dream, she turned to the old man, asking him:

"Then . . . is your son really dead?"

Everybody stared at her. The old man, too, turned to look at her, fixing his great, bulging, horribly watery light gray eyes, deep in her face. For some little time he tried to answer, but words failed him. He looked and looked at her, almost as if only then—at that silly, incongruous question—he had suddenly realized at last that his son was really dead—gone forever—forever. His face contracted, became horribly distorted, then he snatched in haste a handkerchief from his pocket and, to the amazement of everyone, broke into harrowing, heart-rending, uncontrollable sobs.

Discussion of "War"

Luigi Pirandello (1867-1936), of Sicilian birth and parentage, is an internationally celebrated Italian dramatist, novelist, and short-story writer. Two plays, *Six Characters in Search of an Author* and *As You Desire Me*, catapulted him to fame, but gradually he is now becoming recognized as an even greater writer of prose fiction. He received the Nobel Prize for Literature in 1934.

"War" could have been placed in the next section, "Facing Death," but is instead printed in this section on "The Place of Suffering in Life" because it seems concerned not so much with death itself as with the sorrow of those who live.

On one level the story simply reinforces what was said in the discussion of Chekhov's "The Lament": the raw and elemental grief which demands but cannot find solace. Although sorrow is common to the entire human race, it is also and inevitably an ache of loneliness. We can philosophize and sermonize about suffering and the need to bear it with dignity and restraint, but the pain of personal sorrow remains deep, beyond the comfort of words. Perhaps it is as Francois de la Rochefoucauld (1613-1680) once said, "We all have strength enough to bear the misfortunes of others."

A comment of passing interest in the story is that made about the nature of love by one of the passengers, the father with two sons, who says: "Paternal love is not like bread that can be broken into pieces and split amongst the children in equal shares. A father gives *all* his love to each one of his children without discrimination, whether it be one or ten, and if I am suffering now for my two sons, I am not suffering half for each of them but double." As Shelley once said, love is not a material thing which when divided becomes smaller but is a spiritual thing which may divide and divide with each part as large as the beginning whole:

> True love in this differs from gold and clay,
> That to divide is not to take away.
> Love is like understanding, that grows bright,
> Gazing on many truths. . . .
>
> (from *Epipsychidion*)

The most significant development in the story, however, is intimately related to its plot and its structure. There is very little action here, just some gestures and other slight movements of the passengers as they talk to each other. The plot, then, is not in action but in conflict of attitude as the parents argue about how one should feel on giving sons to his country in wartime. For all of them this is a dramatically personal subject because all have sons in the war, and one old man has already lost his son.

The two most opposing positions in the argument are held by the fat woman and the old man whose son has been killed. The woman, whose son is still alive but is being sent to the front, is animal-like in her suffering, and not to be consoled. She grieves anguishedly and sees no way out of her grief. On the other hand, the fat man, even though his loss has been greater, has reasoned himself into an insistence that those who die young, filled with dreams and ideals, before the miseries of the world have beaten upon them, are fortunate; and therefore we should not sorrow but should rejoice.

Miraculously, the fat woman, who has refused to be comforted by her husband and all the others, listens to the old man with persuasion. He has actually lost a son, and yet he does not grieve. She is ready to take strength from him, to believe as he does, and in awe she asks, "Then . . . is your son really dead?"

The question, which serves as the climax of the story, completely catches the old man off guard. It is as if for the first time he realizes that his son really is dead. Before, he has philosophized; now, he is struck by harsh, blunt truth. And so, even as his words changed the attitude of the fat woman, so her words change his attitude. To some extent they reverse positions: Through him, she gained a temporary strength and comfort; through her, he is reduced to unreasoning, animal-like misery—the raw ache of elemental suffering. For her, reasoning triumphs, at least temporarily, over painful emotions; for him, the veneer of his rationalizing cracks under the woman's simple question and a flood of inconsolable feeling engulfs him as he breaks into "harrowing, heart-rending, uncontrollable sobs."

Analyzed in this manner, we see the story as a sharp dramatization of the struggle between the power of the mind to reason sorrow away and the sometimes greater power of the emotions to make it burst forth beyond the control of reason.

Boless

by Maxim Gorky

An acquaintance of mine once told me the following story:

"While still a student at Moscow I happened to be living alongside one of those—well, she was a Polish woman, Teresa by name. A tall, powerfully built brunet with heavy, bushy eyebrows, and a large coarse, vulgar face, as if carved out with an ax—the animal gleam of her eyes, the deep bass voice, the gait and manners of a cabman, and her immense strength like that of a market-woman, inspired me with an inexpressible horror. I lived in the garret of the house, and her room was opposite mine. I never opened my door when I knew that she was in. But this, of course, happened very rarely. Sometimes I chanced to meet her on the landing, staircase, or in the yard, and she would look at me with a smile which seemed to me cynical and rapacious. Occasionally I saw her in her cups, with bleary eyes, her hair and clothes in disorder and with a particularly loathsome smile. On such occasions she would meet my eye with an impudent stare and say:

" 'How are you, Pan Student?'

"And her stupid laugh would increase my dislike for her still more. I would have liked nothing better than to change my quarters in order to get rid of her proximity, but my room was so nice, and the view from my window was so fine, the street below so quiet and peaceful, that I concluded to endure it.

"One morning after I had dressed and was sprawling on the cot, trying to invent some sort of an excuse for not attending my classes, the door of my room suddenly opened, and the disgusting bass voice of the Polish woman sounded from the threshold:

" 'Good morning, Pan Student.'[1]

" 'What is it you wish?' I asked her. I saw she looked confused and had in her face a kind of pleading expression, something unusual with her.

" 'You see, Pan Student, I came to beg you to do me a great favor. Don't refuse me, please!'

"Lying there on my cot I thought that it was just some pretext or other to make my further acquaintance. Take care, my boy!

" 'You see, I have to send a letter to my native country,' she continued in a supplicating, low, tremulous voice.

" 'Well,' I thought, 'the devil take you. If you wish I will write

---

[1]*Pan* is Polish for Mister.

it for you.' And springing to my feet I sat down to the table, took some paper and said: 'Well, come nearer; sit down and dictate.'

"She came over; sat down cautiously on the edge of the chair and looked at me in rather a guilty way.

" 'To whom shall I write?'

" 'To Boleslav Kapshat, in the town Sventsiani, on the Warsaw railroad.'

" 'Well, what shall I write? Speak.'

" 'My dearest Boless, my heart's delight, my beloved. May the Mother of God protect you! My golden heart, why have you not written for so long a time to your sorrowing dove, Teresa—'

"I could hardly keep from laughing. A sorrowing dove, indeed! Almost six feet tall, with the fists of a prize-fighter, and a face so black that it seemed as if the 'dove' had been sweeping chimneys all her life and had never thoroughly washed herself. But I somehow kept my face straight and asked:

" 'Who is this Bolesst?'

" 'Boless, Pan Student,' she replied, seemingly offended because of my mispronouncing the name. 'He is my affianced.'

" 'Affianced!'

" 'And why are you so astonished? Can not I, a girl, have an affianced?'

"She—a girl! well, this beats everything I ever heard. Oh, well, who can tell about such matters! Everything is possible in this world.

" 'And have you been long engaged? '

" 'The sixth year.'

" 'Oh, oh!' I thought and then said aloud: 'Well, go ahead with your letter.'

"And I must confess—so tender and loving was this message—that I would have willingly exchanged places with this Boless had the fair correspondent been any one else but Teresa.

" 'I thank you from my inmost soul for your favor, Pan Student,' Teresa said, bowing low. 'Can I in any way be of service to you?'

" 'No, thank you.'

" 'But maybe the Pan's shirts or trousers need mending?'

"This made me quite angry. I felt that this mastodon in petticoats was making the blood mount to my cheeks, and I told her quite sharply that her services were not required; and she departed.

"Two weeks or so passed. One evening I was sitting at my window, softly whistling and thinking hard how to get away from myself. I felt very bored. The weather was as nasty as it could be. To go out that evening was out of the question, and having nothing better to do I began from sheer ennui a course of self-analysis. This proved dull enough work, but there was nothing else to do. Suddenly the door opened, thank God! Some one was coming to see me.

" 'Are you very busy just now, Pan Student?'

" 'Teresa! H'm—' I thought I would have preferred any one at all to her. Then I said aloud:

" 'No, what is it you want now?'

" 'I wish to ask the Pan Student to write me another letter.'

" 'Very well. Is it again to Boless you wish me to write?'

" 'No, this time I want you to write a letter from Boless to me.'

" 'Wha-at?'

" ' I beg your pardon, Pan Student. How stupid of me! It is not for me, this letter, but for a friend of mine, a man acquaintance; he has a fiancee. Her name is like mine, Teresa. He does not know how to write, so I want the Pan Student to write for him a letter to that Teresa—'

"I looked at her. She seemed very confused and frightened, and her fingers trembled. And tho I failed at first to understand what was the matter with her, I at last understood.

" 'Look here, my lady,' I said to her. 'You have been telling me a pack of lies. There are no Bolesses nor Teresas among your acquaintances. It is only a pretext for coming in here. I tell you outright that there is no use of coming sneaking around me, as I do not wish to have anything to do with you. Do you understand?'

"She grew very red in the face and I saw that she was strangely frightened and confused, and moved her lips so oddly, wishing to say something, without being able to say it. And somehow I began to think that I had misjudged her a little. There was something behind all this. But what?

" 'Pan Student,' she suddenly began, but broke off, and turning toward the door, walked out of the room.

"I remained with a very unpleasant feeling in my heart. I heard her shut her own door with a bang; evidently the poor girl was very angry—I thought the matter over and decided to go in to her and induce her to return; I would write her the letter she wished.

"I entered her room. She was sitting at the table with her head pressed in her hands.

" 'Teresa,' I said, 'will you listen to me a moment?'

"Whenever I come to this turn of the story I always feel very awkward and embarrassed. But let us return to my narrative. Seeing that she did not reply I repeated:

" 'Listen to me, my girl—'

"She sprang to her feet, came close up to me, with eyes flashing, and placing her two hands on my shoulders she began to whisper, or rather to hum in her deep bass voice:

" 'Look you here, Pan Student. What of it, what of it if there is no Boless? And what if there is no Teresa? What difference does it make to you? Is it so hard for you to draw a few lines on the paper! Oh, you! And I thought you such a good fellow, such a nice fair-haired little boy. Yes, it is true—there is no Boless, and there is no Teresa, there is only me! Well, what of it?'

" 'Allow me,' I said, greatly disconcerted by this reception. 'What is it you are saying? Is there no Boless?'

" 'Yes, there is none. But what of it?'

" 'And no Teresa either?'

" 'No, no Teresa either; that is, yes, I am her.'

"I could not understand a word. I stared straight into her eyes, trying to determine which of us two had lost our reason. And she returned once more to the table, rummaged for some time in the drawer, and coming back to me said in an offended tone:

" 'Here is the letter you wrote for me, take it back. You do not wish to write me a second one anyway. Others will probably be kinder than you and would do so.'

"I recognized the letter she held out to me as the one I wrote for her to Boless. Humph!

" 'Look here, Teressa,' I said to her. 'Will you please explain to me what it all means? Why do you ask people to write letters for you when you do not find it necessary even to post them?'

" 'Post them? Where to?'

" 'Why, to this Boless, of course.'

" 'But he does not exist!'

"I really could not understand a word. There was nothing left for me to do but to spit and walk out of the room. But she explained herself.

" 'Well, what of it?' she began in an offended voice. 'He does not exist. He does not, so,' and she extended her hands as if she could not herself clearly understand why he did not exist in reality. 'But I want him to. Am I not as much of a human being as the others? Of course I—I know—But it does no harm to any one, that I am writing to him—'

" 'Allow me—to whom?'

" 'To Boless, of course.'

" 'But he does not exist.'

" 'Oh! what if he does not exist? He does not; still to me he does. And Teresa—this is myself, and he replies to my letters, and I write to him again.'

. "I understood. I felt so sick at heart, so ashamed of myself to know that alongside of me, only three paces removed, lived a human being who had no one in the whole world to love and sympathize with her, and that this being had to invent a friend for herself.

" 'Here you have written a letter from me to Boless, and I gave it to another to read, and when I hear it read it really begins to seem to me as if there is a Boless. And then I ask that a letter be written from Boless to Teresa—that is to me. And when such a letter is written and is read to me then I am almost entirely convinced that there is a Boless, and that makes my life easier.'

"Yes, . . ." continued my acquaintance. "To make a long story short I began from that time on to write with the greatest punctuality twice a week letters to Boless and vice versa. I wrote splendid replies to her. She used to listen to my reading of those epistles and to weep in her bass voice. In return for this she used to mend my clothes and darn my socks.

"Three months later she was thrown into prison for some reason or other and by now she must surely be dead."

My acquaintance blew the ashes from his cigaret, looked thoughtfully at the sky, and concluded:

"Y-e-s, the more a human being has drunk of the cup of bitterness the more ardently he longs for sweetness. And we, enveloped in our worn-out virtues and gazing at each other through the haze of self-sufficiency and convinced of our righteousness, fail to understand it.

"And the whole affair turns out very stupid, and very cruel. Fallen people we say—but who and what are those fallen ones? First of all they are human beings of the very same bone and blood, of the very same flesh and nerves as ourselves. We have been told the very same thing for whole ages, day in and day out. And we listen and—and the devil alone knows how stupid it all is! In reality we, too, are but fallen people and more deeply fallen too, probably—into the abyss of self-sufficiency, convinced of our own sinlessness and superiority, the superiority of our own nerves and brains over the nerves and brains of those who are only less crafty than we are, and who can not, as we can, feign a goodness they do not possess—but enough of this. It is all so old and stale—so old and stale indeed that one is ashamed to speak of it—"

Discussion of "Boless"

Maxim Gorky is the pseudonym of Alexey Maximovich Peshkov (1868-1936), Russian short-story writer and dramatist. Among his works are *Twenty-six and One, The Outcasts, A Night's Lodging, The Lower Depths,* and *Stories of the Steppe.* Generally recognized as his best are his early stories dealing with the socially outcast and downtrodden.

"Boless" is a story within a story, and because of this it is a better story than it otherwise would be.

The "inner" story deals with the Polish woman Teresa, whom Pan Student describes as a "tall, powerfully built brunet with heavy, bushy eyebrows, and a large coarse, vulgar face, as if carved out with an ax—the animal gleam of her eyes, the deep bass voice, the gait and manners of a cabman, and her immense strength like that of a market-woman." Her story is pathetic, touching our hearts with sympathy and reminding us that large and homely women have hearts just as tender, desires for love just as intense, loneliness just as deep, and capacity for companionship just as great as beautiful women—perhaps even more tender, more intense, deeper, and greater. That in her total isolation from all human affection and understanding she should have to invent a "Boless" to whom she can write love letters, signing them "your sorrowing dove," and from whom she can receive them—this is pathetic. And even more pathetic are her clumsy, blundering efforts to open up a friendship with Pan Student.

However, this isn't really Teresa's story. Pan Student, the narrator, is the central character. Only two sentences in the entire story are not spoken by him: the opening sentence, in which Gorky comments, "An acquaintance of mine once told me the following story," and a sentence near the end, which nudgingly reminds us that Pan Student is the narrator, and which reads, "My acquaintance blew the ashes from his cigaret, looked thoughtfully at the sky, and concluded."

The story is principally a character sketch of Pan Student, his qualities revealed to us mostly through his comments on Teresa. He confesses that at first he was filled with "an inexpressible horror" by Teresa's appearance. She seemed to him to have a "loathsome smile," a "stupid laugh," and a "disgusting bass voice." When she referred to herself in her letter to Boless as "a sorrowing dove," Pan Student mocked her in his mind. "I could hardly keep from laughing," he says. "A sorrowing dove, indeed. Almost six feet tall, with the fists of a prize-fighter, and a face so black that it seemed as if the 'dove' had been sweeping chimneys all her life and had never thoroughly washed herself."

Pan Student keeps referring to Teresa as crude and stupid. But who is really crude and stupid? If he were refined in human relationships, wouldn't he have sensed that underneath this "mastodon in petticoats" there was a pleadingly lonely woman? And if he were really intelligent, would it have taken him so long to catch on that Teresa was writing letters to and from an imaginary Boless? After a long conversation with Teresa, Pan Student says, "I could not understand"—and finally, long after the reader is annoyed with Teresa's need to keep explaining, Pan Student at last says, "I understand."

Even then, does he fully understand? He says, "I felt so sick at heart, so ashamed of myself to know that alongside of me, only three paces removed, lived a human being who had no one in the whole world to love and sympathize with her, and that this being had to invent a friend for herself." But is he really, genuinely sympathetic? Just a few sentences later he callously comments, "Three months later she was thrown into prison for some reason or other and by now she must surely be dead." He thinks he has become understanding and sympathetic. But isn't he actually still sort of bored, sort of mouthing words that don't really touch his heart? The last two paragraphs, spoken by Pan Student, preach an eloquent sermon against self-sufficiency and self-righteousness, asking for more compassion in human relationships. But their speaker would seem more genuine, less rhetorical, if he didn't add, "It is all so old and stale—so old and stale." Are human love and understanding, and the need for them, really "old and stale"? The reader knows they are not. Gorky, the author, knows they are not. Teresa knows they are not. But what about Pan Student?

Thou Art Indeed Just, Lord

by Gerard Manley Hopkins

Thou art indeed just, Lord, if I contend
With thee; but, sir, so what I plead is just.
Why do sinners' ways prosper? and why must
Disappointment all I endeavour end?
    Wert thou my enemy, O thou my friend,
How wouldst thou worse, I wonder, than thou dost
Defeat, thwart me? Oh, the sots and thralls of lust
Do in spare hours more thrive than I that spend,
Sir, life upon thy cause. See, banks and brakes
Now, leaved how thick! laced they are again
With fretty chervil, look, and fresh wind shakes
Them; birds build—but not I build; no, but strain,
Time's eunuch, and not breed one work that wakes.
Mine, O thou Lord of life, send my roots rain.

Discussion of "Thou Art Indeed Just, Lord"

Exposing a problem rather than suggesting any answer or solution to it is the sonnet "Thou Art Indeed Just, Lord" by Gerard Manley Hopkins (1844-1889).[1] Hopkins was a deeply religious and a genuinely good man. But he was troubled, as was Job before him, by the knowledge that sometimes sinners seem to prosper more than do good men. I know you are my friend, Hopkins says to God, but if you were my enemy would I suffer any worse? Those who lust after pleasure seem to thrive more than I who spend my hours in Thy cause, he adds. And the sonnet ends with the powerful plea, "O thou Lord of life, send my roots rain."

[1]For a brief discussion of the life and works of Hopkins, see p. 96.

The problem explored in this poem should not be ignored. It needs to be faced and, if possible, answered. While it is generally true that righteous people prosper in business and health more than do sinners, all of us also know that sometimes righteous people suffer both financial collapse and broken health. One of the most thoughtful comments on the problem is the following by Lowell Bennion:

> The gospel of Christ is not an escape from the hard realities of life. . . . Both the person who follows Christ and the person who mocks Him live in the world among the same men and where the same laws of nature operate. Many things happen alike to saint and sinner. Cancer takes over in the human body with no regard for a person's spiritual or moral worth. . . . Innocent children suffer from it, and some of the most wonderful Christians we have known are not spared its merciless attack. Death itself . . . appears to be without discrimination. Clean-living Christian boys fall on the battlefield with those who curse God. A young and beloved husband and father is taken while a mean and feared husband and father is left to curse his wife and children. On the highway, death takes the careless, the sleepy, and innocent victims alike with no regard for their Church attendance, tithing records, or love of neighbor that we can observe. The wicked prosper as well as the righteous, and sometimes more quickly. Individual prosperity is no proof of Christian discipleship; neither is poverty. . . . Living the gospel of Jesus Christ does not necessarily bring with it physical health, freedom from accident and misfortune, freedom from pain and suffering, prosperity and long life. As a matter of fact, some who have lived it best with great devotion have shortened their lives and brought considerable suffering upon themselves.

This is an honest acceptance of the realities of human experience. But within the framework of religion there is an answer, comforting and unassailable. The true and absolute fruits of religious living are spiritual, not material, as Brother Bennion goes on to explain:

> The religion of Jesus does not enable us to escape tribulation, but it does fortify the spirit of man to accept and face it when

it comes. . . . The life founded in the gospel can suffer with patience, can meet adversity with hope, can take malice with forgiveness, can recompense hate with love, and can face death with equanimity. The religious person can find himself in no circumstance . . . in which his religion is not a source of strength to him. In weakness, he knows where to turn for strength; in strength, he remains humble; in poverty he knows whereof his riches consist; in wealth he remembers his brethren in mercy; in health, he is grateful; in illness, he exercises faith.[1]

A wise student of the Gospel knows, as Hopkins must also have known, even though he did not express it in this powerful poem, that the great reward of righteous living, available to all, is not material prosperity and freedom from hardship, but spiritual peace of mind and the serenity that comes with a free conscience and a testimony of truth.

(Emerson's philosophical discussion of this question in the section immediately following is also very pertinent.)

---

[1]Lowell Bennion, *Teachings of the New Testament* (Salt Lake City: Deseret Sunday School Union Board, 1953), pp. 178-180.

Compensation

by Ralph Waldo Emerson

Ever since I was a boy I have wished to write a discourse on Compensation; for it seemed to me when very young that on this subject life was ahead of theology and the people knew more than the preachers taught. . . .

I was lately confirmed in these desires by hearing a sermon at church. The preacher, a man esteemed for his orthodoxy, unfolded in the ordinary manner the doctrine of the Last Judgment. He assumed that judgment is not executed in this world; that the wicked are successful; that the good are miserable; and then urged from reason and from Scripture a compensation to be made to both parties in the next life. . . . .

Yet what was the import of this teaching? What did the preacher mean by saying that the good are miserable in the present life? Was it that houses and lands, offices, wine, horses, dress, luxury, are had by unprincipled men, whilst the saints are poor and despised; and that a compensation is to be made to these last hereafter, by giving them the like gratifications another day—bank-stock and doubloons, venison and champagne? This must be the compensation intended; for what else? Is it that they are to have leave to pray and praise? to love and serve men? Why, that they can do now. The legitimate inference the disciple would draw was— 'We are to have *such* a good time as the sinners have now'; or, to push it to its extreme import—'You sin now, we shall sin by and by; we would sin now, if we could; not being successful we expect our revenge to-morrow.'

The fallacy lay in the immense concession that the bad are successful; that justice is not done now. The blindness of the preacher consisted in deferring to the base estimate of the market of what constitutes a manly success, instead of confronting and convicting the world from the truth; announcing the presence of the soul; the omnipotence of the will; and so establishing the standard of good and ill, of success and falsehood. . . .

Polarity, or action and reaction, we meet in every part of nature; in darkness and light; in heat and cold; in the ebb and flow of waters; in male and female; in the inspiration and expiration of plants and animals; in the equation of quantity and quality in the fluids of the animal body; in the systole and diastole of the heart; in the undulations of fluids and of sound; in the centrifugal and centripetal gravity; in electricity, galvanism, and chemical affinity. Superinduce magnetism at one end of a needle, the opposite magnetism takes place at the other end. If the south attracts, the north repels. To empty here, you must condense there. An inevitable dualism bisects nature, so that each thing is a half, and suggests another thing to make it whole; as, spirit, matter; man, woman; odd, even; subjective, objective; in, out; upper, under; motion, rest; yea, nay.

Whilst the world is thus dual, so is every one of its parts. The entire system of things gets represented in every particle. There is somewhat that resembles the ebb and flow of the sea, day and night, man and woman, in a single needle of the pine, in a kernel of corn, in each individual of every animal tribe. The reaction, so grand in the elements, is repeated within these small boundaries. For example, in the animal kingdom the physiologist has observed that no creatures are favorites, but a certain compensation balances every gift and every defect. A surplusage given to one part is paid out of a reduction from another part of the same creature. If the head and neck are enlarged, the trunk and extremities are cut short.

The theory of the mechanic forces is another example. What we gain in power is lost in time, and the converse. The periodic or compensating errors of the planets is another instance. The influences of climate and soil in political history is another. The cold climate invigorates. The barren soil does not breed fevers, crocodiles, tigers or scorpions.

The same dualism underlies the nature and condition of man. Every excess causes a defect; every defect an excess. Every sweet hath its sour; every evil its good. Every faculty which is a receiver of pleasure has an equal penalty put on its abuse. It is to answer for its moderation with its life. For every grain of wit there is a grain of folly. For every thing you have missed, you have gained something else; and for every thing you gain, you lose something. If riches increase, they are increased that use them. If the gatherer gathers too much, Nature takes out of the man what she puts into his chest; swells the estate, but kills the owner. Nature hates monopolies and exceptions. The waves of the sea do not more speedily seek a level from their loftiest tossing than the varieties of condition tend to equalize themselves. There is always some levelling circumstance that puts down the overbearing, the strong, the rich, the fortunate, substantially on the same ground with all others. . . .

The farmer imagines power and place are fine things. But the President has paid dear for his White House. It has commonly cost him all his peace, and the best of his manly attributes. To preserve for a short time so conspicuous an appearance before the world, he is content to eat dust before the real masters who stand erect behind the throne. Or do men desire the more substantial and permanent grandeur of genius? Neither has this an immunity. He who by force of will or of thought is great and overlooks thousands, has the charges of that eminence. . . .

These appearances indicate the fact that the universe is represented in every one of its particles. Every thing in nature contains all the powers of nature. Every thing is made of one hidden stuff; as the naturalist sees one type under every metamorphoses, and regards a horse as a running man, a fish as a swimming man, a bird as a flying man, a tree as a rooted man. Each new form repeats not only the main character of the type, but part for part all the details, all the aims, furthurances, hindrances, energies and whole system of every other. Every occupation, trade, art, transaction, is a compend of the world and a correlative of every other. Each one is an entire emblem of human life; of its good and ill, its trials, its enemies, its course and its end. And each one must somehow accommodate the whole man and recite all his destiny. . . . The value of the universe contrives to throw itself into every point. If the good is there, so is the evil; if the affinity, so the repulsion; if the force, so the limitation.

Thus is the universe alive. All things are moral. That soul which within us is a sentiment, outside of us is a law. . . . The world looks like a multiplication-table, or a mathematical equation, which, turn it how you will, balances itself. Take what figure you will, its exact value, nor more nor less, still returns to you. Every secret is told, every crime is punished, every virtue rewarded, every wrong redressed, in silence and certainty. What we call retribution is the universal necessity by which the whole appears wherever a part appears. If you see smoke, there must be fire. If you see a hand or a limb, you know that the trunk to which it belongs is there behind. . . .

Crime and punishment grow out of one stem. Punishment is a fruit that unsuspected ripens within the flower of the pleasure which concealed it. Cause and effect, means and ends, seed and fruit, cannot be severed; for the effect already blooms in the cause, the end pre-exists in the means, the fruit in the seed. . . .

All things are double, one against another.—Tit for tat; an eye for an eye; a tooth for a tooth; blood for blood; measure for measure; love for love.—Give, and it shall be given you.—He that watereth shall be watered himself.—What will you have? quoth

God; pay for it and take it.—Nothing venture, nothing have.—Thou shalt be paid exactly for what thou hast done, no more, no less.—Who doth not work shall not eat.—Harm watch, harm catch.—Curses always recoil on the head of him who imprecates them.—If you put a chain around the neck of a slave, the other end fastens itself around your own. . . .

A man cannot speak but he judges himself. With his will or against his will he draws his portrait to the eye of his companions by every word. Every opinion reacts on him who utters it. . . .

You cannot do wrong without suffering wrong. "No man had ever a point of pride that was not injurious to him," said Burke. The exclusive in fashionable life does not see that he excludes himself from enjoyment, in the attempt to appropriate it. The exclusionist in religion does not see that he shuts the door of heaven on himself, in striving to shut out others. Treat men as pawns and ninepins and you shall suffer as well as they. If you leave out their heart, you shall lose your own. The senses would make things of all persons; of women, of chidren, of the poor. . . .

All infractions of love and equity in our social relations are speedily punished. They are punished by fear. Whilst I stand in simple relations to my fellow-man, I have no displeasure in meeting him. We meet as water meets water, or as two currents of air mix, with perfect diffusion and interpenetration of nature. But as soon as there is any departure from simplicity and attempt at halfness, or good for me that is not good for him, my neighbor feels the wrong; he shrinks from me as far as I have shrunk from him; his eyes no longer seek mine; there is war between us; there is hate in him and fear in me. . . .

Experienced men of the world know very well that it is best to pay scot and lot as they go along, and that a man often pays dear for a small frugality. The borrower runs in his own debt. Has a man gained any thing who has received a hundred favors and rendered none? Has he gained by borrowing, through indolence or cunning, his neighbor's wares, or horses, or money? There arises on the deed the instant acknowledgment of benefit on the one part and of debt on the other; that is, of superiority and inferiority. The transaction remains in the memory of himself and his neighbor; and every new transaction alters according to its nature their relation to each other. He may soon come to see that he had better have broken his own bones than to have ridden in his neighbor's coach, and that "the highest price he can pay for a thing is to ask for it."

A wise man will extend this lesson to all parts of life, and know that it is the part of prudence to face every claimant and pay every just demand on your time, your talents, or your heart. Always pay; for first or last you must pay your entire debt. Persons and events may stand for a time between you and justice, but it is only a postponement. You must pay at last your own debt. If you are wise you will dread a prosperity which only loads you with more. Benefit is the end of nature. But for every benefit which you receive, a tax is levied. He is great who confers the most benefits. He is base—and that is the one base thing in the universe—to receive favors and render none. In the order of nature we cannot render benefits to those from whom we receive them, or only seldom. But the benefit we receive must be renderd again, line for line, deed for deed, cent for cent, to somebody. . . .

Labor is watched over by the same pitiless laws. . . . Because of the dual constitution of things, in labor as in life there can be no cheating. The thief steals from himself. The swindler swindles himself. For the real price of labor is knowledge and virtue, whereof wealth and credit are signs. These signs, like paper money, may be counterfeited or stolen, but that which they represent, namely, knowledge and virtue, cannot be counterfeited or stolen. These ends of labor cannot be answered but by real exertions of the mind, and in obedience to pure motives. The cheat, the defaulter, the gambler, cannot extort the knowledge of material and moral nature which his honest care and pains yield to the operative. The law of nature is, Do the thing, and you shall have the power; but they who do not the thing have not the power.

Human labor, through all its forms, from the sharpening of a stake to the construction of a city or an epic, is one immense illustration of the perfect compensation of the universe. The absolute balance of Give and Take, the doctrine that every thing has its price— and if that price is not paid, not that thing but something else is obtained, and that it is impossible to get anything without its price. . . .

The league between virtue and nature engages all things to assume a hostile front to vice. The beautiful laws and substances of the world persecute and whip the traitor. He finds that things are arranged for truth and benefit, but there is no den in the wide world to hide a rogue. Commit a crime, and the earth is made of glass. Commit a crime, and it seems as if a coat of snow fell on the ground, such as reveals in the woods the track of every partridge and fox and squirrel and mole. You cannot recall the spoken word, you cannot wipe out the foot-track, you cannt draw up the ladder, so as to

leave no inlet or clew. Some damning circumstance always trans-
pires. The laws and substances of nature — water, snow, wind,
gravitation—become penalties to the thief.

On the other hand the law holds with equal sureness for all
right action. Love, and you shall be loved. All love is mathematic-
ally just, as much as the two sides of an algebraic equation. The good
man has absolute good, which like fire turns every thing to its own
nature, so that you cannot do him any harm. . . .

The good are befriended even by weakness and defect. As no
man had ever a point of pride that was not injurious to him, so no
man had ever a defect that was not somewhere made useful to him.
. . . Every man in his lifetime needs to thank his faults. . . .

Our strength grows out of our weakness. The indignation which
arms itself with secret forces does not awaken until we are picked
and stung and sorely assailed A great man is always willing to be
little. Whilst he sits on the cushion of advantages, he goes to sleep.
When he is pushed, tormented, defeated, he has a chance to learn
something; he has been put on his wits, on his manhood; he has
gained facts; learns his ignorance; is cured of the insanity of conceit; has got moderation and real skill. The wise man throws himself on the side of his assailants. It is more his interest than it is theirs
to find his weak point. The wound cicatrizes and falls off from him
like a dead skin, and when they would triumph, lo! he has passed
on invulnerable. Blame is safer than praise. I hate to be defended
in a newspaper. As long as all that is said is said against me, I feel
a certain assurance of success. But as soon as honeyed words of
praise are spoken for me, I feel as one that lies unprotected before
his enemies. In general, every evil to which we do not succumb is
a benefactor. As the Sandwich Islander believes that the strength
and valor of the enemy he kills passes into himself, so we gain the
strength of the temptation we resist. . . .

The history of persecution is a history of endeavors to cheat
nature, to make water run up hill, to twist a rope of sand. It makes
no difference whether the actors be many or one, a tyrant or a mob.
A mob is a society of bodies voluntarily bereaving themselves of
reason and traversing its work. The mob is man voluntarily descending to the nature of the beast. Its fit hour of activity is night. Its
actions are insane, like its whole constitution. It persecutes a principle; it would whip a right; it would tar and feather justice, by inflicting fire and outrage upon the houses and persons of those who
have these. It resembles the prank of boys, who run with fire-
engines to put out the ruddy aurora streaming to the stars. The
inviolate spirit turns their spite against the wrongdoers. The martyr

cannot be dishonored. Every lash inflicted is a tongue of fame; every prison a more illustrious abode; every burned book or house enlightens the world; every suppressed or expunged word reverberates through the earth from side to side. Hours of sanity and consideration are always arriving to communities, as to individuals, when the truth is seen and the martyrs are justified.

Thus do all things preach the indifferency of circumstances. The man is all. Everything has two sides, a good and an evil. Every advantage has its tax. I learn to be content. But the doctrine of compensation is not the doctrine of indifferency. The thoughtless say, on hearing these representations—What boots it to do well? there is one event to good and evil; if I gain any good I must pay for it; if I lose any good I gain some other; all actions are indifferent. . . .

Neither can it be said, on the other hand, that the gain of rectitude must be bought by any loss. There is no penalty to virtue; no penalty to wisdom; they are proper additions of being. In a virtuous action I properly *am;* in a virtuous act I add to the world; I plant into deserts conquered from Chaos and Nothing and see the darkness receding on the limits of the horizon. There can be no excess to love, none to knowledge, none to beauty, when these attributes are considered in the purest sense. The soul refuses limits, and always affirms an Optimism, never a Pessimism. . . .

In the nature of the soul is the compensation for the inequalities of condition. The radical tragedy of nature seems to be the distinction of More and Less. How can Less not feel the pain; how not feel indignation or malevolence towards More? Look at those who have less faculty, and one feels sad and knows not well what to make of it. He almost shuns their eye; he fears they will upbraid God. What should they do? It seems a great injustice. But see the facts nearly and these mountainous inequalities vanish. Love reduces them as the sun melts the iceberg in the sea. The heart and soul of all men being one, this bitterness of *His* and *Mine* ceases. His is mine. I am my brother and my brother is me. If I feel over-shadowed and outdone by great neighbors, I can yet love; I can still receive; and he that loveth maketh his own the grandeur he loves. . . .

The compensations of calamity are made apparent to the understanding also, after long intervals of time. A fever, a mutilation, a cruel disappointment, a loss of wealth, a loss of friends, seems at the moment unpaid loss, and unpayable. But the sure years reveal the deep remedial force that underlies all facts. The death of a dear friend, wife, brother, lover, which seemed nothing but privation, somewhat later assumes the aspect of a guide or genius; for it commonly operates revolutions in our way of life, terminates an epoch of infancy or of youth which was waiting to be closed, breaks up a wonted occupation, or a household, or style of living, and allows the formation of new ones more friendly to the growth of character. It permits or constrains the formation of new acquaintances and the reception of new influences that prove of the first importance to the next years; and the man or woman who would have remained a sunny garden-flower, with no room for its roots and too much sunshine for its head, by the falling of the walls and the neglect of the gardener is made the banian of the forest, yielding shade and fruit to wide neighborhoods of men.

Discussion of "Compensation"

One of the wisest, most profound, most provocative explorations ever made into the whole matter of grief and suffering in life and the basic morality of the universe is the essay "Compensation" by Ralph Waldo Emerson (1803-1882), that great romantic transcendentalist who still stands as America's foremost philosophical essayist. Is it true *in this life,* as Emerson says, that in every triumph there is also defeat, and in every defeat triumph; that in every gain there is loss, and in every loss gain; that in every pleasure there is pain, and in every pain pleasure; that all experiences of success and failure, health and sickness, happiness and sorrow so balance themselves that inherent within them is inevitable compensation and equalization?

Less than half of the essay is quoted here, but even in fragmentary form it so forcefully and eloquently speaks its message that no further comment on it is needed. It invites absorption and stimulates meditation, but paraphrase or explanation would ruin it—would dilute its thought and lessen the rich figurativeness of its literary style. One comment only seems desirable, and that is to remind ourselves that whatever laws of compensation govern our earthly experiences, our responsibility as individuals is to do all that we can to live according to the ideals of the Gospel, with complete confidence in God's eternal justice.

Michael

A Pastoral Poem

by William Wordsworth

If from the public way you turn your steps
Up the tumultuous brook of Greenhead Ghyll,
You will suppose that with an upright path
Your feet must struggle; in such bold ascent
The pastoral mountains front you, face to face.
But, courage! for around that boisterous brook
The mountains have all opened out themselves,
And made a hidden valley of their own.
No habitation can be seen; but they
Who journey thither find themselves alone
With a few sheep, with rocks and stones, and kites
That overhead are sailing in the sky.
It is in truth an utter solitude;
Nor should I have made mention of this Dell
But for one object which you might pass by,
Might see and notice not. Beside the brook
Appears a straggling heap of unhewn stones!
And to that simple object appertains
A story—unenriched with strange events,
Yet not unfit, I deem, for the fireside,
Or for the summer shade. It was the first
Of those domestic tales that spake to me
Of shepherds, dwellers in the valleys, men
Whom I already loved; not verily
For their own sakes, but for the fields and hills
Where was their occupation and abode.
And hence this Tale, while I was yet a Boy
Careless of books, yet having felt the power
Of Nature, by the gentle agency
Of natural objects, led me on to feel
For passions that were not my own, and think
(At random and imperfectly indeed)
On man, the heart of man, and human life.
Therefore, although it be a history
Homely and rude, I will relate the same
For the delight of a few natural hearts;

And, with yet fonder feeling, for the sake
Of youthful Poets, who among these hills
Will be my second self when I am gone.

    Upon the forest-side in Grasmere Vale
There dwelt a Shepherd, Michael was his name;
An old man, stout of heart, and strong of limb.
His bodily frame had been from youth to age
Of an unusual strength: his mind was keen,
Intense, and frugal, apt for all affairs,
And in his shepherd's calling he was prompt
And watchful more than ordinary men.
Hence had he learned the meaning of all winds,
Of blasts of every tone; and, oftentimes,
When others heeded not, he heard the South
Make subterraneous music, like the noise
Of bagpipes on distant Highland hills.
The Shepherd, at such warning, of his flock
Bethought him, and he to himself would say,
"The winds are now devising work for me!"
And, truly, at all times, the storm, that drives
The traveller to a shelter, summoned him
Up to the mountains: he had been alone
Amid the heart of many thousand mists,
That came to him, and left him, on the heights.
So lived he till his eightieth year was past.
And grossly that man errs, who should suppose
That the green valleys, and the streams and rocks,
Were things indifferent to the Shepherd's thoughts.
Fields, where with cheerful spirits he had breathed
The common air; hills, which with vigorous step
He had so often climbed; which had impressed
So many incidents upon his mind
Or hardship, skill or courage, joy or fear;
Which, like a book, preserved the memory
Of the dumb animals, whom he had saved,
Had fed or sheltered, linking to such acts
The certainty of honorable gain;
Those fields, those hills—what could they less?—had laid
Strong hold on his affections, were to him
A pleasurable feeling of blind love,
The pleasure which there is in life itself.

His days had not been passed in singleness,
His Helpmate was a comely matron, old—
Though younger than himself full twenty years.
She was a woman of a stirring life,
Whose heart was in her house: two wheels she had
Of antique form; this large, for spinning wool;
That small, for flax; and if one wheel had rest
It was because the other was at work.
The Pair had but one inmate in their house,
An only Child, who had been born to them
When Michael, telling o'er his years, began
To deem that he was old,—in shepherd's phrase,
With one foot in the grave. This only Son,
With two brave sheep-dogs tried in many a storm,
The one of an inestimable worth,
Made all their household. I may truly say,
That they were as a proverb in the vale
For endless industry. When day was gone,
And from their occupations out of doors
The Son and Father were come home, even then,
Their labor did not cease; unless when all
Turned to the cleanly supper-board, and there,
Each with a mess of pottage and skimmed milk,
Sat round the basket piled with oaten cakes,
And their plain home-made cheese. Yet when the meal
Was ended, Luke (for so the Son was named)
And his old Father both betook themselves
To such convenient work as might employ
Their hands by the fireside; perhaps to card
Wool for the Housewife's spindle, or repair
Some injury done to sickle, flail, or scythe,
Or other implement of house or field.

Down from the ceiling, by the chimney's edge,
That in our ancient uncouth country style
With huge and black projection overbrowed
Large space beneath, as duly as the light
Of day grew dim the Housewife hung a lamp;
An aged utensil, which had performed
Service beyond all others of its kind.
Early at evening did it burn—and late,
Surviving comrade of uncounted hours,

Which, going by from year to year, had found,
And left, the couple neither gay perhaps
Nor cheerful, yet with objects and with hopes,
Living a life of eager industry.
And now when Luke had reached his eighteenth year,
There by the light of this old lamp they sate,
Father and Son, while far into the night
The Housewife plied her own peculiar work,
Making the cottage through the silent hours
Murmur as with the sound of summer flies.
This light was famous in its neighborhood,
And was a public symbol of the life
That thrifty Pair had lived. For, as it chanced,
Their cottage on a plot of rising ground
Stood single, with large prospect, north and south,
High into Easedale, up to Dunmail-Raise,
And westward to the village near the lake;
And from this constant light, so regular
And so far seen, the House itself, by all
Who dwelt within the limits of the vale,
Both old and young, was named The Evening Star.

Thus living on through such a length of years,
The Shepherd, if he loved himself, must needs
Have loved his Helpmate; but to Michael's heart
This son of his old age was yet more dear—
Less from instinctive tenderness, the same
Fond spirit that blindly works in the blood of all—
Than that a child, more than all other gifts
That earth can offer to declining man,
Brings hope with it, and forward-looking thoughts,
And stirrings of inquietude, when they
By tendency of nature needs must fail.
Exceeding was the love he bare to him,
His heart and his heart's joy! For oftentimes
Old Michael, while he was a babe in arms,
Had done him female service, not alone
For pastime and delight, as is the use
Of fathers, but with patient mind enforced
To acts of tenderness; and he had rocked
His cradle, as with a woman's gentle hand.

And, in a later time, ere yet the Boy
Had put on boy's attire, did Michael love,
Albeit of a stern unbending mind,
To have the Young-one in his sight, when he
Wrought in the field, or on his shepherd's stool
Sate with a fettered sheep before him stretched
Under the large old oak, that near his door
Stood single, and, from matchless depth of shade,
Chosen for the Shearer's covert from the sun,
Thence in our rustic dialect was called
The Clipping Tree, a name which yet it bears.
There, while they two were sitting in the shade,
With others round them, earnest all and blithe,
Would Michael exercise his heart with looks
Of fond correction and reproof bestowed
Upon the Child, if he disturbed the sheep
By catching at their legs, or with his shouts
Scared them while they lay still beneath the shears.

And when by Heaven's good grace the boy grew up
A healthy Lad, and carried in his cheek
Two steady roses that were five years old;
Then Michael from a winter coppice cut
With his own hand a sapling, which he hooped
With iron, making it throughout in all
Due requisites a perfect shepherd's staff,
And gave it to the Boy; wherewith equipped
He as a watchman oftentimes was placed
At gate or gap, to stem or turn the flock;
And, to his office prematurely called,
There stood the urchin, as you will divine,
Something between a hindrance and a help;
And for this cause not always, I believe,
Receiving from his Father hire of praise;
Though nought was left undone which staff, or voice,
Or looks, or threatening gestures, could perform.

But soon as Luke, full ten years old, could stand
Against the mountain blasts; and to the heights,
Not fearing toil, nor length of weary ways,
He with his Father daily went, and they
Were as companions, why should I relate

That objects which the Shepherd loved before
Were dearer now? that from the Boy there came
Feelings and emanations—things which were
Light to the sun and music to the wind;
And that the old Man's heart seemed born again?

   Thus in his Father's sight the Boy grew up:
And now, when he had reached his eighteenth year,
He was his comfort and his daily hope.

   While in this sort the simple household lived
From day to day, to Michael's ear there came
Distressful tidings. Long before the time
Of which I speak, the Shepherd had been bound
In surety for his brother's son, a man
Of an industrious life, and ample means;
But unforeseen misfortunes suddenly
Had pressed upon him; and old Michael now
Was summoned to discharge the forfeiture,
A grievous penalty, but little less
Than half his substance. This unlooked-for-claim,
At the first hearing, for a moment took
More hope out of his life than he supposed
That any old man ever could have lost.
As soon as he had armed himself with strength
To look his trouble in the face, it seemed
The Shepherd's sole resource to sell at once
A portion of his patrimonial fields.
Such was his first resolve; he thought again,
And his heart failed him. "Isabel," said he,
Two evenings after he had heard the news,
"I have been toiling more than seventy years,
And in the open sunshine of God's love
Have we all lived; yet if these fields of ours
Should pass into a stranger's hand, I think
That I could not lie quiet in my grave.
Our lot is a hard lot; the sun himself
Has scarcely been more diligent than I;
And I have lived to be a fool at last
To my own family. An evil man
That was, and made an evil choice, if he
Were false to us; and, if he were not false,

There are ten thousand to whom loss like this
Had been no sorrow. I forgive him;—but
'Twere better to be dumb than to talk thus.

When I began, my purpose was to speak
Of remedies and of a cheerful hope.
Our Luke shall leave us, Isabel; the land
Shall not go from us, and it shall be free;
He shall possess it, free as is the wind
That passes over it. We have, thou know'st,
Another kinsman—he will be our friend
In this distress. He is a prosperous man,
Thriving in trade—and Luke to him shall go,
And with his kinsman's help and his own thrift
He quickly will repair this loss, and then
He may return to us. If here he stay,
What can be done? Where every one is poor,
What can be gained?"

At this the old man paused,
And Isabel sat silent, for her mind
Was busy, looking back into past times.
There's Richard Bateman, thought she to herself,
He was a parish-boy—at the church door
They made a gathering for him, shillings, pence,
And halfpennies, wherewith the neighbors bought
A basket, which they filled with pedlar's wares;
And, with this basket on his arm, the lad
Went up to London, found a master there,
Who, out of many, chose the trusty boy
To go and overlook his merchandise
Beyond the seas; where he grew wondrous rich,
And left estates and monies to the poor,
And, at his birth-place, built a chapel, floored
With marble, which he sent from foreign lands.
These thoughts, and many others of like sort,
Passed quickly through the mind of Isabel,
And her face brightened. The old Man was glad,
And thus resumed:—"Well, Isabel! this scheme,
These two days, has been meat and drink to me
Far more than we have lost is left us yet.
We have enough—I wish indeed that I

Were younger;—but this hope is a good hope.
Make ready Luke's best garments, of the best
Buy for him more, and let us send him forth
To-morrow, or the next day, or to-night:
If he *could* go, the Boy should go to-night."

   Here Michael ceased, and to the fields, went forth
With a light heart. The Housewife for five days
Was restless morn and night, and all day long
Wrought on with her best fingers to prepare
Things needful for the journey of her son.
But Isabel was glad when Sunday came
To stop her in her work: for, when she lay
By Michael's side, she through the last two nights
Heard him, how he was troubled in his sleep;
And when they rose at morning she could see
That all his hopes were gone. That day at noon
She said to Luke, while they two by themselves
Were sitting at the door, "Thou must not go:
We have no other Child but thee to lose,
None to remember—do not go away,
For if thou leave thy Father he will die."
The Youth made answer with a jocund voice;
And Isabel, when she had told her fears,
Recovered heart. That evening her best fare
Did she bring forth, and all together sat
Like happy people round a Christmas fire.

   With daylight Isabel resumed her work;
And all the ensuing week the house appeared
As cheerful as a grove in Spring: at length
The expected letter from their kinsman came,
With kind assurances that he would do
His utmost for the welfare of the Boy;
To which, requests were added, that forthwith
He might be sent to him. Ten times or more
The letter was read over; Isabel
Went forth to show it to the neighbors round;
Nor was there at that time on English land
A prouder heart than Luke's. When Isabel
Had to her house returned, the old Man said,
"He shall depart to-morrow." To this word

The Housewife answered, talking much of things
Which, if at such short notice he should go,
Would surely be forgotten. But at length
She gave consent, and Michael was at ease.

    Near the tumultuous brook of Greenhead Ghyll,
In that deep valley, Michael had designed
To build a Sheepfold; and, before he heard
The tidings of his melancholy loss,
For this same purpose he had gathered up
A heap of stones, which by the streamlet's edge
Lay thrown together, ready for the work.
With Luke that evening thitherward he walked:
And soon as they had reached the place he stopped,
And thus the old Man spake to him:—"My son,
To-morrow thou wilt leave me: with full heart
I look upon thee, for thou art the same
That wert a promise to me ere thy birth,
And all thy life hast been my daily joy.
I will relate to thee some little part
Of our two histories; 'twill do thee good
When thou art from me, even if I should touch
On things thou canst not know of.—After thou
First cam'st into the world—as oft befalls
To new-born infants—thou didst sleep away
Two days, and blessings from thy Father's tongue
Then fell upon thee. Day by day passed on,
And still I loved thee with increasing love.
Never to living ear came sweeter sounds
Than when I heard thee by our own fireside
First uttering, without words, a natural tune;
While thou, a feeding babe, didst in thy joy
Sing at thy Mother's breast. Month followed month,
And in the open fields my life was passed
And on the mountains; else I think that thou
Hadst been brought up upon thy Father's knees.
But we were playmates, Luke: among these hills,
As well thou knowest, in us the old and young
Have played together, nor with me didst thou
Lack any pleasure which a boy can know."
Luke had a manly heart; but at these words
He sobbed aloud. The old Man grasped his hand,

And said, "Nay, do not take it so—I see
That these are things of which I need not speak.
—Even to the utmost I have been to thee
A kind and a good Father: and herein
I but repay a gift which I myself
Received at others' hands; for, though now old
Beyond the common life of man, I still
Remember them who loved me in my youth.
Both of them sleep together: here they lived,
As all their Forefathers had done; and when
At length their time was come, they were not loth
To give their bodies to the family mould.
I wished that thou should'st live the life they lived:
But 'tis a long time to look back, my Son,
And see so little gain from threescore years.
These fields were burthened when they came to me;
Till I was forty years of age, not more
Than half of my inheritance was mine.
I toiled and toiled; God blessed me in my work,
And till these three weeks past the land was free.
—It looks as if it never could endure
Another Master. Heaven forgive me, Luke,
If I judge ill for thee, but it seems good
That thou should'st go."

                              At this the old Man paused;
Then, pointing to the stones near which they stood,
Thus, after a short silence, he resumed:
"This was a work for us; and now, my Son,
It is a work for me. But, lay one stone—
Here, lay it for me, Luke, with thine own hands.
Nay, Boy, be of good hope;—we both may live
To see a better day.   At eighty-four
I still am strong and hale;—do thou thy part;
I will do mine.—I will begin again
With many tasks that were resigned to thee:
Up to the heights, and in among the storms,
Will I without thee go again, and do
All works which I was wont to do alone,
Before I knew thy face.—Heaven bless thee, Boy!
Thy heart these two weeks has been beating fast
With many hopes; it should be so—yes—yes—
I knew that thou could'st never have a wish

To leave me, Luke: thou hast been bound to me
Only by links of love: when thou art gone,
What will be left to us!—But I forget
My purposes. Lay now the corner-stone,
As I requested; and hereafter, Luke,
When thou art gone away, should evil men
Be thy companions, think of me, my Son,
And of this moment; hither turn thy thoughts,
And God will strengthen thee: amid all fear
And all temptation, Luke, I pray that thou
May'st bear in mind the life thy Fathers lived,
Who, being innocent, did for that cause
Bestir them in good deeds. Now, fare thee well—
When thou return'st, thou in this place wilt see
A work which is not here: a covenant
'Twill be between us; but, whatever fate
Befall thee, I shall love thee to the last,
And bear thy memory with me to the grave."

The Shepherd ended here; and Luke stooped down,
And, as his Father had requested, laid
The first stone of the Sheepfold. At the sight
The old Man's grief broke from him; to his heart
He pressed his Son, he kissed him and wept;
And to the house together they returned.
—Hushed was that House in peace, or seeming peace,
Ere the night fell:—with morrow's dawn the Boy
Began his journey, and when he had reached
The public way, he put on a bold face;
And all the neighbors, as he passed their doors,
Came forth with wishes and with farewell prayers,
That followed him till he was out of sight.

A good report did from their Kinsman come,
Of Luke and his well-doing; and the Boy
Wrote loving letters, full of wondrous news,
Which, as the Housewife phrased it, were throughout
"The prettiest letters that were ever seen."
Both parents read them with rejoicing hearts.
So, many months passed on: and once again
The Shepherd went about his daily work
With confident and cheerful thoughts; and now
Sometimes when he could find a leisure hour

He to that valley took his way, and there
Wrought at the Sheepfold. Meantime Luke began
To slacken in his duty; and, at length,
He in the dissolute city gave himself
To evil courses: ignominy and shame
Fell on him, so that he was driven at last
To seek a hiding-place beyond the seas.

There is a comfort in the strength of love;
'Twill make a thing endurable, which else
Would overset the brain, or break the heart:
I have conversed with more than one who well
Remember the old Man, and what he was
Years after he had heard this heavy news.
His bodily frame had been from youth to age
Of an unusual strength. Among the rocks
He went, and still looked up to sun and cloud,
And listened to the wind; and, as before,
Performed all kinds of labor for his sheep,
And for the land, his small inheritance.
And to that hollow dell from time to time
Did he repair to build the Fold of which
His flock had need. 'Tis not forgotten yet
The pity which was then in every heart
For the old Man—and 'tis believed by all
That many and many a day he thither went,
And never lifted up a single stone.

There, by the Sheepfold, sometimes was he seen
Sitting alone, or with his faithful Dog,
Then old, beside him, lying at his feet.
The length of full seven years, from time to time,
He at the building of this Sheepfold wrought,
And left the work unfinished when he died.
Three years, or little more, did Isabel
Survive her Husband: at her death the estate
Was sold, and went into a stranger's hand.
The Cottage which was named The Evening Star
Is gone—the ploughshare has been through the ground
On which it stood; great changes have been wrought
In all the neighborhood:—yet the oak is left
That grew beside their door; and the remains
Of the unfinished Sheepfold may be seen
Beside the boisterous brook of Greenhead Ghyll.

Discussion of "Michael"

As indicated earlier in this book, two closely related themes are dominant above all others in the poetry of William Wordsworth[1] (1770-1850): (1) the power of nature to elevate and ennoble the mind of man and (2) the dignity and nobility inherent in all human life. In "Michael," Wordsworth's greatest narrative poem, we find his most impressive treatment of these two themes, as well as a very significant handling of the place of suffering in human experience.

To be fully appreciated "Michael" must be read aloud from beginning to end so that its stately story and blank-verse structure can be felt in total strength. It is a story of such dignity and tragic power that so read it will never be forgotten. It is like a parable of Christ—both in the eloquent simplicity of its style and the memorable message of its story—or perhaps even more like an incident out of Old Testament history.

"Michael" opens with a 39-line introduction which sets the dignified, reverent tone of the poem and in which Wordsworth explains why he is writing it: that in a remote mountain valley which as a boy he knew there is a "straggling heap of unhewn stones" around which centers an old and moving legend which he wishes to recount "for the delight of a few natural hearts." He then goes on to tell the story of the shepherd Michael, who years earlier was "an old man, stout of heart, and strong of limb," whose "bodily frame had been from youth to age of an unusual strength." In every way Michael was noble and good, and, like Abraham of old, he was blessed in his old age with a son, whom he loved deeply and with whom he formed a beautiful comradeship as the son became a young man. When the son, named Luke, was eighteen, and Michael eighty-four, financial difficulties pressed upon the family in the form of a "debt of honor" to the extent that Luke was sent to work

---

[1]For an introductory discussion of Wordsworth's life and work, see pp. 53-70.

for a distant kinsman to relieve the financial stress. Deciding to send him away was most difficult for Michael and his wife Isabel, for they loved the boy deeply. But their love for their land was equally great. And the only possibility for keeping the land as an inheritance for the son was to allow the son away for a few years, thus earning sufficient money to discharge the indebtedness and return to his parents and the land they all loved. So arrangements were made for his departure.

But before old father and young son separated, Michael took Luke into the hills where they laid the cornerstone of a sheepfold as a covenant of their faith in and devotion to each other. Michael assured Luke that at eighty-four he still was "strong and hale" and while Luke was gone would use the pile of gathered stones to build the sheepfold and do the other work now performed by the two together. He counseled his son:

> Should evil men
> Be thy companions, think of me, my Son,
> And of this moment; hither turn thy thoughts,
> And God will strengthen thee, amid all fear
> And all temptation. . . . But whatever fate
> Befall thee, I shall love thee to the last,
> And bear thy memory with me to the grave.

Then Michael and Luke separated. At first good reports came of the son, but months later Luke "began to slacken in his duty" and "in the dissolute city gave himself to evil courses: ignominy and shame fell on him, so that he was driven at last to seek a hiding-place beyond the seas." Old Michael was somewhat sustained in his grief by his deep love, for

> There is a comfort in the strength of love;
> 'Twill make a thing endurable, which else
> Would overset the brain, or break the heart.

But partly his love was in very fact responsible for his grief, for there is no grief more harsh than that of faith betrayed.

Thus, bearing the burden of his sorrow, Michael went about his daily work suffering in silence, often sitting in numb loneliness at the site of the unfinished sheepfold ("and 'tis believed by all that many and many a day he thither went, and never lifted up a single stone"), anguishedly disappointed in his erring son, but still loving him, even as God must feel for his erring earth children.

It is a powerful and unforgettably sad and beautiful story. In a way, although perhaps Wordsworth did not think of this, it is the Prodigal Son parable re-told but with the son not returning. Its ethical message is not only to parents who may suffer as Michael suffered but even more to children—and all of us are children—who may falter as Luke faltered, and who through the poem may be strengthened in our desire to fulfill the faith in us of those who love us.

As one aspect of the story, note that old Michael becomes a greater, more heroic figure through his suffering. Suffering dignifies and deepens him. Someone has defined tragedy as the spectacle of a heroic figure suffering heroically. We admire as well as pity a character of tragic stature, even as Michael is. Wordsworth once said of himself, "A deep distress hath humanized my soul."[1] Is there a kind of understanding, a largeness of the soul, which comes through personal suffering, and can come in no other way? Is there a majesty of the human spirit that becomes most clearly visible only in a moment of defeat and disaster?

---

[1] See his poem "Elegiac Stanzas." The "deep distress" was the death of Wordsworth's brother in a storm at sea.

The Sick Child

by Colette

Translated by George Davis

The child wanted to prop himself higher on his pillow but
could not. His mother heard his prayer without words and lifted
him up. He had thought she was no longer watching him, the child
promised to death, yet here was the maternal face bending over him
again, the chestnut hair drawn over the temples in old-fashioned
wings, the thinnish cheeks barely touched with powder, the candidly
set brown eyes so confident of mastery over their fears that often
they forgot to be on guard. . . .

"You are nice and rosy this evening, little boy," she said gaily.

But her brown eyes kept a worried fixity that the little boy had
come to know well. To avoid any tiring movement of his neck,
he raised the pupils of his sea-green eyes upward against their lids
and gravely made a correction:

"I'm rosy because of the lamp shade."

Lady Mother looked sorrowfully at her son, inwardly reproach-
ing him for the word that had erased the color she had seen in his
face. He had closed his eyes, and again with the appearance of
sleep he was a ten-year-old. "She believes that I am sleeping."
With a gentle guile, his mother turned away from the bed, as
though she could now concern herself elsewhere. "He believes that
I believe he is sleeping." Many a time they played this game of outpretending each other. "She believes that I'm not in pain," Jean
would think, his lashes crisping against his hot cheekbones. While
Lady Mother would be thinking: "How well he knows how to imitate a child who is not in pain. Any other mother would be taken
in. But I . . ."

"Doesn't the lavender spray make the most delicious fragrance?
Your room smells so good."

The child agreed without speaking. Practice and the need to
spare his strength had gradually provided him with a repertory of
intricate little signs, a mimicry as delicate as the language of the
animals. He excelled in putting his senses to a fantastic and magical use. For example, he could hear the morning sunlight make a
pink sound as it came through the curtains of white muslin. He
could hold his battered old *Voyage Up the Amazon* under his nose,
and the smell of calfskin binding became the taste of steaming pan-
cakes. . . . Three blinks of his eyelids meant that he wanted water.

And for food . . . oh, but somehow he never seemed to want food, it hardly needed a sign. The other wants of his soft and wasted little body made themselves known by a modest telegraphy. But for anything that was not actually necessary, anything that could still represent pleasure and play in the life of a condemned child, Jean clung to human speech, sought words that were exact and varied, spoke them in a voice to which pain had given its own wan harmony.

"No, it isn't really such a delicious smell," he thought. "I don't remember lavender quite that way. It seems to me that when I used to live standing up. . ."

At that moment a cloud of scent passed under his pinched white nostrils. Swiftly Jean leaped on and galloped away. It was just one of the wonderful stunts he had learned during the long hours in bed, though he never breathed a word about them to his mother.

Bored after a moment with his room, he headed his perfumed steed out through the frosted transom and down the hall. A big silvery moth followed sneezing in their wake, but Jean outdistanced him easily by giving Lavender a few digs with his knees. While people were around, those long legs of Jean's would only lie still, but now they gave him all the strength and skill a rider needed. At times like this, escaped from his bed, he could ride a horse—and right through a wall, too. But best of all he could fly! Bending his body forward like a diver plunging into space, he could feel his forehead cleaving an element that had yielded its every resource to him. Arms spread, he had only to raise one or the other shoulder to shift the direction of his flight. An extra little shove forward always eased the shock of landing.

Not that he landed often. . . . Once he was careless enough to swoop too low, over a cow pasture. Suddenly there he was, right up against the astonished gaze of a beautiful tan cow, her horns sprouting toward him, her eyes like two magnifying lenses whirling bigger and bigger, while from the grass yellow dandelions sped up like bursting planets. Just in the nick of time he managed to grab hold of her horns with his bare hands and vault back into the air. He could still recall the warm glossy feel of the horns, with their blunt and somehow kindly tips, and hear the barking of the shepherd dog grow fainter as the flying boy climbed back into his familiar sky. That morning he had to use all the strength in his arm-feathers to retrace his way across the periwinkle dawn, glide over the slumbering city and tumble into his lacquered bed. The rumples in the blanket had hurt him terribly, with a tenacious hurt that

burned along his back and down his thighs, so that he was unable
to hide the traces of his tears. . . .

"Did something make you cry, Jean darling?"

"No, Lady Mother, only in a dream. . . ."

Now Lavender had reached the end of the hall and was butting
against the door that led to the kitchen. "Ho ho, Ho ho! What a
stupid beast! I knew she wasn't a thoroughbred. These mongrel
ponies will always break your neck if you don't hold right. . . ."
Jean dug severely into her penitent flanks and guided her into the
warm upper region of the kitchen where the wash was drying.
Lowering his head to pass between two clotheslines, he neatly
snipped off an apron string and slipped it into Lavender's mouth.

"Where are we heading? We must get back in time for dinner, and it's already late. . . . Giddyap, Lavender, giddyap. . . ."

They were out the service door, and Jean invented a new game
of racing down the stairs head first, with a couple of spins thrown
in for fun. Lavender was terrified by her master's commands and
tried to balk. "Oh, you big dumb filly" cried the child, and he
burst into laughter, he who never laughed in his sheltered other life.
As they flew madly down, they came on a small dog, the one who
"knew how to do his business all alone," then go back and scratch
on the door. Jean reached out to pull his tail.

"Want a ride, Riki? You can sit behind me!"

Jean swept up the dog with his powerful little hand, bounced
him on to the bulging rump of Lavender, who, spurred by Riki's
frantic clawings, went tumbling down the last two flights. There
Riki leaped from the eiderdown rump and ran off howling.

"You don't know what you're missing!" shouted Jean. "I used
to be scared at first too, but now . . . watch me, Riki!"

Rider and mount flung themselves against the stout street door.
To Jean's astonishment, they were met not with the usual surrender
of obliging oak, melting locks and big bolts which said, "Yes, yes,"
as they slid tamely back, but the inflexible barrier of a chiseled
voice whispering: ". . .back to slumberland. . ."

Breathless with the shock, shaken from head to foot, Jean could
feel the cruelly sharp words "back to, Baktu, Baktu" cutting like
a razor. Behind them the word "slumberland" lay severed in three
pieces.

"Slum . . . ber . . . land . . ." murmured Jean. "It's all over,
my horseback ride. Now it's slum . . . ber . . . land, rolled into
a ball. Good-by . . . good-by . . ."

He had no chance to find out to whom he was saying good-by.
Time was getting horribly short. He miscalculated the landing.

The exhausted Lavender missed the four feet she never had; before vanishing forever into cold droplets she threw her rider from her non-existent back into his lacquered bed, and Jean groaned as he crashed. . . .

"You were sleeping so well . . ." said the voice of Lady Mother.

A voice, thought her son, that was made up of a mixture of straight and curved lines—a curved, a straight—a dry line, a wet line. . . . But there would never be any use in trying to explain this to Lady Mother.

"You woke up as though something were the matter, my darling. Were you in pain?"

He made his "no" sign, wagging from right to left his thin white index finger. Besides, his suffering was not so bad now. He wished the bed were not quite so hard, but he was getting used to his falls. As for Lavender, well, what could you expect from a stinky old nag?

"The next time," thought Jean, "I'll take a ride on Big Scooter." That was his nighttime name for an ennnormous nickel-plated paper cutter; it always took three n's and sometimes four, to give an idea of its size.

"Lady Mother, would you please push Big Scoot—I mean the big paper cutter—over here under the lamp?"

To make sure that everything would be ready for his next expedition, Jean turned on his pillow toward his mother. His hair was cut short in back to keep it from matting. On top and over his forehead and ears he had soft yellow curls with a faint greenish tint, the color of a winter moon, well matched with the sea green of his eyes, the petal white of his face. He watched his mother's practiced hand place the lamp and the paper cutter where he wanted them, so that the polished blade caught a reflection that was like snow at sunset, with bluish streaks; a strange landscape that he loved. He half closed his eyes.

"Jean dearest, it will soon be time for your dinner," said Lady Mother hestitatingly.

The sick child smiled indulgently at his mother. People who are well must be forgiven everything. And he really did feel rather bruised from his fall. "I have lots of time," he thought, and accentuated his smile at the risk of seeing Lady Mother—as whenever his smiles were too accomplished, too charged with a serenity to which she gave only one meaning—break down and rush from the room.

"If you don't mind, dearest, I'll have my dinner all alone in the diningroom, after you have finished with your tray. . . ."

"Okay, okay," answered the index finger condescendingly, closing twice.

Lady Mother bent over him, and he reached up his arms and clasped them according to ritual around her neck.   Thus proudly charged, she hauled up the meager body of her child, too tall for his age, the slender torso followed by the long legs, inert now but which knew how to grip and master the flanks of a skittish cloud steed. . . . Lady Mother gazed at her graceful and ailing creation, sitting against his hard, pulpit-shaped pillow.

"There we are!   Your tray will be right along. Just the same, I think I'll go and hurry Mandore.   She never manages to be on time!"

And out she went once more.

"She goes, she comes. . . . Mostly she goes. She doesn't want to leave me alone, but she is always running out of my room. Probably she was thinking of me and has tears she wants to wipe away. Won't she ever get used to me?   Won't she ever learn to be sensible?   She has a hundred reasons for leaving my room and if by luck, she didn't, I could give her a thousand. . . . Mandore is never late."

Turning his neck cautiously, he watched Mandore enter.   "If it weren't for me," thought Jean, "she would still be calling herself Angelina."   But wasn't Mandore the perfect, inevitable name for her, so round-bellied and golden, sounding tunefully to every touch, harmony in her beautiful voice and in her eyes that gleamed like the precious wood of lutes?   Mandore, Mandore. . .

She crossed the room, and as her yellow-and-chestnut-striped skirt brushed against the furniture, Jean heard the full cello notes that his ear alone could catch.   She put over the bed a little table covered with an embroidered napkin and holding a steaming bowl.

"Here's your dinner, young man!"

"What have you got?"

"Your phosphate salts to start off with, right here! Then . . . well, you'll see."

Over the reclining body of the sick child poured a glance that was like a consoling flood of foamy, thirst-quenching liquid. "How good, how good the dark beer of Mandore's eyes! How kind she is! How kind everybody is to me. . . . If only sometimes they wouldn't be quite so much so. . ." Exhausted by the burden of universal kindness, he shut his eyes, reopening them to the clinking of spoons.

Spoons for his medicine, for his soup, for his desserts. . . . Jean hated spoons, except for one wonderful spoon with a long handle and an ornamented ring on the end. "It's a sugar crusher," was Lady Mother's explanation. "And what's the other end for?" "I'm not quite sure, precious. I believe it is an absinthe spoon. . . ." And her glance had a way of slipping toward a photograph of Jean's father, the husband she had lost so young, "Your dear papa, Jean darling," and to whom Jean referred coldly—with words out of a silence, out of a secret—as "that gentleman hanging in the parlor."

"Now, Jean my pet, open wide. . . ."

He obeyed, gulping down the medicine that was inoffensive enough except for a quick musky taste that seemed to disguise a horror. In Jean's secret vocabulary, this potion was called "the gully of the corpses."

The phosphated soup followed inescapably, with a flavor like the seedy sweepings from a granary. All that saved it was a magical something floating in its depths like a floral breeze; the perfumed powder of cornflowers that Mandore had bought for him last July from a pushcart. . . . A small cube of grilled lamb took no time at all. "Hurry, lamb, hurry, I won't make a face at you, as long as you roll down quick to my stomach. But I wouldn't chew you for the world, I can still hear you saying baaa, and your insides are pink!"

"Aren't you eating faster than usual this evening, Jean?"

Lady Mother's voice came floating down from the shadows overhead, perhaps from the plaster shell cornice, perhaps from somewhere high in the huge wardrobe. By special grant from Jean, Lady Mother had been given the power to penetrate the lofty reaches of the wardrobe, realm of the household linen. Up she would go on a double ladder that was invisible behind the right-hand door, and climb down again carrying great snowy slabs that she had hewed from above. Her ambition was satisfied with this harvest. Jean went farther, higher, leaping ever on toward the pure summits, plunging through an unmatched pair of sheets, reappearing through the even folds of a matched pair—with a perilous slip or two, a dizzy spell, among the stiff damask napkins—then a pause on an Alp to admire the Greek scrolls and the glazed foliage, the sprigs of dried lavender, the big and creamy iris roots. . . . At dawn he would have made the descent again, rigid with cold, white and utterly done in, but still devilish. "Jean! Heavens, he must have thrown off the covers during his sleep. Mandore.

quick, the hot-water bottle!" . . . While Jean was congratulating himself on getting back in time. . . .

"I'm eating fast, Lady Mother, because I'm hungry." He was an old hand at sly tricks, and Lady Mother had only to hear him say, "I'm hungry," to blush with delight.

"If that's so, precious, I feel dreadful that I have only applesauce for your dessert. But I told Mandore to give it a dash of lemon and a stick of vanilla for perfume."

Jean turned stoutly on the applesauce, sour provincial maiden of fifteen summers, who like all girls her age scorns and despises little boys of ten. But Jean could give as good as he took. Couldn't he get around nimbly, with the aid of his vanilla stick? "Too short, always too short, this little stick," he muttered under his breath.

Mandore was back, her skirt billowing out on all sides, so that with the large stripes she looked like a melon. With every step she plucked—zroom, zzrroomm, for Jean alone to hear—those interior chords that were the very soul, the rich harmony of Mandore.

"You've got your dinner finished already? It's not good to eat so fast, you'll only bring it up later. That's not your usual way."

Lady Mother on the one side, Mandore on the other, standing beside his bed. "How big they are!" Not that Lady Mother took up very much room, in her little claret-colored dress. But Mandore, already like a giant fiddle box, added two curved handles by putting her arms akimbo. Jean got rid of the last of the applesauce, scattered in tiny festoons among the gilt curlicues on his plate. Once more the question of dinner was settled.

The winter night had long since fallen. Lingering over his half glass of mineral water, which he thought was green because he drank it from a pale green tumbler, Jean calculated that he still needed a little courage to bring his invalid's day to a close. There was still his toilet for the night, the minute and inescapable chores which called on Lady Mother and even—zroom, zzrroomm—the gay, tuneful assistance of Mandore; still the toothbrush, the sponge glove, the special soap and the luke-warm water; still the tender maternal inquisitions. . . .

"Now, little boy, you won't be able to sleep like this, with your big picture book sticking into your side. And look at all those little books everywhere in your bed, with their sharp corners. Don't you want the night table closer?"

"No, Lady Mother, thank you, I'm fine just the way I am."

His toilet over, Jean fought the drunken fatigue creeping over him. He knew the limits of his strength and was anxious not to

miss the capricious wonders that the night might set as its program.
He was afraid that the solicitude of Lady Mother would prolong
the day unbearably, ruining his structure of books and furniture,
his balance of light and shadows, so reverently assembled. It was
already ten o'clock, and he was utterly used up. "If she stays, if she
insists, if she is still taking care of me when the big hand leans to
the other side of XII, I'll just get whiter and whiter, my eyes will
sink in, I won't be able to say any more of the no-thank-you-I'm
just-fine-Lady-Mother-good-nights that she must always have, and
. . . and . . . it will be awful, she'll begin sobbing. . . ."

He smiled at his mother, and the majesty which suffering bestows on her chosen children was born in a blazing curl of his
hair, descended to his eyelids and settled bitterly on his lips. This
was the hour when Lady Mother could have lost herself forever in
adoration of her shattered and exquisite creation. . . .

"Good night, Lady Mother," whispered Jean.

"Are you tired, dear? Would you like me to leave you alone?"

He made another effort, opened wide his sea green eyes, courageously pulled back his high shoulders. "Do I look like a tired
boy? Lady Mother, I ask you!"

She answered with a mischievous shake of her head, kissed
him and went away carrying the suppressed cries of love, the
stifled entreaties, the hushed litanies that pleaded with the pain to
release her son, to unshackle the fetters from his long legs and
his wasted but not deformed hips, to let the impoverished blood run
freely through the green branches of his veins.

"I have left two oranges on the plate. Should I turn out your
lamp for you?"

"I'll turn it out myself, Lady Mother."

"Heavens, where is my head? I've forgotten to take your
temperature tonight."

A haze came between Lady Mother's claret dress and her
son. Tonight, Jean burned with a fever that had been sending out
a thousand warnings; a little fire smoldering in his palms, a wou-
wou-wou throbbing inside his ears, a hot crown against his temples.

"We'll take it tomorrow without fail, Lady Mother."

"The buzzer is right beside your wrist. Are you sure you
wouldn't like to have a night lamp for company, when you are
alone? You know, one of those pretty night . . ."

The last syllable of the word tumbled into a dark corner, but
Lady Mother never even noticed. "She is too busy with all that
she has gathered up in her skirt," thought Jean. "She can only

worry about her little prayers, the things she wants to tell the doctor, the sadness she feels because I don't want anybody to stay with me at night. . . . And all that, she tries to carry in her skirt, no wonder something falls out and rolls on the carpet. Poor Lady Mother . . . how can I make her understand that I'm not unhappy? It seems that a boy my age can't lie in bed, can't be pale and unable to use his legs, can't feel pain, without being unhappy. Yes, I was unhappy when they used to take me out for a ride, and everybody used to look at me and I could hear them saying, 'Such a beautiful child, isn't it a dreadful pity?' Now I'm only unhappy when my cousin Charlie comes to visit me, with his scraped knees, his hob-nail shoes and that word 'boy scout,' half steel and half rubber, he is always pestering me with. . . . But when night comes and I'm alone, everything is fine. . . ."

He turned out the lamp and watched peacefully while his nocturnal visitors rose to greet him in a chorus of forms and colors. He awaited a symphonic blaze and the troupe that Lady Mother called his loneliness. He reached for the luminous buzzer, and put it on the bedside table. "Now shine!" he commanded.

It did not obey immediately. The night outside was not too black to distinguish, tapping against one of the panes, the farthest branch of a chestnut tree, stripped of its leaves and imploring help. Its swollen tip was trying hard to look like a sickly rosebud. "Yes, you are still trying to work on my sympathy by pretending to be the first bud of spring. You should know by now that I don't want any talk about next year. Stay outside. Vanish! As Charlie would say, 'Get the hell out!'"

His purity drew itself up to its full height, inflicting yet another rebuke on his cousin with the scratched and purplish knees, and his vocabulary studded with "Says you!" and "I get it!"—as though thought and comprehension would not have fled in terror, as fast as their wise old cricket legs could carry them, from such a boy with his hobnails and dried mud. . . .

Just at the sight of his cousin Charlie, Jean would wipe his fingers with his handkerchief as if to rid them of some filth. Because Lady Mother and Mandore, standing between the child and ugliness, the child and abusive language, the child and coarse reading, had taught him to know and cherish only two luxuries: fastidiousness and suffering. Protected, precocious, he had mastered the hieroglyphics of print, racing as madly through books as over clouds, uncovering countrysides inscribed under glossy surfaces and gathering around him all that, for privileged folk like him, secretly people the air.

But he no longer used the silver fountain pen engraved with his initials, since the day his agile handwriting had surprised and somehow antagonized the doctor with the cold hands. "Is this the writing of a young child, Madam?" Yes, yes, Doctor, my son has a grownup way of writing. . . ." And the worried eyes of Lady Mother seemed to ask apologetically: "At least, it isn't a dangerous symptom, Doctor?"

"Wouldn't you like a drawing book, my young friend, with a box of crayons? They are an excellent pastime and just the thing for a boy your age." This extramedical suggestion Jean answered with a narrowed look between his lashes, a grave and virile look that took the measure of this doctor so free with his advice: "It wouldn't be my nice barber who would talk such nonsense!" He had never forgiven the doctor for asking, out of the maternal presence: "And why the devil do you call your mother, *Lady* Mother?" This time the angered male look, the weak musical voice merged in: "I didn't think it would be the devil's business."

The nice barber went about his task quite differently. It was the account of his dominical activities that absorbed Jean. Every Sunday he went fishing with a bamboo rod and line. With a dazzling wave of scissors, he would demonstrate to Jean how he cast the bobber and bait. Jean could always see the cool spray fly up, then the expanding circles as the victorious fisherman drew up his catch.

"When you are well, Master Jean, I'll take you with me up the river."

"Yes, yes . . ." Why did they all want him to get well? He *was* up the river now. And what would he do with a bass-as-big-as-my hand-here and a pickerel-as-long-as-that-paper-cutter? "Tell me some more. . . ."

And then he would hear the tall tale of the cloud of fish flies that the barber had spied sticking under the little bridge, an impromptu bait that had landed a wagonful of trout, calling for the biggest stringer the barber could find, and three lengths of cord knotted one to the other. The story began to the edgy refrain of the clipping scissors. "You follow the river until you get to a little branch that begins big-as-my-behind, then spreads out as you go up the meadow. You see two, three willow trees together and a clump of bushes. Well, sir, that's the spot. . . ."

Around the two, three willows, Jean had transplanted, the first day he saw them, some thick-spiked agrimony *eupatoria*, dug from his big botanical album, and a bed of hemp, whose pink blossoms put butterflies and tired children to sleep. The raggedly

pruned face of the oldest willow winks monstrously at Jean from
under a crown of white morning-glories. A fish leaps through the
mirrored surface of the river, then two more. . . . The kind barber,
busy with his bait, turns around:

"They think they can tease me! I'll have 'em on my hook!"

"No, no," protests Jean, "it was just me throwing pebbles. . . ."

A frog sings, the imaginary afternoon drowses away. . . . "The
frog sings," dreams Jean, "because he begins with *fr* and hides
under his lily pad . . . but if he began with *l* he would be a log
instead, and he wouldn't be able to sing, just float where the river
carried him. . . ."

The barber-fisherman, the river and the meadow faded like a
daydream, their only trace a sweetish perfume on Jean's forehead,
a wind-blown tuft of blond hair. . . . Wide awake, Jean heard a
long whispering, coming from the parlor, a low-voiced conference
between Lady Mother and the doctor. A word escaped and ran,
frizzled and frisky, to find Jean: *crisis*. It appeared again, but cere-
moniously this time, like a girl receiving a prize at school. She
had an *h* behind her ear and a *y* in her corsage: Chrysis, Chrysis
Turnapoynt. "Truly? truly?" pressed the voice of Lady Mother.
"I said *perhaps*," replied the voice of the doctor, a voice unable to
stand straight on its two legs. "A crisis . . . turning point . . ."
Chrysis Turnapoynt, a young West Indian girl in flowing white
veils, flitting through the forest. . . .

The subtle ear of the sick child caught another name, one he
was positive they did not wish him to hear. It was only part of
the name—something like Infanta Peralla, Fantil Lysis. . . . Jean
concluded finally that she was a little girl who had to lie painfully
still, like him, her long legs stretched out on the bed. They never
mentioned her name in front of him because they were afraid he
might be jealous. . . .

Obedient to his harsh command, the branch of the chestnut
tree, with its false message of spring, had sunk into the night. But
the buzzer had disobeyed a second time, refusing to shed its faint
opaline glow over the night table where Lady Mother had arranged
the green tumbler, the oranges, the paper cutter, the myopic watch
with its bulging crystal.

None of Jean's books were on the table. No matter what
their size or weight, whether they were sleeping tight or keeping
watch, they were lodged in the sick child's bed. Down at the
foot, one big volume heavy as a tile weighed against those legs in
which life moved in a miserly flow, but Jean had no complaint.

With his still active arms, he groped around him, bringing up paper-covered books, tattered and warm. These he heaped into a prop alongside his meager hips, while he pressed his cheek against a tan calfskin binding a century old. Under his left shoulder, Jean felt the presence of a favorite companion, a book chunky as a paving stone.

Cardboard corners fitted against the frail body in boon companionship. A momentary bruise taught patience for the chronic pain. Certain little tortures inflicted between the ear and the shoulder by a tan calfskin horn seemed to ease the larger torment in the same region and around his winged shoulder blades. . . "What do you have here?" Lady Mother would say, suddenly. "Really, it's beyond my understanding what happens. As though you had been hit. . . ." In truth, the bruised child would have to reflect for a moment before he told himself: "There . . . but let's see, yes. . . . It must have been that tree I flew against. It might have been that roof I was leaning on, watching the sheep being brought in. Or maybe that big rake that fell on me while I was drinking at the fountain. At that, it's lucky Lady Mother didn't see the nick in the corner of my eye, where that swallow's beak caught me. . . . I didn't have time to get out of his way. . . . It's true that the sky is such a small place. . . ."

Around him rose the nocturnal hum, expected if not always familiar, varying according to the dreams, the fever, the weakness, the fancies that had made up a day that Lady Mother had sadly thought must be like all the others. But this night bore no resemblance to yesterday's. Darkness can be many, many blacks. "Now tonight black is like purple. I have a terrible pain . . . but where? In my forehead. No, what am I saying? It must be in my back, as always. . . . No, though, it's a weight, two weights, hanging from my hips, two weights like the pine cones on the cuckoo clock in the kitchen. Aren't you going to shine, you buzzer you?"

In order to snap another command to the buzzer, he leaned his temple against the tan calfskin binding and shivered to find it so cold. "It must be me that's on fire." No light came from the buzzer on the night table. "What's wrong with it? And what's wrong with me, that the service door wouldn't let me fly through, this afternoon?" He reached out in the swarming blackness and without a fumble managed to find the buzzer. But now the light played a mischievous trick on him and shone suddenly from the fat, myopic face of the spherical watch. "What are you sticking your nose in for?" murmured Jean.

Mortified, the watch dimmed its light, and Jean breathed a sigh of appeased power. But from his stiffened sides he was able to wrest no more than a moan. Now a wind was rising that was the one Jean knew best; the wind that blows down the pines, dishevels the larches, builds and tears down the dunes. Its roar filled Jean's ears, and images that his ordinary daydreams could never summon up, that could not push past the lashes of his poor eyelids, now burst into rebellion, leaped free to roam the vast reaches of the room. Queerly horizontal ones crossed others that had bolted straight up, making a luminous quivering plaid. "Those must be Scotch," thought Jean.

His bed trembled slightly, shaken by the vibrant rise of the Great Fever. He felt three or four years slipping away from him, and suddenly, almost for the first time in his life, he knew fear. He was on the point of calling: "Help, help, Lady Mother! Your little boy is being kidnaped!"

Not in his wildest rides, not in his rich domain of strange sounds—hunchbacked sounds wearing radio tubes on their heads, sounds with pointed snouts like weasels—never anywhere had Jean envisioned such a mad swarm. His hearing drank them in like a mouth, his sight was held in a kind of enraptured agony. "Help me, Lady Mother! You know that I can't walk! I only know how to fly, to swim, to glide from cloud to cloud. . . ." At that moment, something indescribable and long forgotten stirred within his body, far off, infinitely far off, at the very end of his useless legs, something like a frantic scatter of lost ants. "Help me, Mother!"

But another being, whose decisions did not defer to maternal hope or despair, made an imperious sign that imposed silence. A magic spell held Lady Mother in her room, dreaming timidly of a time when she might be as grownup as her own little boy.

So he did not cry out. Already his fabulous, unknown visitors had begun their assault. Surging up everywhere, they poured fire and ice over him, a shrilling torture. Lying in motionless agony, listening in vain for the maternal footsteps, Jean made a sudden decision and flung himself into a headlong flight that shot him over meteors, above the battle of thunderbolts, through mists that hid and shielded him. Now the boy who had been so gay and so spoiled, so at home in his loneliness, so wrapped up in his privileges as a fatherless invalid, knew that only a sad little sound, as of crystal breaking, remained between him and a happiness whose hollow name he had still to learn: death. A sad, frail little breaking

sound, coming from a planet he might never see again . . . a clear
and grieving sound, somehow connected with the child who might
die, and so penetrating that Jean could not outdistance it in his
dazzling flight.

Perhaps his journey lasted a long time. He had lost all sense
of time passing so he could only judge by what he experienced.
Often he believed that he was following a shadowy guide, one
who had difficulty himself in finding the trail. Then he whimpered
because he could not take the lead and, hearing his own wail of
humbled pride or of utter exhaustion, he wheeled sharply, plunged
through the wake of a cyclone, in search of a corner where he might
find refuge. Now he was gripped with the agony of inhabiting a
country where there were no corners, only a freezing current of
dark air, a night on whose breast he was nothing more than a lost
and weeping lad. Then he stood up, on legs that suddenly grew
in number, that stretched to stilts through which pain cut like a
scythe. Then everything vanished, and he had only the blind
wind rushing past to tell him how fast was his speed. As he fled
from a familiar continent over an uncharted sea, he caught a few
words spoken in a language he was surprised to understand:
"The noise of the green tumbler breaking woke me . . ."
"Look, Madam, he's moving his lips like he's thirsty. Would
he be wanting some water?"
He would have loved to know whose voice he had heard last
. . . *thirsty* . . . *water*. . . . But already the words and his memory of
them were swallowed up by time and space. Once again during
the night, after a sudden halt that set his temples throbbing, he
overheard a snatch of human talk and longed to say over the
fragmentary syllables. He had been brought up abruptly and ach-
ingly against a rough, solid object that seemed to arrive from
nowhere; it was finely striped, shaggy, mysteriously allied—he was
to discover later—to horrid *my-young-friends*. "It's a . . . I know
. . . a sleeve. . . ." With that he winged out again, head lowered,
into chaos.
Another time he saw a hand. With slender fingers, skin
slightly chapped, and white spots on the nails, it was repelling some
strange monster that would make a mouthful of it. And Jean began
to laugh. "Poor little hand, the monster will make a mouthful of
it. And it's such a clever-looking monster, with those black and
yellow stripes!" The weak little hand was fighting as hard as it
could, fingers outstretched, and the parallel stripes began to swell
out, to diverge, to bend like molten bars. A great opening ap-

peared between them and swallowed the frail hand. Somehow the
spectacle had filled Jean with a vague grief, and he found it difficult to strike out on his travels. The grief went along with him,
like the obstinate tinkling of shattered green glass, in an age long,
long past. From that time on, through the cradling giddiness of
swirling eddy and sudden fall, Jean's journey was troubled by
echoes, the sound of weeping, the anxious try at something like a
thought, by a strangely insistent pity.

A sharp barking ripped through space, and Jean murmured,
"Riki. . . ." Far away he heard a kind of sob: "Riki! Madam, he
said Riki!" And another voice stammered, "He said Riki . .. Oh,
God, he said Riki . . ."

Some obstinate, quivering force seemed to be tugging under
his arms, trying to lift him high, high, toward an unknown peak.
The pressure was hurting him, and he grumbled. Things were
simply not done that way to a traveler who was used to motors
without engines, steeds that had never been shod, sleighs that
sped down the multicolored ways of the rainbow. . . . He must
not be bothered by outsiders . . . only if the night had unleashed
and commanded them. For example, the pigeon that was just
now snuggling its breast against his cheek had no right. . . .
Not that it *could* be a bird's breast, because it wasn't feathered,
only bordered with a lock of long hair. "It would be a cheek,"
he thought, "if there were another cheek besides mine in the
universe . . . but it's an impostor. . . . I forbid anybody touching
me, I forbid . . ."

To find the strength to speak, Jean drew in deep breaths.
With the air entered the wonder, the enchantment of memory, the
fragrance of hair and skin that he had forgotten on the other side
of the world and which set loose within him now a torrent of
remembrance. He coughed, trying to keep down something that
was knotting his throat, moistening his dry lips, overflowing his
eyes . . . and mercifully veiling his descent to the hard bed. Next
he heard a voice, echoing to infinity: "He's crying . . . dear, dear
God, he's crying. . . ." The voice subsided into a kind of storm,
over which rose disjointed syllables, calls to someone hidden in
the room: "Come, come quickly!"

"So noisy, so noisy," thought the child reproachfully. But he
pressed his cheek more and more against the smooth, soft surface
framed with hair and felt against his mouth a briny dew. He
turned away his head, meeting on the way a narrow valley, a
nest molded to his measure. He just had time to say to himself

what it was—"Lady Mother's shoulder"—before he lost consciousness. Or did he only fall asleep?

It was his own voice, clear and teasing, that brought him back. "Where have you been all this time, Lady Mother?"

There was no answer, but a slice of orange slipped between his lips, told him of the presence of the one he had sought. He knew that she was bending over him, submissive, unmindful of her own comfort. Completely exhausted, Jean lay still. But already a thousand worries were plaguing him, and he momentarily conquered his faintness to settle the most urgent: "Did you change my pajamas, Lady Mother, while I was sleeping? When I went to bed last night I had on my blue ones and now these are the green. . . ."

"Can you believe it Madam? He remembers that he was wearing his blue pajamas, the night when . . ."

He did not listen to the rest of the sentence whispered in a warm, husky voice but gave himself over to the hands that were removing his damp garments, hands as nimble as a cloud steed, rocking him weightlessly.

"He is soaked. Wrap him in the big bathrobe, Mandore, but don't bother with the sleeves."

"The furnace is sending up heat, Madam, don't worry. And I've just given him another hot-water bottle. He's all damp, bless him. . . ."

"If they knew where I've come from . . . getting a little damp would be the least of it," thought Jean. "I wish I could scratch my legs or else that they would get rid of those ants. Lady Mother . . ."

He recognized, absorbed, the silence, the still vigilance that was Lady Mother's guarded reply.

"Would you please . . . would you scratch above my ankles, where the ants have been crawling? . . ."

Out of the depths of silence, someone murmured, with a queer awe: "He says there are ants. That's what he said, ants."

Snug within the oversized bathrobe, he tried to raise his shoulders. Why, naturally, he said ants. What was there so amazing just because he said Riki and ants. An airy, carefree dream bore him off to the borderline between waking and sleep, until he was revived by something brushing against him. Through his lashes he saw that it was the hateful sleeve, right there beside him, with its blue stripes, its woolen hairs. Resentment brought him wide awake. He refused to see more, but then he heard a voice that made him open his eyes, a voice saying: "Well, my young friend. . . ."

"I'll drive him out!" cried Jean to himself. "Yes, him, his sleeve, his *my-young-friend*, his mean little eyes, I hate them and I'll drive them all out!" In his fury he began gasping.

"Well, well, what's this? Yes, there's really movement. . . . There . . . there . . ."

A hand rested on Jean's head. Powerless to rebel, the child hoped to crush the aggressor with a glance. But his eyes discovered, in the bedside chair that was reserved for Lady Mother, a man who wasn't so bad after all, heavyish, rather bald, whose eyes moistened when they met Jean's.

"Well, my boy, well, well. . . . Is it true you can feel ants crawling on your legs? Honest to goodness? That's good news, on my word. . . . Would you like to have a glass of orange juice? Or a few spoonfuls of lemon ice? Or maybe a few swallows of milk?"

Jean's hand let itself go in the clasp of the gentle big fingers, the pleasantly warm palm. He murmured confused acceptance, not sure whether he had said he wanted or did not want the orange juice, the lemon ice, the milk. . . . With eyes faded to a pale gray, between deeply creased circles and dark eyebrows, he greeted eyes that were gaily blue, twinkling, tender. . . .

The remainder of this new time in Jean's life passed in a succession of jumbled moments, in a mixture of short naps and tight slumbers, of quickening urges and hazy thrills. The good doctor spent himself in a holiday of well-wells and there-theres, satisfied harrumphings and repetitions of "Happy days, my dear lady! We're out of the woods now!" Indeed, if Jean had not been in a state of sublime indifference, he would surely have asked what was the joyous occasion. As it was, the hours slipped away, with only the arrival of a glass of milk or a dish of stewed berries, to mark them off. A boiled egg would tip its lid, revealing a yellow as gay as a gold button.

Through the half-opened window entered a heady breeze, a wine of spring, while outside the rosy chestnut buds swelled more and more each day. Up and down Jean's legs ran ants armed with tiny pincers. "This time I've caught one, Lady Mother!" But it was his own transparent skin that he was pinching; the ant had escaped to the other side of his tree of veins. The eighth day of this new time, a long scarf of sunlight wound across the bed, arousing in Jean an emotion stronger than he could bear. He made up his mind that in his nocturnal fever he would retrieve all that he had missed for the past week; his periods of sleep had become like blocks of black stone, separating him from his faceless companions, his wild flights, his round of firmaments, his security as a soaring angel. . . .

"Lady Mother, if you please, I'd like my books."

"But darling, the doctor said that . . ."

"Oh, but I don't want to read them, Lady Mother. I just want them to get used to me again. . . ."

She protested no more, but brought him somewhat apprehensively his tattered books—the surly old paving stone, the one bound in tan calf smooth as his own cheek, his *Horticulture* with its lusciously colored fruits, his *Zoology* with its flat-faced lion and duck-bill platypuses cowering under beetles bigger than islands. . . .

Evening, and he had stuffed himself greedily with all the food Mandore had brought on his tray. He pretended that he was ready to drowse off, crooned his good nights in a wandering sly song. Having attended to the departure of Lady Mother and Mandore, he took command of his raft of folios and atlasses and embarked. A new moon behind the branch of the chestnut tree revealed that, thanks to an indulgent April, the buds were about to burst into forked leaves.

He sat up without help, dragging along legs that were still heavy and swarming with ants. Beyond the window, in the heavenly waters of the night, bathed a curved moon and the blurred reflection of a child with long hair, to whom Jean beckoned. The other child docilely repeated the gesture. Intoxicated with his old sense of power and wonder, he summoned back his companions of the cruel and privileged hours he used to know, the visible sounds, the tangible images, the breathable seas, the nourishing and navigable air, the defiant wings, the laughing stars. . . .

Above all, he summoned back a certain impetuous boy who used to shake with secret mirth as he hurtled into the air, who as lord and master of Lady Mother's every emotion made her the victim of a hundred tender hoaxes.

He waited, but nothing came. Not that night, nor the next; nothing came again ever. The landscape of pink snow had vanished from the nickel paper cutter, and nevermore would Jean glide through a periwinkle dawn, skimming the sharp horns of cattle blue with morning mist. . . . Nevermore would a yellow and brown Mandore entrance him—zroom, zzrroomm—with the melodies of her expansive skirts. Nevermore would the damask Alp indulge

the child, who was soon to be cured, in the hardy exploits that had
been his as a helpless lad, leaping over imaginary glaciers. . . .

A time comes to give oneself to life. A time comes to turn
away utterly, irrevocably, from death. Jean waved farewell to
his haloed reflection, and the salute was returned to him from a
night that had lost its magic, the meek and disenchanted night
that is the lot of children on whom death has no more claim.

Discussion of "The Sick Child"

Colette is the pen-name of Sidonie Gabrielle Claudine
Colette (1873-   ), French writer of semi-autobiographical stories, essays, and plays. Especially distinguished as
a writer of prose fiction, she has written many works, including *The Vagrant, Backs and Purrs, The Gentle Liber-
tine, Young Lady of Paris,* and *The Indulgent Husband.*

"The Sick Child" is a delicate, lovely story, and will
seem especially so to any parent who has spent long weeks
of anxious waiting at the side of a dangerously sick child.
Beyond all the fear and pain, beyond all the apprehension
and suffering, there is—or can be—beauty too. Our hearts
ache for the child lying small and helpless on the too-big
bed, his flesh hot with fever, his arms and legs and body
shrunken to a pitiful thinness, his eyes seeming over-large in
the white face. But when is a child more beautiful? When
is a child dearer to us, or closer to God? Truly, as Colette
says, there is a "majesty which suffering bestows on her
chosen children."

The story is written from the point of view of the sick
child, and is all the more lovely for this point of view. We
experience with him his wonderful dreams, heightened
rather than diminished by the fever. We share the harsh-
ness of realism too, the slipping in and out of the pain of

reality, and the terrible unconsciousness of the infantile paralysis that almost claims him, this child "promised to death." But most of all we ride with him on his marvelous adventures with Lavender and his other play-mates of fancy in the world of his fevered imagination. Or we play with him the heart-touching game of "outpretending" his mother and nurse, lest they feel pity for him when he doesn't want pity. He wants love, and freedom to let his fancies wander—but not pity.

The whole work is beautifully written, so beautifully that few stories claim our hearts as fully as this delicate portrayal of a child and his weeks of hovering in the fevered dream-world between life and death. Michael was dignified through suffering; this child is beatified.

SECTION SIX

Facing Death

FACING DEATH

Introductory Comments

The most solemn experience shared by the whole human race is the inescapable fact of death—which comes to every mortal being regardless of how good or evil, how beautiful or ugly, how ready or unready the individual may be. Two possibilities confront us: either we can die young and bring sorrow to family and friends, or we can live long and feel sorrow as family and friends one by one die. Such a statement is not pessimistic; it is simply true. For, soon or late, in one way or another, all must die.

How we as human beings act and react in the face of death is and has always been one of the principal concerns of literature. Even more than love, death has been the central focus of literally thousands of novels, dramas, stories, and poems. We see it in the old medieval morality play *Everyman,* written about 1500 A.D. in which Death summons Everyman, who appears to Fellowship, Kindred, Goods, Beauty, Strength, etc., to accompany him, but, abandoned by all, he is accompanied only by Good-Deeds as he exits through the door of death. We see it in such modern works as Hemingway's *For Whom the Bell Tolls* or Miller's *The Death of a Salesman.* And we see it in a multitude of works between then and now.

In their views on death writers tend to reflect the variant attitudes of people as a whole. Sometimes they fear it as mysterious and unknown; sometimes they dread it as a condition of suffering in consequence of mortal sin, or anticipate it as a place of bliss after mortal suffering; sometimes they are merely curious about it, or defiant of it, or resigned to it. Sometimes they treat it tenderly and sometimes brutally, sometimes optimistically and sometimes pessimistically, sometimes with sad beauty and sometimes with grotesque ugliness. Theologically, a writer may either look at death as the end of existence, or he may look on it as a doorway to continued life in some form.

The selections in this section on "Facing Death" are divided into four groups:

(1) First, one story, "The Death of the Dauphin," dramatizing the idea of the universality of death.

(2) Second, excerpts from several poems sampling works which show a negative attitude towards death.

(3) Third, six poems showing an affirmative attitude towards death and life after death.

(4) Fourth, three poems exploring some special problems on death.

The Death of the Dauphin[1]

by *Alphonse Daudet*

The little Dauphin is ill—the Dauphin is going to die. In all the churches the Host is elevated and tall candles burn for the recovery of the royal child. The streets of the ancient residence are sad and silent, the bells are mute, citizens peer curiously through the palace gratings, porters talk in solemn tones in the courts.

All the palace is astir. Chamberlains and majordomos hurry up and down the marble steps; the galleries are thronged with pages; courtiers in silken robes pass from group to group, asking the news in smothered accents. On the broad stairways weeping maids of honor bow low, and wipe their eyes with beautiful embroidered kerchiefs.

An assemblage of robed doctors gathers in the orangery. Through the glasses they can be seen waving their long black sleeves and inclining doctorally their perukes. Before the door walk the tutor and riding-master of the little Dauphin. They are waiting for decisions of the faculty. The riding-master swears like a trooper, the tutor quotes Horace. From the stable comes a long, plaintive neigh. It is the little Dauphin's chestnut, who, forgotten by the grooms, calls sadly from his empty crib.

And the king—where is the king? Shut up all alone at the farther end of the palace. Kings must not be seen to weep. Not so, however, the queen. Seated by the Dauphin's side, her lovely face all bathed in tears, she sobs before us all like the veriest serving-woman.

In his lace bed lies the little Dauphin. He is whiter than the pillow upon which his head reclines. They believe that he is asleep; but no, he is not asleep. The little Dauphin turns to his mother. "Madame the queen, why do you weep? Do you believe, like the rest, that I am going to die?" The queen tries to answer; sobs choke her utterance.

"Do not weep, madame the queen. You forget that I am the Dauphin; Dauphins do not die thus." The queen sobs more piteously. The little Dauphin is frightened. "Halloo!" exclaims he, "I do not want to die! Order instantly forty stout lansquenets to keep guard around our bed. Set a hundred large guns to watch night and day before our windows. And woe to Death should he dare approach us!"

---

[1]The Dauphin was the eldest son of the French King and heir to the throne.

To humor the royal child the queen makes a sign. In a twinkling, cannon are heard rolling in the court; forty stoutly lansquenets with their partisans range themselves around the room. They are old troopers and their mustaches are gray. The Dauphin recognizes one. "Lorrain!" he cries. The old soldier draws closer, "Let me look at your big sword. If Death comes for me you will kill him, will you not?" "Yes, monseigneur." And two big tears roll down his tanned cheeks.

The priest approaches the Dauphin. He speaks long in subdued tones and holds up the crucifix. The Dauphin shows surprise. Suddenly he interrupts him. "I see what you mean, monsieur the abbé; but would not my little friend Beppo die in my place if we pay him plenty of money?" The priest continues to speak. The Dauphin looks more and more surprised. When the priest ceases, he says, with a sigh, "All that is very sad, monsieur the abbé, but there is one comfort for me. When I get to the paradise of the stars I shall still be the Dauphin. The good God is my cousin, and will treat me according to my rank."

Then he turned to his mother, and said, "Let them bring my best clothes—the ermine doublet and velvet pumps. I want to make myself smart for the angels, and enter paradise dressed like the Dauphin." Again the priest bends over the Dauphin, and speaks to him in low tones. In the midst of the discourse the royal child interrupts him angrily: "What! it is nothing, then, to be a Dauphin, after all!" and refusing to hear more, he turns his head to the wall and weeps bitterly.

Discussion of "The Death of the Dauphin"

Alphonse Daudet (1840-1897) is a French novelist and short-story writer generally referred to as of the realistic-naturalistic school. However, his writings are less somber than those of most of the other Naturalists, and sometimes he even has a warmth of attitude suggestive of Dickens. Most of his works are concerned with a realistic portrayal of life as he observed it.

"The Death of the Dauphin" is a very short and very simple story. Its characterization is simple; its setting and plot are simple; and its message (theme), although of central importance, is also clear and simple. Everyone must die, even a Dauphin; and in death all are equal. Death is no respecter of persons. The story is not intended to be either pessimistic or optimistic, but just realistic, emphasizing the universality and inevitability of the fact of death. And in the face of death neither power nor wealth nor the young Dauphin's haughty manner makes any difference. Some readers may find the story very sad; others may find grim satisfaction in the ironic truth of its message. Most will simply accept it for what it is: a moving comment on the inescapable fact of death. It is here intended as an introduction to a group of selections all concerned with the problem of facing death.

Out of the Best Books

Some Negative Views on Death

Most writers through the centuries, however different their views as to its details, have been believers in some form of life after death. But occasionally a writer has become convinced that death closes all—or should. If he arrives at such a conviction, he then either, like Edward Fitzgerald in "The Rubaiyat of Omar Khayyam," endorses a hedonistic philosophy that we should eat, drink, and be merry, for tomorrow we die. Or, with such writers as the English James Thomson or the American Robinson Jeffers, he rejoices that the misery of life will end in the oblivion of the grave.

As brief samples of some of these extremely "negative" views on death, we print the following passages:

From "The City of Dreadful Night" by James Thomson (1834-1882)

The world rolls round forever like a mill;
It grinds out death and life and good and ill;
It has no purpose, heart or mind or will.

While air of Space and Time's full river flow
The mill must blindly whirl unresting so;
It may be wearing out, but who can know?

Man might know one thing were his sight less dim;
That it whirls not to suit his petty whim,
That it is quite indifferent to him.

Nay, does it treat him harshly as he saith?
It grinds him some slow years of bitter breath,
Then grinds him back into eternal death.
(lines 456-467)

O length of the intolerable hours,
  O nights that are as aeons of slow pain,
O Time, too ample for our vital powers,
   O Life, whose woeful vanities remain
Immutable for all of all our legions
Through all the centuries and in all the regions,
  Not of your speed and variance *we* complain.

We do not ask a longer term of strife,
  Weakness and weariness and nameless woes;
We do not claim renewed and endless life
  When this which is our torment here shall close,
An everlasting conscious inanition
We yearn for speedy death in full fruition,
  Dateless oblivion and divine repose.
               (lines 672-685)

This little life is all we must endure,
The grave's most holy peace is ever sure,
  We fall asleep and never wake again;
Nothing is of us but the moldering flesh,
Whose elements dissolve and merge afresh
  In earth, air, water, plants, and other men.

We finish thus; and all our wretched race
Shall finish with its cycle, and give place
  To other beings, with their own time-doom;
Infinite aeons ere our kind began;
Infinite aeons after the last man
  Has joined the mammoth in earth's tomb and womb.
               (lines 734-745)

From "The Rubaiyat of Omar Khayyam"

by Edward Fitzgerald (1809-1883)

A Book of Verses underneath the Bough,
A Jug of Wine, a Loaf of Bread—and Thou
    Beside me singing in the Wilderness—
Oh, Wilderness were Paradise enow!

Some for the Glories of This World; and some
Sigh for the Prophet's Paradise to come;
    Ah, take the Cash, and let the Credit go,
Nor heed the rumble of a distant Drum!
                          (stanzas 12 & 13)

For some we loved, the loveliest and the best
That from his Vintage rolling Time hath prest,
    Have drunk their Cup a Round or two before,
And one by one crept silently to rest.

And we, that now make merry in the Room
They left, and Summer dresses in new bloom,
    Ourselves must we beneath the Couch of Earth
Descend—ourselves to make a Couch—for whom?

Ah, make the most of what we yet may spend,
Before we too into the Dust descend;
    Dust into Dust, and under Dust, to lie,
Sans Wine, sans Song, sans Singer, and—sans End!
                          (stanzas 22, 23, 24)

Then to the Lip of this poor earthern Urn
I learned, the Secret of my Life to learn;
    And Lip to Lip it murmured—"While you live,
Drink,—for, once dead, you never shall return."
                          (stanza 35)

Oh threats of Hell and Hopes of Paradise!
One thing at least is certain—*this* life flies;
    One thing is certain and the rest is Lies—
The Flower that once has blown forever dies.
                          (stanza 63)

From "The Garden of Proserpine" by A. C. Swinburne (1837-1909)

I am tired of tears and laughter,
  And men that laugh and weep,
Of what may come hereafter
  For men that sow to reap;
I am weary of days and hours,
Blown buds of barren flowers,
Desires and dreams and powers
  And everything but sleep.
              (lines 9-16)

From too much love of living,
  From hope and fear set free,
We thank with brief thanksgiving
  Whatever gods may be
That no life lives forever;
That dead men rise up never;
That even the weariest river
  Winds somewhere safe to sea.

Then star nor sun shall waken,
  Nor any change of light;
Nor sound of waters shaken,
  Nor any sound or sight;
Nor wintry leaves nor vernal,
Nor days nor things diurnal;
Only the sleep eternal
  In an eternal night.
              (lines 81-96)

From "May-June, 1940" by Robinson Jeffers (1887-1962)

. . . But not enough death to serve us, not enough death. It
   would be better for men
To be few and live far apart, where none could infect another; then
   slowly the sanity of field and mountain
And the cold ocean and glittering stars might enter their minds.

(lines 5-7)

And why do you cry, my dear, why do you cry?
   It is all in the whirling circles of time.
   If millions are born millions must die,

   . . . .

   All in the turning of time.
   If civilization goes down, that
   Would be an event to contemplate.
   It will not be in our time, alas, my dear,
   It will not be in our time.

(lines 16-18 & 21-25)

Affirmative Views on Death and Life After Death

Such poems as those sampled on the preceding several pages are powerful and vivid; but they are also grimly, brutally, bleakly pessimistic, especially with regard to death and resurrection. However strong as poetry, they are, of course, completely out of harmony with all Christian philosophy and are false in their views but are included here to serve as contrasts and heighten the beauty of the poems that follow.

Much more harmonious with Latter-day Saint philosophy are thousands of poems and stories that affirm a life after death. And we now turn to six poems expressing affirmative, positive, optimistic views with regard to death and life after death.

Sonnet 146

by William Shakespeare

Poor soul, the centre of my sinful earth,
Rebuke these rebel powers that thee array!
Why dost thou pine within and suffer dearth,
Painting thy outward walls so costly gay?
Why so large cost, having so short a lease,
Dost thou upon thy fading mansion spend?
Shall worms, inheritors of this excess,
Eat up thy charge? Is this thy body's end?
Then, soul, live thou upon thy servant's loss,
And let that pine to aggravate thy store;
Buy terms divine in selling hours of dross:
Within be fed, without be rich no more.
  So shalt thou feed on Death that feeds on men,
  And Death once dead, there's no more dying then.

Discussion of Shakespeare's Sonnet #146

William Shakespeare (1564-1616) is surely the greatest writer of the English language and perhaps the greatest
writer of the world. Altogether he wrote thirty-seven
dramas, two fairly long poems ("Venus and Adonis" and
"The Rape of Lucrece"), a cycle of 154 sonnets, and a few
other short poems. His supreme genius is seen principally
in the dramas, where he surpassed all his contemporaries
in the brilliant Elizabethan renaissance in the three types of
drama—history plays (chronicles), comedies, and tragedies
—with his apex of achievement in the four great tragedies,
Hamlet, Othello, King Lear, and *Macbeth.*

Shakespeare is not a didactic writer in the ordinary
sense. That is, he does not write primarily to teach moral
lessons. Instead, he writes to explore the complexities of
human relationships, problems, and values. Even so, it is
abundantly clear to any reader of Shakespeare that
throughout his writings he is fundamentally a believer in
God and in the dignity of man.

Sonnet 146 vividly counsels man to stop wasting so
much attention on fancy dress and other external, worldly
matters that pertain merely to the body. For the body is
temporary and mortal, a "fading mansion." Instead, man
should give attention to divine matters that his soul may
grow and he may "within be fed." The sonnet climaxes
with the powerful closing couplet asserting that men should
"feed on Death, that feeds on men" — that is, mature
through death to immortality, and once Death is conquered,
men may live eternally.

The following notes on words will assist in understanding the poem: In line 1, "earth" means "body," as also
does "servant" in line 9. In line 10, "aggravate" means
"increase." And in line 11, "terms divine" means "eternity
in heaven."

Death Be Not Proud

by John Donne

Death, be not proud, though some have called thee
Mighty and dreadful, for thou art not so;
For those whom thou think'st thou dost overthrow
Die not, poor Death; nor yet canst thou kill me.
From rest and sleep, which but thy pictures be,
Much pleasure; then from thee much more must flow;
And soonest our best men with thee do go—
Rest of their bones and souls' delivery!
Thou art slave to fate, chance, kings, and desperate men,
And dost with poison, war, and sickness dwell;
And poppy or charms can make us sleep as well
And better than thy stroke. Why swell'st thou then?
One short sleep past, we wake eternally,
And Death shall be no more: Death, thou shalt die!

Discussion of "Death Be Not Proud"

A few decades ago John Donne (1571-1631) was regarded as an interesting minor poet of the early seventeenth
century. But during the past half century such attention
has been given to Donne as the first and greatest of the
brilliantly experimental Metaphysical Poets and the forerunner of twentieth-century "modern" poetry that he is
now generally recognized as the most important English
poet between Shakespeare and Milton.

Donne grew up in a devoutly religious Roman Cath-
olic family; renounced this background to spend several
years in riotous and fleshly living as a young man in his
twenties; then at the age of thirty fell deeply and permanently in love with and married Anne More, a love so
spiritual and so lasting that it transformed his life; and

finally, after years of poverty and of religious searching, became a minister in the Church of England, in which position he wrote such brilliant sermons that he became recognized as one of the most eloquent preachers in the Anglican Church and was appointed Dean of St. Paul's Cathedral. Donne's poems vividly reflect all the torturous phases of his emotional, intellectual, and spiritual progress through life.

"Death Be Not Proud" is one of Donne's *Holy Sonnets*. In it he eloquently declares that death, however powerful, does not have power to destroy the immortal spirit which, after a short sleep, wakes eternally and wakes in joy. Note how similar in message and how equally rich in poetic vividness this poem and Shakespeare's Sonnet 146 are.

And Death Shall Have No Dominion

by Dylan Thomas

And death shall have no dominion.
Dead men naked they shall be one
With the man in the wind and the west moon;
When their bones are picked clean and the clean bones gone,
They shall have stars at elbow and foot;
Though they go mad they shall be sane,
Though they sink through the sea they shall rise again;
Though lovers be lost love shall not;
And death shall have no dominion.

And death shall have no dominion.
Under the windings of the sea
They lying long shall not die windily;
Twisting on racks when sinews give way,
Strapped to a wheel, yet they shall　not break;
Faith in their hands shall snap in two,
And the unicorn evils run them through;
Split all ends up they　shan't crack;
And death shall have no dominion.

And death shall have no dominion.
No more may gulls cry at their ears
Or waves break loud on the seashores;
Where blew a flower may a flower no more
Lift its head to the blows of the rain;
Though they be mad and dead as nails,
Heads of the characters hammer through daisies;
Break in the sun till the sun breaks down,
And death shall have no dominion.

Discussion of "And Death Shall Have No Dominion"

At the time of his tragically early death a few years
ago, Dylan Thomas (1914-1953) had already established
himself as not only the foremost of modern Welsh poets
but also one of the few contemporary poets writing the

English language whose poetry is so clearly marked by an individual style that it could not be confused with the work of any other writer. So rapidly were his expressive powers developing that, had he lived, he almost certainly would have become one of the great poets of the twentieth century. Perhaps he is that already. And his prose fiction is hardly less striking.

Hearing Dylan Thomas read "And Death Shall Have No Dominion" in his rich, resonant bass was an unforgettable experience. Fortunately, his reading of this and other poems was recorded and is easily available.

The poem vigorously declares the power of life over the power of death. Though the body be lost in the depths of the sea or smashed into fragments or otherwise totally destroyed, yet that which is vital and eternal shall live on—"And death shall have no dominion." Though even the mind, broken by disease or experience, may go mad, yet it shall be restored to its full faculties—"And death shall have no dominion." Moreover, not only the life but also the ideals we live by are eternal: lovers may be untrue, men may lose their faith, and evil may dominate a human personality; but still Love and Faith and Goodness shall live on—"And death shall have no dominion."

Two Poems by Robert Browning

Earlier in this book we saw Browning's vigorous faith in God and man[1] and his hatred of self-righteousness, hypocrisy, and related attitudes.[2] Now we turn to two other poems to see his robust confidence in life after death.

Prospice

Fear death?—to feel the fog in my throat,
    The mist in my face,
When the snows begin, and the blasts denote
    I am nearing the place,
The power of the night, the press of the storm,
    The post of the foe;
Where he stands, the Arch Fear in a visible form,
    Yet the strong man must go.
For the journey is done and the summit attained,
    And the barriers fall,
Though a battle's to fight ere the guerdon be gained,
    The reward of it all.
I was ever a fighter, so—one fight more,
    The best and the last!
I would hate that death bandaged my eyes, and forbore,
    And bade me creep past.
No! let me taste the whole of it, fare like my peers,
    The heroes of old,
Bear the brunt, in a minute pay glad life's arrears
    Of pain, darkness, and cold.
For sudden the worst turns the best to the brave,
    The black minute's at end,
And the elements' rage, the fiend-voices that rave,
    Shall dwindle, shall blend,
Shall change, shall become first a peace out of pain,
    Then a light, then thy breast,
O thou soul of my soul! I shall clasp thee again,
    And with God be the rest!

[1]See discussions of "A Grammarian's Funeral" and "An Epistle of Karshish" on pp. 73-90.
[2]See discussions of "Johannes Agricola in Meditation" and "Soliloquy of the Spanish Cloister" on pp. 235-42.

Discussion of "Prospice"

"Prospice," which means "look forward," is Browning's most direct expression of belief in immortality. Two ideas form the poem. One is simply a courageous attitude towards the experience of death: he has faced all life's experiences with vigor, and he will not now shrink from this final experience. The other idea, more philosophical, is the climax that ends the poem as with great confidence Browning anticipates the time when he will reach through death to reunite with his beloved wife ("O thou soul of my soul"). who had recently died.

In order to appreciate the intense emotion of this poem we need to be reminded of the courtship and marriage of Robert Browning and Elizabeth Barrett, the most beautiful courtship and marriage in the history of English literature. When they met in 1845, Miss Barrett, six years older than Browning, was already a celebrated poetess. She was also a semi-invalid who for years of delicate health had hidden in the seclusion of her rooms. Browning, aged 33, was not yet acclaimed as a poet but already showed all the robustness and vigor that set him above ordinary men. He first learned of Miss Barrett through her poems, wrote her an admiring letter, met her, fell in love with her, as she with him, and after a whirlwind series of letters and visits, swept her "on" her feet for a secret wedding in 1846 that resulted in fifteen years of beautiful marriage ending only with her death in 1861. All of this forms the background for "Prospice," written in 1861 shortly after Mrs. Browning's death.

Rabbi Ben Ezra

by Robert Browning

1   Grow old along with me!
The best is yet to be,
The last of life, for which the first was made.
Our times are in his hand
Who saith, "A whole I planned;
Youth shows but half. Trust God; see all, nor be afraid!"

2   Not that, amassing flowers,
Youth sighed, "Which rose make ours,
Which lily leave and then as best recall?"
Not that, admiring stars,
It yearned, "Nor Jove, nor Mars;
Mine be some figured flame which blends, transcends them all!"

3   Not for such hopes and fears
Annulling youth's brief years,
Do I remonstrate—folly wide the mark!
Rather I prize the doubt
Low kinds exist without,
Finished and finite clods, untroubled by a spark.

4   Poor vaunt of life indeed,
Were man but formed to feed
On joy, to solely seek and find and feast.
Such feasting ended, then
As sure an end to men;
Irks care the crop-full bird? Frets doubt the maw-crammed
    beast?

5   Rejoice we are allied
To that which doth provide
And not partake, effect and not receive!
A spark disturbs our clod;
Nearer we hold of God
Who gives, than of his tribes that take, I must believe.

6   Then, welcome each rebuff
That turns earth's smoothness rough,
Each sting that bids nor sit nor stand but go!
Be our joys three-parts pain!
Strive, and hold cheap the strain;
Learn, nor account the pang; dare, never grudge the throe!

7   For thence—a paradox
     Which comforts while it mocks—
     Shall life succeed in that it seems to fail:
     What I aspired to be,
     And was not, comforts me;
     A brute I might have been, but would not sink i' the scale.

8   What is he but a brute
     Whose flesh has soul to suit,
     Whose spirit works lest arms and legs want play?
     To man, propose this test—
     Thy body at its best,
     How far can that project thy soul on its lone way?

9   Yet gifts should prove their use:
     I own the past profuse
     Of power each side, perfection every turn;
     Eyes, ears took in their dole,
     Brain treasured up the whole;
     Should not the heart beat once, "How good to live and learn"?

10   Not once beat, "Praise be thine!
     I see the whole design,
     I, who saw power, see now Love perfect too;
     Perfect I call thy plan.
     Thanks that I was a man!
     Maker, remake, complete—I trust what thou shalt do!"

11   For pleasant is this flesh;
     Our soul, in its rose-mesh
     Pulled ever to the earth, still yearns for rest.
     Would we some prize might hold
     To match those manifold
     Possessions of the brute—gain most, as we did best!

12   Let us not always say,
     "Spite of this flesh today
     I strove, made head, gained ground upon the whole!"
     As the bird wings and sings,
     Let us cry, "All good things
     Are ours, nor soul helps flesh more, now, than flesh helps soul!"

13 Therefore I summon age
To grant youth's heritage,
Life's struggle having so far reached its term.
Thence shall I pass, approved
A man, for aye removed
From the developed brute—a god, though in the germ.

14 And I shall thereupon
Take rest, ere I be gone
Once more on my adventure brave and new;
Fearless and unperplexed,
When I wage battle next,
What weapons to select, what armor to indue.[1]

15 Youth ended, I shall try
My gain or loss thereby;
Leave the fire ashes, what survives is gold.
And I shall weigh the same,
Give life its praise or blame.
Young, all lay in dispute; I shall know, being old.

16 For note, when evening shuts,
A certain moment cuts
The deed off, calls the glory from the gray;
A whisper from the west
Shoots—"Add this to the rest,
Take it and try its worth, Here dies another day."

17 So, still within this life,
Though lifted o'er its strife,
Let me discern, compare, pronounce at last,
"This rage was right i' the main,
That acquiescence vain;
The Future I may face, now I have proved the Past."

18 For more is not reserved
To man, with soul just nerved
To act tomorrow what he learns today;
Here, work enough to watch
The Master work, and catch
Hints of the proper craft, tricks of the tool's true play.

---

[1] *To indue* means to put on.

19 As it was better, youth
    Should strive, through acts uncouth,
    Toward making, than repose on aught found made;
    So, better, age, exempt
    From strife, should know, than tempt
    Further. Thou waitedst age; wait death nor be afraid!

20 Enough now, if the Right
    And Good and Infinite
    Be named here, as thou callest thy hand thine own,
    With knowledge absolute,
    Subject to no dispute
    From fools that crowded youth, nor let thee feel alone.

21 Be there, for once and all,
    Severed great minds from small,
    Announced to each his station in the Past!
    Was I, the world arraigned,
    Were they, my soul disdained,
    Right? Let age speak the truth and give us peace at last!

22 Now, who shall arbitrate?
    Ten men love what I hate,
    Shun what I follow, slight what I receive;   .
    Ten, who in ears and eyes
    Match me. We all surmise,
    They this thing, and I that; whom shall my soul believe?

23 Not on the vulgar mass
    Called "work," must sentence pass—
    Things done, that took the eye and had the price;
    O'er which, from level stand,
    The low world laid its hand,
    Found straitway to its mind, could value in a trice:

24 But all, the world's coarse thumb
    And finger failed to plumb,
    So passed in making up the main account;
    All instincts immature,
    All purposes unsure,
    That weighed not as his work, yet swelled the man's amount:

25   Thoughts hardly to be packed
Into a narrow act,
Fancies that broke through language and escaped;
All I could never be,
All, men ignored in me,
This, I was worth to God, whose wheel the pitcher shaped.

26   Aye, note that Potter's wheel,[1]
That metaphor! and feel
Why time spins fast, why passive lies our clay—
Thou, to whom fools propound,
When the wine makes its round,
"Since life fleets, all is change; the Past gone, seize today!"

27   Fool! All that is, at all,
Lasts ever, past recall;
Earth changes, but thy soul and God stand sure.
What entered into thee,
That was, is, and shall be.
Time's wheel runs back or stops; Potter and clay endure.

28   He fixed thee 'mid this dance
Of plastic circumstance,
This Present, thou, forsooth, would fain arrest—
Machinery just meant
To give thy soul its bent,
Try thee and turn thee forth, sufficiently impressed.

29   What though the earlier grooves,
Which ran the laughing loves
Around thy base, no longer pause and press?
What though, about thy rim,
Skull-things in order grim
Grow out, in graver mood, obey the sterner stress?

30   Look not thou down but up!
To uses of a cup,
The festal board, lamp's flash, and trumpet's peal,
The new wine's foaming flow,
The Master's lips aglow!
Thou, heaven's consummate cup, what needst thou with earth's
      wheel?

---

[1]*That Potter's wheel* refers to *Isaiah,* 64:8.—"But now, O Lord, thou art our father; we are the clay, and thou our potter; and we all are the work of thy hand."

31   But, I need, now as then,
      Thee, God, who moldest men;
      And since, not even while the whirl was worst,
      Did I—to the wheel of life
      With shapes and colors rife,
      Bound dizzily—mistake my end, to slave Thy thirst.

32   So, take and use Thy work;
      Amend what flaws may lurk,
      What strain o' the stuff, what warpings past the aim!
      My times be in Thy hand!
      Perfect the cup as planned!
      Let age approve of youth, and death complete the same!

Discussion of "Rabbi Ben Ezra"

Rabbi Ben Ezra was a distinguished Jewish philosopher, doctor, astronomer, and poet of the 12th century. Although the ideas in the poem are drawn somewhat from Ben Ezra's writings, they are also one of the fullest expressions of Browning's own philosophy.

The poem begins with a robust assertion that God formed man's life as a united whole, youth being the first half and old age the second and best half—"the last of life, for which the first was made." He then moves, starting with stanza 3, to a rejoicing that man is not a mere animal living in the selfish needs of the flesh. Instead, we are allied to God, who provides the example of unselfishness for us. "A spark disturbs our clod"—the spark of the divine spirit that inhabits the mortal body and separates man from the animals. Therefore, because of our immortal spirits that need to grow through the challenges of earthly experience, we should "welcome each rebuff" and "sting" and "pain" that are steps along the road of endless progression. We should accept life's challenge to "strive," "learn," "dare." Man is a mere brute unless the spirit within his body aspires to subdue and live above the desires of the animal flesh. But man does aspire. This is why he is man, and all according to the "whole design" of the Creator. "Perfect I call the plan," says Browning in stanza 10. And even as youth and age are two halves of mortal life, so body and spirit are two halves of man's total essence, each necessary to the other, he says in stanzas 11 and 12.

Stanza 13 is a key passage in the poem, for here Browning states that, matured by life's experiences, man is "a god, though in the germ"—one of the most explicit statements in all literature harmonizing with the L.D.S. doctrine that men and women have the potential to become gods and goddesses. Note also Browning's rejection of the "scientific" theory of evolution that man is merely a "developed brute." Man has a divine spirit, says Browning, setting him forever apart from all other forms of life on earth.

Beginning in stanza 14 Browning makes another analogy: Even as youth and age are halves of the whole of mortal life, and body and spirit are halves of the whole of man's essence, so mortal life and life after death are related parts of continuous existence—and Browning says he is ready to start on his "adventure brave and new" of life beyond death. The past and the present are both preparations for the future, and all are united in a perfect plan. Therefore, do not be afraid to face death, he says in stanza 19; for even as *seeking* should characterize youth, so *knowledge* should characterize age. And this can be "knowledge absolute" he says in stanza 20, reaffirming his position in stanza 21 when he adds, "Let age speak the truth and give us peace at last."

I realize, Browning says in stanza 22, that for every man who believes as I do about life and death and immortality there may be ten who believe otherwise. The way of the world is to be weak in faith and to argue (see stanza 26) that since life is fleeting and the future uncertain we should seize the pleasures of today. In answer to this point of view Browning makes one of his strongest statements in the poem:

> Fool! All that is, at all,
> Lasts ever, past recall;
> Earth changes, but thy soul and God stand sure.
> What entered into thee,
> *That* was, is, and shall be.
>   (from stanza 27)

Man's mortal existence, Browning repeats in stanza 28, is simply part of God's perfect and immortal plan, a school wherein man's soul can be given direction and growth. Therefore, look up, not down (stanza 30), and trust in God's divine wisdom, following His plan that will shape men to perfection for the eternal life ahead.

   Surely this is one of the great short religious poems of the world, and especially so to Latter-day Saint readers because its views are so beautifully harmonious with truth. Compare what Browning says here with his comment in "A Grammarian's Funeral" that we should "trust death" and with his famous statement "A man's reach should exceed his grasp—or what's a heaven for!" in "Andrea del Sarto." (One "trusts death" by believing in life after death, and heaven is for progressing eternally are the implied answers.) Browning does not give L.D.S. readers theological knowledge beyond that we already have. The Gospel gives us a fulness of religious truth. Even so, it is reassuring to discover that one of the great poets of the world in poem after poem expresses thoughts harmonizing with the truths of the scriptures.

We Are Seven

by William Wordsworth

˗ ˗ ˗ A simple Child,
That lightly draws its breath,
And feels its life in every limb,
What should it know of death?

I met a little cottage Girl:
She was eight years old, she said:
Her hair was thick with many a curl
That clustered round her head.

She had a rustic, woodland air,
And she was wildly clad:
Her eyes were fair, and very fair:
—Her beauty made me glad.

"Sisters and brothers, little Maid,
How many may you be?"
"How many? Seven in all," she said,
And wondering looked at me.

"And where are they? I pray you tell."
She answered, "Seven are we;
And two of us at Conway dwell,
And two are gone to sea.

"Two of us in the church-yard lie,
My sister and my brother;
And, in the church-yard cottage, I
Dwell near them with my mother."

"You say that two at Conway dwell,
And two are gone to sea,
Yet ye are seven!—I pray you tell,
Sweet Maid, how this may be."

Then did the little Maid reply,
"Seven boys and girls are we;
Two of us in the church-yard lie,
Beneath the church-yard tree."

"You run about, my little Maid,
Your limbs they are alive;
If two are in the church-yard laid,
Then ye are only five."

"Their graves are green, they may be seen,"
The little Maid replied,
"Twelve steps or more from my mother's door,
And they are side by side.

"My stockings there I often knit,
My kerchief there I hem;
And there upon the ground I sit,
And sing a song to them.

"And often after sunset, Sir,
When it is light and fair,
I take my little porringer,
And eat my supper there.

"The first that died was sister Jane;
In bed she moaning lay,
Till God released her of her pain;
And then she went away.

"So in the church-yard she was laid;
And, when the grass was dry,
Together round her grave we played,
My brother John and I.

"And when the ground was white with snow,
And I could run and slide,
My brother John was forced to go,
And he lies by her side."

"How many are you, then," said I,
"If they two are in heaven?"
Quick was the little Maid's reply,
"O Master! we are seven."

"But they are dead; those two are dead!
Their spirits are in heaven!"
'Twas throwing words away; for still
The little Maid would have her will,
And said, "Nay, we are seven!"

Discussion of "We Are Seven"

One of the firmest of Wordsworth's convictions was expressed in that much attacked but really lovely little poem "We Are Seven." Like the "Intimations of Immortality" ode,[1] "We Are Seven" has an especial appeal to Latter-day Saint readers, because, although among all people there is a hopeful yearning that the family unit may endure beyond the grave, the Church of Jesus Christ of Latter-day Saints is apparently the only Christian church which officially teaches that the family unit may so endure. On this theme, and on the scriptural idea that we can sometimes be led by children and learn wisdom out of their spontaneous, intuitive feelings, "We Are Seven" is written.

In the poem Wordsworth tells of meeting a little eight-year-old cottage girl and of asking her how many brothers and sisters she has. The girl replies that, counting herself, there are seven. In response, the speaker in the poem argues that, since two are dead and others have moved away, the family is broken apart; but the little girl repeatedly insists, "Nay, we are seven!" She feels close through the bond of love not only to those who have moved away but also, especially, to the two who have died.

The poem, despite the attacks of those who regard its childish sentiment as sentimental and its simple loveliness as repetitiously shallow, is as tender and beautifully meaningful a poem as Wordsworth ever wrote, even though it doesn't have the rich artistic and philosophic complexity of some of his greater poems. Those who criticize the poem for being monotonous and childish in its phrasing miss its whole point. Of course it is repetitious, for no amount of arguing will shake the little girl's intuitive knowledge that the family unit is eternal, as she repeats again and again, "Nay, we are seven." And of course its language is child-

---

[1] For a discussion of this poem and of Wordsworth's work in general, see pp. 53-70. Also, for a discussion of Wordsworth's "Michael" see pp. 417-19 and of "The World Is Too Much With Us" see pp. 229-30.

ish, for how else should a child talk but in the language of a child? The poem can be a pleasing source of comfort for all who have lost a beloved one in death. For, as Wordsworth through the little girl says, the family unit can be eternal, and it is through faith, like that of a believing child, that one can know this.

In this poem, as in many others by him, we see Wordsworth's wisdom and religious insight and feel the "healing power" of his genius, this "friend of the wise and teacher of the good."[1]

---

[1]The quoted phrases are from Matthew Arnold and Samuel Taylor Coleridge.

Three Poems Exploring Special Problems on Death

In addition to the preceding selections presenting pessimistic and optimistic attitudes towards death, we wish to include three poems touching on special problems in relation to death: Tennyson's "Tithonus," Owen's "Dulce et Decorum Est," and Shapiro's "Auto Wreck":

Tithonus

by Alfred, Lord Tennyson

The woods decay, the woods decay and fall,
The vapors weep their burthen to the ground;
Man comes and tills the field and lies beneath,
And after many a summer dies the swan.
Me only cruel immortality
Consumes; I wither slowly in thine arms,
Here at the quiet limit of the world,
A white-haired shadow roaming like a dream
The ever-silent spaces of the East,
Far-folded mists, and gleaming halls of morn.
    Alas! for this gray shadow, once a man—
So glorious in his beauty and thy choice,
Who madest him they chosen, that he seemed
To his great heart none other than a god!
I asked thee, "Give me immortality."
Then didst thou grant mine asking with a smile,
Like wealthy men who care not how they give.
But thy strong Hours[1] indignant worked their wills,
And beat me down and marred and wasted me,
And though they could not end me, left me maimed
To dwell in presence of immortal youth,
Immortal age beside immortal youth,
And all I was in ashes. Can thy love,
Thy beauty, make amends, though even now,
Close over us, the silver star, thy guide,
Shines in those tremulous eyes that fill with tears
To hear me? Let me go; take back thy gift.
Why should a man desire in any way
To vary from the kindly race of men,
Or pass beyond the goal of ordinance
Where all should pause, as is most meet for all?
    A soft air fans the cloud apart; there comes
A glimpse of that dark world where I was born.
Once more the old mysterious glimmer steals
From thy pure brows, and from thy shoulders pure,
And bosom beating with a heart renewed.
Thy cheek begins to redden through the gloom,
Thy sweet eyes brighten slowly close to mine,

---

[1]The Hours were goddesses.

Ere yet they blind the stars, and the wild team
Which love thee, yearning for thy yoke, arise,
And shake the darkness from their loosened manes,
And beat the twilight into flakes of fire.
    Lo! ever thus thou growest beautiful
In silence; then, before thine answer given,
Departest, and thy tears are on my cheek.
    Why wilt thou ever scare me with thy tears,
And make me tremble lest a saying learnt,
In days far-off, on that dark earth, be true?
"The gods themselves cannot recall their gifts."
    Ay me! ay me! with what another heart
In days far-off, and with what other eyes
I used to watch—if I be he that watched—
The lucid outline forming round thee; saw
The dim curls kindle into sunny rings;
Changed with thy mystic change, and felt my blood
Glow with the glow that slowly crimsoned all
Thy presence and thy portals, while I lay,
Mouth, forehead, eyelids, growing dewy-warm
With kisses balmier than half-opening buds
Of April, and could hear the lips that kissed
Whispering I knew not what of wild and sweet,
Like that strange song I heard Apollo sing,
While Ilion like a mist rose into towers.
    Yet hold me not forever in thine East;
How can my nature longer mix with thine?
Coldly thy rosy shadows bathe me, cold
Are all thy lights, and cold my wrinkled feet
Upon thy glimmering thresholds, when the steam
Floats up from those dim fields about the homes
Of happy men that have the power to die,
And grassy barrows of the happier dead.
Release me, and restore me to the ground.
Thou seest all things, thou wilt see my grave;
Thou wilt renew thy beauty morn by morn,
I earth in earth forget these empty courts,
And the returning on thy silver wheels.

Discussion of "Tithonus"

Alfred, Lord Tennyson (1809-1892) was a poet undeniably great but with undeniable weaknesses and limitations. In hundreds of short poems and dozens of long poems he for more than half a century showed his lyric richness to the world, re-creating in modern language tales of the heroic past and legends of the even more distant mythological past, and endeavoring to compromise the conflicts in his age between science and religion. He was, especially in his masterpiece, *In Memoriam*, the spiritual guide and phrase-maker of nineteenth-century England. But with the passage of time Tennyson has seemed less and less the giant poet of his age, as Browning has emerged larger and larger above him. Even so, and in spite of a sentimental lushness that characterizes most of Tennyson's poems, he still stands, and probably will always stand, as one of the great lyric poets of the world.

"Tithonus" is one of many poems by Tennyson built on ancient mythology. And like almost everything that Tennyson wrote, it contains memorable lines and phrases— such as the powerful "Man comes and tills the field and lies beneath"; or "After many a summer dies the swan," which became the title of a novel by Aldous Huxley.

The poem tells the story of Tithonus, son of the king of Troy, who was married to Aurora, goddess of the dawn. Tithonus was a mortal being, subject to ageing and death, and Aurora was immortal, beyond the effects of either ageing or death. At the request of Aurora, the gods granted Tithonus eternal life, but she neglected to request eternal youth for him. Therefore, as the years came and went, he grew forever older, forever more feeble, but could not die. In lamentation for his plight, Tithonus in the poem cries out, "Me only cruel immortality consumes; I wither slowly in thine arms, . . . immortal age beside immortal youth." Later he pleads, "Let me go; take back thy gift." He would die, but cannot. Finally, according to the old legend, but beyond the limits of Tennyson's poem, Tithonus grew so withered and ugly that Aurora turned him into a grasshopper. (Let all husbands beware!)

The poem is included here because it gives an interesting slant on death. Most people, even the most religious of people, fear death and cling to life. A confidence in the resurrection and in the reuniting of loved ones after death lessens the fear of death — but still fear remains for most people.

The truth is, of course, that there are many things worse than death. And the truth also surely is that one thing worse than death would be to grow forever older, forever more subject to the sicknesses and deteriorations of the body characterizing old age, and be unable to die. If one could live on in full health, endless life in this world might be attractive; but to live on in ever-declining physical and mental health would be a terrible curse, far worse than the blessed release of death. This central idea of the poem is worth thinking about.

Dulce et Decorum Est

by Wilfred Owen

Bent double, like old beggars under sacks,
Knock-kneed, coughing like hags, we cursed through sludge,
Till on the haunting flares we turned our backs,
And towards our distant rest began to trudge.
Men marched asleep. Many had lost their boots,
But limped on, blood-shod. All went lame, all blind;
Drunk with fatigue; deaf even to the hoots
Of gas-shells dropping softly behind.

Gas! Gas! Quick, boys!—An ecstasy of fumbling,
Fitting the clumsy helmets just in time,
But someone still was yelling out and stumbling
And flound'ring like a man in fire or lime.
Dim through the misty panes and thick green light,
As under a green sea, I saw him drowning.

In all my dreams before my helpless sight
He plunges at me, guttering, choking, drowning.

If in some smothering dreams, you too could pace
Behind the wagon that we flung him in,
And watch the white eyes wilting in his face,
His hanging face, like a devil's sick of sin,
If you could hear, at every jolt, the blood
Come gargling from the froth-corrupted lungs
Bitten as the cud
Of vile, incurable sores on innocent tongues,—
My friend, you would not tell with such high zest
To children ardent for some desperate glory,
The old lie: *Dulce et decorum est
Pro patria mori.*[1]

---

[1]"It is sweet and proper to die for one's country."

Discussion of "Dulce et Decorum Est"

Wilfred Owen (1893-1918) was probably the most gifted, the most promising, the greatest of the young English poets killed in World War I. The story of his life is pitifully brief. Until 1916 he spent most of his time just growing up and getting educated. Then, in spite of delicate health, he served for over a year as a rifleman with the British Army in France, was wounded, and after a year of convalescence, returned to the Western Front, was awarded the Military Cross for gallantry, and—with tragic irony—was killed just a week before the Armistice, in November 1918.

Owen did not write many poems, but the few he did write are characterized by force, realism, and the ring of authentic literary genius.

When death comes after a full life of goodness and service, it is surely to be looked on not as a tragedy but as a step toward eternal progression. However, avoidable deaths that needlessly cut short lives of earthly usefulness are another matter. A young father or mother severed from a dependent family through war or accident—this seems hardest to explain.

Often war has been romanticized as something heroic and glorious. Owen's poem labels it more accurately for what it truly is—a grim waste. And the poem gains strength through the signature of his own testament in death.

Auto Wreck

by Karl Shapiro

Its quick soft silver bell beating, beating,
And down the dark one ruby flare
Pulsing out red light like an artery,
The ambulance at top speed floating down
Past beacons and illuminated clocks
Wings in a heavy curve, dips down,
And brakes speed, entering the crowd.
The doors leap open, emptying light;
Stretchers are laid out, the mangled lifted
And stowed into the little hospital.
Then the bell, breaking the hush, tolls once,
And the ambulance with its terrible cargo
Rocking, slightly rocking, moves away,
As the doors, and afterthought, are closed.

We are deranged, walking among the cops
Who sweep glass and are large and composed.
One is still making notes under the light.
One with a bucket douches ponds of blood
Into the street and gutter.
One hangs lanterns on the wrecks that cling,
Empty husks of locusts, to iron poles.

Our throats were tight as tourniquets,
Our feet were bound with splints, but now
Like convalescents intimate and gauche,
We speak through sickly smiles and warn
With the stubborn saw of common sense,
The grim joke and the banal resolution.
The traffic moves around with care,
But we remain, touching a wound
That opens to our richest horror.

Already old, the question Who shall die?
Becomes unspoken Who is innocent?
For death in war is done by hands;
Suicide has cause and stillbirth, logic.
But this invites the occult mind,
Cancels our physics with a sneer,
And spatters all we knew of denouement
Across the expedient and wicked stones.

Discussion of "Auto Wreck"

In the twentieth century it is customary for us to look more clearly at harsh reality than it was in some preceding generations. Partly this is true because harsh reality confronts us on all sides in the rush and challenge of the modern world. Partly it is that we want to be honest and not hide truth, even when truth may be ugly. And so modern poems about death often are harsh poems, especially if the death seems cruel and purposeless, as it does in Owen's "Dulce et Decorum Est," or in "Auto Wreck" by Karl Shapiro (gifted young American poet, 1913-).

Readers will not find this a pretty description. It is ugly, as ugly as real death in a grinding highway accident. But we should not close our eyes and ears to the poem. We should read it, letting all of its brutal horror sink into our senses, from the opening description of the flashing beam on the speeding ambulance "pulsing out red light like an artery" to the closing comments that the terrible deaths of war and still-birth and even suicide are more explainable than the mangling death of an automobile accident, as fatal to the innocent as to the guilty. We should read it because maybe it will forever after make us a little more careful and determined that we will never be responsible for an accident such as that described. Shapiro's purpose, of course, is to impress his readers with the sacredness of life and to shock them with the awfulness of the totally useless and needless death of a highway accident.

Much of the power of the poem, and certainly its unity, comes from the sustained image of describing the whole scene, including the viewers of the accident, in terms of an injured victim—the already mentioned ambulance beam "pulsing . . . like an artery," the spectators with throats "tight as tourniquets," the final spattering "of denouement across the expedient and wicked stones." All of this focuses to illuminate the central question, "Who is innocent?" with the clear implication that, even as all of us suffer from the slaughter of lives on the world's highways, so all of us in varying degrees are guilty of the carelessness that causes the slaughter.

And on this somber but important thought we end our book.

Index of References to Authors